Means

Electrical Estimating Methods

Second Edition

Senior Editors
Paul H. DeLong
John H. Chiang, PE

Contributing Editors
Mary P. Greene
Suzanne Morris

Illustrator
Carl W. Linde

Means

Electrical Estimating Methods

Second Edition

Copyright 1995

R.S. MEANS COMPANY, INC.
CONSTRUCTION PUBLISHERS & CONSULTANTS

100 Construction Plaza
P.O. Box 800
Kingston, MA 02364-0800
(617) 585-7880

Southam
Construction
Information
Network

The editors for this book were John Chiang and Suzanne Morris; the managing editor was Mary Greene. The production manager was Helen Marcella; the production coordinator was Marion Schofield. Composition was supervised by Karen O'Brien. The book and jacket were designed by Norman Forgit.

10   9   8   7   6   5   4   3   2   1

Library of Congress Cataloging in Publication Data

ISBN 0-87629-358-5

Table of Contents

Foreword

This new edition of ***Means Electrical Estimating Methods*** has been updated and revised to address some important changes that have taken place in the construction industry over the past few years. All of these issues are covered with revisions and/or new text in this book. For example, the Construction Specifications Institute has revised and updated their MasterFormat numbering system to bring it into close alignment with current technology and quality, and to include broader coverage of installation methods and materials. Consequently, electrical construction items are now classified somewhat differently. All MasterFormat references in this book are current with the latest available CSI designations. The sample estimate is supported by data from Means' annual cost publication, ***Means Electrical Cost Data***, which also conforms with the current MasterFormat and with Means' numbering system.

New systems, such as fiber optics, uninterruptible power supply systems, and power transmission and distribution, have become standard features in today's electrical plans and must be covered in the corresponding estimates. These new systems have been added to Part II, "Components of Electrical Systems," which includes methods and units of takeoff for each, as well as general guidance for selecting and estimating these items.

Furthermore, computers are used increasingly to plan and schedule electrical work and to estimate it. While the book shows how to fill in sample estimate sheets for a handwritten estimate, the sample project estimate shows the kinds of estimate sheets generated by a computerized estimating program.

As with the original edition, this book is intended to provide sound, practical methods and standards for accurate electrical estimating. The entire process, updated for the most current electrical installations, is demonstrated, step by step, through to the finished estimate. It includes interpreting drawings, performing the takeoff, pricing, labor costing, figuring of overhead and profit, bidding, and scheduling.

Part 1

The Estimating Process

Components of an Estimate

The term "estimating accuracy" is a relative concept. What is the correct or accurate cost of a given construction project? Is it the total price paid to the contractor? Might not another reputable contractor perform the same work for a different cost, whether higher or lower? There is no one correct estimated cost for a given project. There are too many variables in construction. At best, the estimator can determine a very close approximation of what the final costs will be. The resulting accuracy of this approximation is directly affected by the amount of detail provided and the amount of time spent on the estimate.

Every cost estimate requires three basic components. The first is the establishment of standard *units of measure*. The second component of an estimate is the determination of the *quantity* of units for each component, which is an actual counting process: how many linear feet of wire, how many outlet boxes, etc. The third component, and perhaps the most difficult to obtain, is the determination of a reasonable *cost* for each unit.

The first element, the designation of measurement units, is the step that determines and defines the level of detail, and thus the degree of accuracy, of a cost estimate. In electrical construction, such units could be as all-encompassing as the number of watts per square foot of floor area, or as detailed as a linear foot of wire. Depending on the estimator's intended use, the designation of the "unit" may describe a complete system, or it may imply only an isolated entity. The choice and detail of units also determines the time required to do an estimate.

The second component of every estimate, the determination of quantity, is more than the counting of units. In construction, this process is called the "quantity takeoff" or "quantity survey." To perform this function successfully, the estimator should have a working knowledge of the materials, methods, and codes used in electrical construction. An understanding of the design specifications is particularly important. This knowledge helps to ensure that each quantity is correctly tabulated and that essential items are not forgotten or omitted. The estimator with a thorough knowledge of construction is also more likely to account for all requirements in the estimate. Many of the items to be quantified (counted) may not involve any material but, rather, entail labor costs only. Testing is an example of a labor-only item. Experience is, therefore, invaluable to ensure a complete estimate.

The third component is the determination of a reasonable cost for each unit. This aspect of the estimate is significantly responsible for variations in estimating. Rarely do two estimators arrive at exactly the same material cost for a project. Even if material costs for an installation are the same for competing contractors, the labor costs for installing that material can vary considerably, as a result of varying productivity and pay scales in different areas. The use of specialized equipment can decrease installation time and, therefore, cost. Finally, material prices do fluctuate within the market. These cost differences occur from city to city and even from supplier to supplier in the same town. It is the experienced and well-prepared estimator who can keep track of these variations and fluctuations and use them to his or her best advantage when preparing accurate estimates.

This third component of the estimate, the determination of costs, can be defined in three different ways by the estimator. With one approach, the estimator uses a unit cost that includes all the elements (i.e., material, installation, overhead, and profit) in one number expressed in dollars per unit. A variation of this approach is to use a unit cost that includes total material and installation only, adding a percent markup for overhead and profit to the "bottom line."

A second method is to use unit costs — in dollars — for material and for installation. This is done separately for each item, without markups. These are sometimes called "bare costs." Different profit and overhead markups are applied to each item before the material and installation prices are added; the result is the total "selling" cost.

A third method of unit pricing uses unit costs for materials, and labor-hours as the units of labor. Again, these figures are totalled separately; one represents the value of materials (in dollars), and the other shows the total labor-hours for installation. The average cost per hour of craft labor is determined by allowing for the expected ratios of foremen, journeymen, and apprentices. This is sometimes called the "composite labor rate." This rate is multiplied by the total labor-hours to get the total bare cost of installation. Different overhead and profit markups can then be applied to each, material and labor, and the results added to get the total selling cost.

The word *unit* is used in many ways, as can be seen in the above definitions. Keeping the concepts of units clearly defined is vital to achieving an accurate, professional estimate. For the purposes of this book, the following references to different types of units are used:

Unit of Measure: The standard by which the quantities are counted, such as *linear feet* of conduit, *number* of boxes.

Cost Units: The total dollar price per each installed unit of measure, including the costs of material and installation. This figure may or may not include overhead and profit.

Material Unit Cost: The cost to purchase each unit of measure. This cost represents material dollars only — with no overhead and profit.

Installation Unit Cost: The cost for installing each unit of measure. This cost includes labor dollars only — with no overhead and profit.

Labor Unit: The labor-hours required to install a unit of measure. (Note: Labor units multiplied by the labor rate per hour equals the installation unit cost in dollars.)

Very often, two or three of these different numerical values may appear on the same estimate sheet under columns all titled simply "UNITS." The estimator must, therefore, exercise care to utilize these columns correctly and consistently for the format of each particular estimate.

Types of Estimates

Estimators use four basic types of estimates. These types may be referred to by different names and may not be recognized by all as definitive. Most estimators, however, will agree that each type has its place in the construction estimating process. These types of estimates are as follows:

- **Order of Magnitude Estimate:** The order of magnitude estimate could be loosely described as an educated guess. It can be completed in a matter of minutes. Accuracy may be plus or minus 20%.
- **Square Foot and Cubic Foot Estimate:** This type is most often useful when only the proposed size and use of a planned building is known. This method can be completed within an hour or two. Accuracy may be plus or minus 15%.
- **Systems (or Assemblies) Estimate:** A systems estimate is best used as a budgetary tool in the planning stages of a project when some parameters have been decided. This type of estimate could require as much as one day to complete. Accuracy is expected to be plus or minus 10%.
- **Unit Price Estimate:** Working drawings and full specifications are required to complete a unit price estimate. It is the most accurate of the four types but is also the most time-consuming. Used primarily for bidding purposes, the accuracy of a unit price estimate can be plus or minus 5%.

Figure 2.1 graphically demonstrates the relationship of required time versus resulting accuracy of a complete building estimate for each of these four basic estimate types. As an estimator *and* his or her company gain repetitive experience on similar or identical projects, the accuracy of all four types of estimates should improve dramatically. In fact, given enough experience, Order of Magnitude and Square Foot Estimates may closely approach the accuracy of Unit Price Estimates.

Order of Magnitude Estimates

The Order of Magnitude Estimate can be completed with a minimum of information. The "units," as described in Chapter 1, can be very general for this type of estimate and need not be well defined. For example: "The electrical work for the office building of a small service company in a suburban industrial park will cost about $26,000." This type of statement (or estimate) can be made after a few minutes of thought, drawing on experience and making comparisons with similar projects from the past. While this rough figure might be appropriate for a project in one region of the country, substantial adjustments may be required for a change of geographic location and for cost changes over time resulting from, for example, changes of materials, inflation, or code changes.

Figure 2.2, from *Means Electrical Cost Data,* includes data for a refined approach to the Order of Magnitude Estimate. This format is based on unit of use. Please note at the bottom of the category "Hospitals," for example, that costs are given "per bed" or "per person." The proposed use and magnitude of the planned structure—such as the number of beds for a hospital building or the number of apartments in a complex—may be the only parameters known at the time the Order of Magnitude Estimate is done. The data given in Figure 2.2 does not require that details of the proposed project be known to determine rough costs; the only required information is the intended use and capacity of the building. What is lacking in accuracy (plus or minus 20%) is more than compensated by the minimal time required to complete the Order of Magnitude Estimate—a matter of minutes.

Square Foot and Cubic Foot Estimates

The use of Square Foot and Cubic Foot Estimates is most appropriate prior to the preparation of plans or preliminary drawings, when budgetary parameters are being analyzed and established. Please refer again to Figure 2.2 and note that costs for each type of project are presented first as "total project costs" by square foot and by cubic foot. These costs are broken down into different components, and then into the relationship of each component to the project as a whole, in terms of costs per square foot. This breakdown enables the designer, planner, or estimator to adjust certain components according to the unique requirements of the proposed project.

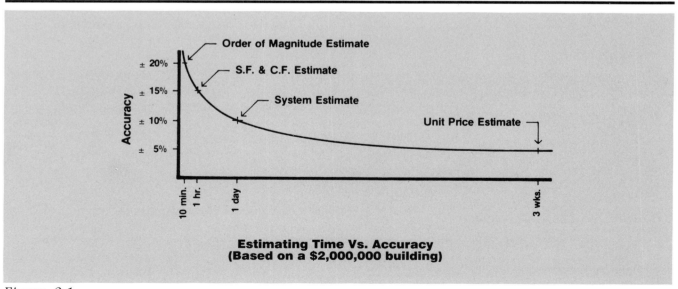

Figure 2.1

171 000	S.F. & C.F. Costs		UNIT	UNIT COSTS			% OF TOTAL			
				1/4	MEDIAN	3/4	1/4	MEDIAN	3/4	
390	1800	Equipment	S.F.	2.05	4.29	7.05	3.60%	6.40%	8.40%	**390**
	2720	Plumbing		2.30	3.48	6.90	4.90%	7.40%	11%	
	2730	Heating & ventilating		3.23	4.43	5.35	5.20%	7.20%	9.50%	
	2900	Electrical		3.18	4.97	7	7.10%	9%	11.10%	
	3100	Total: Mechanical & Electrical	↓	6.30	12.50	18.05	15.40%	20.20%	26.40%	
400	0010	**GARAGES, MUNICIPAL** (Repair)	S.F.	50.70	67.35	94.35				**400**
	0020	Total project costs	C.F.	3.25	4.07	5.80				
	0500	Masonry	S.F.	4.96	9.50	14.60	7%	10%	19%	
	2720	Plumbing		2.34	4.28	8.45	3.50%	6.60%	7.90%	
	2730	Heating & ventilating		2.85	4.56	7.70	4.90%	7.20%	11.60%	
	2900	Electrical		3.84	5.70	8.65	6.30%	8.10%	11.10%	
	3100	Total: Mechanical & Electrical	↓	10.10	17.60	29	15.20%	22.90%	31.50%	
410	0010	**GARAGES, PARKING**	S.F.	19.60	27.15	45				**410**
	0020	Total project costs	C.F.	1.76	2.45	3.68				
	2720	Plumbing	S.F.	.51	.89	1.37	2.20%	3.30%	3.80%	
	2900	Electrical		.83	1.25	1.84	4.20%	5.40%	6.30%	
	3100	Total: Mechanical & Electrical	↓	1.43	1.94	3.21	6.80%	8.70%	9.50%	
	3200									
	9000	Per car, total cost	Car	8,400	9,700	13,400				
430	0010	**GYMNASIUMS**	S.F.	53.50	69.30	87.25				**430**
	0020	Total project costs	C.F.	2.81	3.58	4.64				
	1800	Equipment	S.F.	1.19	2.41	4.92	2%	3.30%	6.70%	
	2720	Plumbing		3.18	4.40	5.45	5.30%	7.20%	8.20%	
	2770	Heating, ventilating, air conditioning		3.83	5.85	11.75	7.60%	9.70%	22.60%	
	2900	Electrical		4.33	5.35	7.30	6.50%	8.20%	10.40%	
	3100	Total: Mechanical & Electrical	↓	8.10	12.80	18.80	15.70%	19.60%	26.30%	
	3500	See also division 114-801 & 114-805								
460	0010	**HOSPITALS**	S.F.	115	135	213				**460**
	0020	Total project costs	C.F.	8.40	10.55	14.40				
	1800	Equipment	S.F.	2.80	5.20	8.85	1.60%	3.80%	5.90%	
	2720	Plumbing		9.50	12.60	17.35	7.20%	9.10%	10.80%	
	2770	Heating, ventilating, air conditioning		13.65	18.15	25	8.40%	13.80%	16.70%	
	2900	Electrical		11.60	15.45	23.65	9.80%	11.90%	14.70%	
	3100	Total: Mechanical & Electrical	↓	32.20	43.25	66.15	26.10%	33.60%	39.90%	
	9000	Per bed or person, total cost	Bed	32,400	63,300	80,600				
	9900	See also division 117-001								
480	0010	**HOUSING** For the Elderly	S.F.	52.80	67.40	83.20				**480**
	0020	Total project costs	C.F.	3.84	5.35	6.80				
	0100	Site work	S.F.	3.69	5.95	8.55	5%	8.20%	12.10%	
	0500	Masonry		1.27	5.80	8.85	2.10%	7%	11.50%	
	1140	Dampproofing		.31	.47	1.01	.30%	.50%	.90%	
	1580	Painting		1.94	2.43	2.82	2.40%	2.80%	3.30%	
	1800	Equipment		1.28	1.77	2.80	1.80%	3.20%	4.30%	
	2510	Conveying systems		1.30	1.73	2.36	1.80%	2.20%	2.80%	
	2720	Plumbing		3.97	5.35	6.92	8.10%	9.70%	10.70%	
	2730	Heating, ventilating, air conditioning		1.87	2.87	4.08	3.20%	5.60%	7.10%	
	2900	Electrical		3.97	5.40	7.20	7.40%	8.80%	10.50%	
	3100	Total: Mechanical & Electrical	↓	9.65	13.60	17	18.20%	21.60%	24.70%	
	9000	Per rental unit, total cost	Unit	46,600	55,400	61,600				
	9500	Total: Mechanical & Electrical	"	9,300	11,400	13,900				
500	0010	**HOUSING** Public (Low Rise)	S.F.	44.80	61.60	79.35				**500**
	0020	Total project costs	C.F.	3.52	4.91	6.18				

Figure 2.2

The costs on this and other pages of *Means Electrical Cost Data* were derived from more than 10,200 projects contained in the Means Data Bank of Construction Costs. These costs include the contractor's overhead and profit but do not include architectural fees or land costs. The 1/4 column shows the value at which 25% of the projects had lower costs and 75% had higher. The 3/4 column value denotes that 75% of the projects had lower costs and 25% had higher. The median column value shows that 50% of the projects had lower costs and 50% had higher.

Historical data for square foot costs of new construction are plentiful (see *Means Electrical Cost Data,* Division 171). However, the best source of square foot costs is the estimator's own cost records for similar projects, adjusted to the parameters of the project in question. While helpful for preparing preliminary budgets, Square Foot and Cubic Foot Estimates can also be useful as checks against other, more detailed estimates. While slightly more time is required than with Order of Magnitude Estimates, a greater accuracy (plus or minus 15%) is achieved because of a more specific definition of the project.

Systems (or Assemblies) Estimates

One of the primary advantages of Systems (or Assemblies) Estimates is that they enable alternate construction techniques to be readily compared for budgetary purposes. Rapidly rising design and construction costs in recent years have made budgeting and cost-effectiveness studies increasingly important in the early stages of building projects. Never before has the estimating process had such a crucial role in the initial planning. Unit Price Estimates, because of the time and detailed information required, are not well suited as budgetary or planning tools. A faster and more cost-effective method is needed for the planning phase of a building project; this is the "Systems," or "Assemblies," Estimate.

The Systems method is a logical, sequential approach that reflects how a building is constructed. Twelve "UniFormat" divisions organize building construction into major components that can be used in Systems Estimates. These UniFormat divisions are listed below:

Systems Estimating Divisions:
   Division 1 — Foundations
   Division 2 — Substructures
   Division 3 — Superstructures
   Division 4 — Exterior Closure
   Division 5 — Roofing
   Division 6 — Interior Construction
   Division 7 — Conveying Systems
   Division 8 — Mechanical
   Division 9 — Electrical
   Division 10 — General Conditions and Profit
   Division 11 — Special Construction
   Division 12 — Site Work

Each division is further broken down into systems. Division 9, which covers electrical construction, is comprised of the following groups of systems: Service, Lighting and Power, and Special.

Each system incorporates several different components into an assemblage that is commonly used in construction. Figure 2.3 is an example of a typical system, in this case "Lighting and Power — Fluorescent Fixture" (from *Means Electrical Cost Data*).

A. Strip Fixture   **B. Surface Mounted**

C. Recessed   **D. Pendent Mounted**

Design Assumptions:

1. A 100 footcandle average maintained level of illumination.
2. Ceiling heights range from 9' to 11'.
3. Average reflectance values are assumed for ceilings, walls and floors.
4. Cool white (CW) fluorescent lamps with 3150 lumens for 40 watt lamps and 6300 lumens for 8' slimline lamps.
5. Four 40 watt lamps per 4' fixture and two 8' lamps per 8' fixture.
6. Average fixture efficiency values and spacing to mounting height ratios.
7. Installation labor is average U.S. rate as of January 1.

System Components	QUANTITY	UNIT	COST PER S.F.		
			MAT.	INST.	TOTAL
SYSTEM 9.2-212-0520					
FLUORESCENT FIXTURES MOUNTED 9'-11" ABOVE FLOOR, 100 FC					
TYPE A, 8 FIXTURES PER 400 S.F.					
Steel intermediate conduit, (IMC) 1/2" diam	.404	L.F.	.45	1.39	1.84
Wire, 600V, type THWN-THHN, copper, solid, #12	.008	C.L.F.	.05	.25	.30
Fluorescent strip fixture 8' long, surface mounted, two 75W SL	.020	Ea.	1.20	1.11	2.31
Steel outlet box 4" concrete	.020	Ea.	.13	.34	.47
Steel outlet box plate with stud, 4" concrete	.020	Ea.	.05	.09	.14
TOTAL			1.88	3.18	5.06

9.2-212	Fluorescent Fixtures (by Type)	COST PER S.F.		
		MAT.	INST.	TOTAL
0520	Fluorescent fixtures, type A, 8 fixtures per 400 S.F.	1.88	3.18	5.06
0560	11 fixtures per 600 S.F.	1.77	3.08	4.85
0600	17 fixtures per 1000 S.F.	1.70	3.02	4.72
0640	23 fixtures per 1600 S.F.	1.52	2.87	4.39
0680	28 fixtures per 2000 S.F.	1.52	2.87	4.39
0720	41 fixtures per 3000 S.F.	1.47	2.86	4.33
0800	53 fixtures per 4000 S.F.	1.44	2.79	4.23
0840	64 fixtures per 5000 S.F.	1.44	2.79	4.23
0880	Type B, 11 fixtures per 400 S.F.	3.82	4.65	8.47
0920	15 fixtures per 600 S.F.	3.51	4.47	7.98
0960	24 fixtures per 1000 S.F.	3.41	4.44	7.85
1000	35 fixtures per 1600 S.F.	3.19	4.23	7.42
1040	42 fixtures per 2000 S.F.	3.09	4.25	7.34
1080	61 fixtures per 3000 S.F.	3.14	4.09	7.23
1160	80 fixtures per 4000 S.F.	2.99	4.19	7.18
1200	98 fixtures per 5000 S.F.	2.99	4.16	7.15
1240	Type C, 11 fixtures per 400 S.F.	3.10	4.89	7.99
1280	14 fixtures per 600 S.F.	2.72	4.58	7.30
1320	23 fixtures per 1000 S.F.	2.71	4.55	7.26
1360	34 fixtures per 1600 S.F.	2.57	4.48	7.05
1400	43 fixtures per 2000 S.F.	2.62	4.45	7.07
1440	63 fixtures per 3000 S.F.	2.54	4.38	6.92
1520	81 fixtures per 4000 S.F.	2.47	4.32	6.79
1560	101 fixtures per 5000 S.F.	2.47	4.32	6.79
1600	Type D, 8 fixtures per 400 S.F.	3.02	3.79	6.81
1640	12 fixtures per 600 S.F.	3.01	3.78	6.79
1680	19 fixtures per 1000 S.F.	2.89	3.68	6.57
1720	27 fixtures per 1600 S.F.	2.68	3.59	6.27
1760	34 fixtures per 2000 S.F.	2.67	3.55	6.22
1800	48 fixtures per 3000 S.F.	2.54	3.46	6
1880	64 fixtures per 4000 S.F.	2.54	3.46	6
1920	79 fixtures per 5000 S.F.	2.54	3.46	6

Figure 2.3

A great advantage of the Systems Estimate is that the estimator/designer is able to substitute one system for another during design development and can quickly determine the relative cost differential. The owner can then anticipate budget requirements before the final details and dimensions are established.

The Systems method does not require the degree of final design details needed for a Unit Price Estimate, but estimators who use this approach must have a solid background knowledge of construction materials and methods, code requirements, design options, and budget considerations.

The Systems Estimate should not be used as a substitute for the Unit Price Estimate. While the Systems approach can be an invaluable tool in the planning stages of a project, it should be supported by Unit Price Estimating whenever greater accuracy is required.

Unit Price Estimates

The Unit Price Estimate is the most accurate and detailed of the four estimate types and, therefore, takes the most time to complete. Detailed working drawings and specifications must be available to the unit price estimator. All decisions regarding the project's materials and methods must have been made to complete this type of estimate. Because there are fewer variables, the estimate can be more accurate. Working drawings and specifications are used to determine the quantities of materials, equipment, and labor. Current and accurate unit costs for these items are also necessary. These costs can come from different sources. Wherever possible, estimators should use prices based on experience or developed from actual, similar projects. If these kinds of records are not available, prices may be determined from an up-to-date industry source book, such as *Means Electrical Cost Data.*

Because of the detail involved and the need for accuracy, completion of a Unit Price Estimate entails a great deal of time and expense. For this reason, Unit Price Estimating is best suited for construction bidding. It can also be an effective method for determining certain detailed costs in a conceptual budget or during design development.

Most construction specification manuals and cost reference books, such as *Means Electrical Cost Data,* divide unit price information into the 16 MasterFormat divisions as adopted by the Construction Specifications Institute, Inc.

MasterFormat Divisions:
  Division 1 — General Requirements
  Division 2 — Site Work
  Division 3 — Concrete
  Division 4 — Masonry
  Division 5 — Metals
  Division 6 — Wood & Plastics
  Division 7 — Thermal and Moisture Protection
  Division 8 — Doors and Windows
  Division 9 — Finishes
  Division 10 — Specialties
  Division 11 — Equipment
  Division 12 — Furnishings
  Division 13 — Special Construction
  Division 14 — Conveying Systems

Division 15—Mechanical
Division 16—Electrical

Division 16, Electrical, is further divided into the following Means subdivisions:

160 Raceways
161 Conductors and Grounding
162 Boxes and Wiring Devices
163 Motors, Starters, Boards and Switches
164 Transformers and Bus Ducts
165 Power Systems and Capacitors
166 Lighting
167 Electric Utilities
168 Special Systems
169 Power Transmission and Distribution

This method of organizing the various components provides a standard of uniformity that is widely used by construction industry professionals: contractors, material suppliers, engineers, and architects.

A sample unit price page from the 1995 edition of *Means Electrical Cost Data* is shown in Figure 2.4. This page lists various types of cable connectors. (Please note that the heading "161 Conductors and Grounding" denotes the MasterFormat subdivision classification for these items in Division 16.) Each page contains a wealth of information useful in developing Unit Price Estimates. The type of work to be performed is described in detail: typical crew make-ups, unit man-hours, units of measure, and separate costs for material and installation. Total costs are extended to include the installing contractor's overhead and profit.

As a refinement to the Unit Price Estimate, a fifth type of estimate warrants mention. The "Scheduling Estimate" involves the application of realistic manpower allocations. A complete Unit Price Estimate is a prerequisite for the preparation of a Scheduling Estimate. The purpose of the Scheduling Estimate is to determine costs based on actual working conditions. This is done using data obtained from the Unit Price Estimate. A "human factor" can be applied. For example, if a task requires 7.5 hours to complete, based on unit price data, a worker will most likely take 8 hours to complete the work. Costs can be adjusted accordingly.

A thorough discussion of scheduling and Scheduling Estimates is beyond the scope of this book, but a brief overview is included in Chapter 9. This subject is covered in detail in *Means Scheduling Manual,* 3rd edition, by F. William Horsley.

161 100 | Conductors

		CREW	DAILY OUTPUT	MAN-HOURS	UNIT	1995 BARE COSTS				TOTAL INCL O&P	
						MAT.	LABOR	EQUIP.	TOTAL		
165 6110	700 MCM	1 Elec	1.80	4.444	C.L.F.	220	127		347	435	165
6120	750 MCM	▼	1.70	4.706	▼	225	134		359	450	

161 500 | Terminations

		CREW	DAILY OUTPUT	MAN-HOURS	UNIT	MAT.	LABOR	EQUIP.	TOTAL	TOTAL INCL O&P	
510 0010	**CABLE CONNECTORS**										510
0100	600 volt, nonmetallic, #14-2 wire	1 Elec	160	.050	Ea.	.30	1.43		1.73	2.48	
0200	#14-3 wire to #12-2 wire		133	.060		.30	1.71		2.01	2.91	
0300	#12-3 wire to #10-2 wire		114	.070		.30	2		2.30	3.34	
0400	#10-3 wire to #14-4 and #12-4 wire		100	.080		.30	2.28		2.58	3.77	
0500	#8-3 wire to #10-4 wire		80	.100		.89	2.85		3.74	5.30	
0600	#6-3 wire		40	.200		1.37	5.70		7.07	10.10	
0800	SER aluminum, 3 #8 insulated + 1 #8 ground		32	.250		1.37	7.15		8.52	12.25	
0900	3 #6 + 1 #6 ground		24	.333		1.67	9.50		11.17	16.15	
1000	3 #4 + 1 #6 ground		22	.364		1.67	10.35		12.02	17.45	
1100	3 #2 + 1 #4 ground		20	.400		3.10	11.40		14.50	20.50	
1200	3 1/0 + 1 #2 ground		18	.444		6.90	12.65		19.55	26.50	
1400	3 2/0 + 1 #1 ground		16	.500		8.40	14.25		22.65	31	
1600	3 4/0 + 1 #2/0 ground		14	.571		9.90	16.30		26.20	35.50	
1800	600 volt, armored, #14-2 wire		80	.100		.33	2.85		3.18	4.66	
2200	#14-4, #12-3 and #10-2 wire		40	.200		.33	5.70		6.03	8.95	
2400	#12-4, #10-3 and #8-2 wire		32	.250		.40	7.15		7.55	11.20	
2600	#8-3 and #10-4 wire		26	.308		1.36	8.75		10.11	14.70	
2650	#8-4 wire		22	.364		2.10	10.35		12.45	17.90	
2700	PVC jacket connector, #6-3 wire, #6-4 wire		16	.500		5.40	14.25		19.65	27.50	
2800	#4-3 wire, #4-4 wire		16	.500		5.40	14.25		19.65	27.50	
2900	#2-3 wire		12	.667		5.40	19		24.40	34.50	
3000	#1-3 wire, #2-4 wire		12	.667		8.20	19		27.20	37.50	
3200	1/0-3 wire		11	.727		8.20	20.50		28.70	40	
3400	2/0-3 wire, 1/0-4 wire		10	.800		8.20	23		31.20	43.50	
3500	3/0-3 wire, 2/0-4 wire		9	.889		10.95	25.50		36.45	50	
3600	4/0-3 wire, 3/0-4 wire		7	1.143		10.95	32.50		43.45	61	
3800	250 MCM-3 wire, 4/0-4 wire		6	1.333		20.50	38		58.50	80	
4000	350 MCM-3 wire, 250 MCM-4 wire		5	1.600		20.50	45.50		66	91	
4100	350 MCM-4 wire		4	2		29	57		86	118	
4200	500 MCM-3 wire		4	2		29	57		86	118	
4250	500 MCM-4 wire, 750 MCM-3 wire		3.50	2.286		55	65		120	159	
4300	750 MCM-4 wire		3	2.667		55	76		131	176	
4400	5 KV, armored, #4		8	1		34.50	28.50		63	81	
4600	#2		8	1		34.50	28.50		63	81	
4800	#1		8	1		34.50	28.50		63	81	
5000	1/0		6.40	1.250		43	35.50		78.50	101	
5200	2/0		5.30	1.509		43	43		86	113	
5500	4/0		4	2		57	57		114	149	
5600	250 MCM		3.60	2.222		67	63.50		130.50	169	
5650	350 MCM		3.20	2.500		82	71.50		153.50	197	
5700	500 MCM		2.50	3.200		82	91		173	227	
5720	750 MCM		2.20	3.636		120	104		224	288	
5750	1000 MCM		2	4		163	114		277	350	
5800	15 KV, armored, #1		4	2		55	57		112	147	
5900	1/0		4	2		55	57		112	147	
6000	3/0		3.60	2.222		72	63.50		135.50	175	
6100	4/0		3.40	2.353		72	67		139	180	
6200	250 MCM		3.20	2.500		80	71.50		151.50	195	
6300	350 MCM		2.70	2.963		92	84.50		176.50	228	
6400	500 MCM	▼	2	4	▼	92	114		206	273	

Figure 2.4

Before Starting the Estimate

The "Invitation to Bid" — to the contractor, this can mean the prospect of weeks of hard work with only a chance of bidding success. It can also mean the opportunity to obtain a contract for a successful and lucrative project. It is not uncommon for the contractor to bid ten or more jobs to win just one. The successful bid depends heavily on estimating accuracy and thus the preparation, organization, and care that go into the estimating process. (If a job is won because of omissions in the estimate, it is likely *not* to be a "successful bid.")

The first step before starting the estimate is to obtain copies of the plans and specifications in *sufficient quantities*. Most estimators mark up plans with colored pencils and make numerous notes and references. For one estimator to work from plans that have been used by another is difficult at best and may easily lead to errors. Most often, only two complete sets are provided by the architect to the general contractor. More sets must be purchased, if needed. When more than one estimator works on a particular project, especially if they are working from the same plans, careful coordination is required to prevent omissions or duplications.

The estimator should be aware of and note any instructions to bidders, which may be included in the specifications or in a separate document. To avoid future confusion, the bid's due date, time, and place should be clearly stated and understood upon receipt of the construction documents (plans and specifications). The due date should be marked on a calendar and a schedule. Completion of the takeoff should be made as soon as possible, not two days prior to the bid deadline.

If bid security, or a bid bond, is required, then time must be allowed for arrangements to be made, especially if the bonding capability or capacity of a contractor is limited or has not previously been established.

The estimator should attend all pre-bid meetings with the owner or architect, preferably *after* reviewing the plans and specifications. Important points are often brought up and details clarified at such meetings. Attendance is important, not only to show the owner your interest in the project, but also to assure equal and competitive bidding. For many projects, attendance is required or the bid will not be accepted. It is to the estimator's advantage to examine and review the plans and specifications before any such meetings and before the initial site visit. It is important to become familiar with the project as soon as possible.

All contract documents should be read thoroughly. They exist to protect all parties involved in the construction process. If they are not provided, the estimator should make a list of all appropriate documents to be checked with the engineer and listed in the bid. The contract documents are written so that the contractors will be bidding equally and competitively, and to ensure that all items in a project are included. The contract documents protect the designer (the architect or engineer) by ensuring that all work is supplied and installed as specified. The owner also benefits from thorough and complete construction documents by being assured of a quality job and a complete, functional project. Finally, the contractor benefits from good contract documents because the scope of work is well defined, eliminating the gray areas of what is implied but not stated. "Extras" are more readily avoided. Change orders, if required, are accepted with less argument if the original contract documents are complete, well stated, and, most importantly, read by all concerned parties. The Appendix of this book contains a reproduction of the two electrical pages from Spec-Aid, a preliminary checklist for detailed project specifications from *Means Forms for Building Construction Professionals.* Spec-Aid was created not only to assist designers and planners when developing project specifications, but also as an aid to the contractor's estimator. The electrical section of Spec-Aid lists the electrical division (MasterFormat 16) components and variables. The estimator can use this form as a means of outlining a project's requirements, and as a checklist to be sure that all items have been included.

During the first review of the specifications, any items to be priced should be identified and noted. All work to be contracted should be examined for "related work" required from other trades or contractors. Such work is usually referenced and described in a thorough project specification. "Work by others" or "Not in Contract" should be clearly defined on the drawings. Certain materials are often specified by the designer and purchased by the owner to be installed (labor only) by the contractor. These items should be noted and the responsibilities of each party clearly understood. An example of such an item might involve allocating responsibility for receiving, temporary storage, and maintenance of motors furnished by others but installed by electricians.

The "General Conditions," "Supplemental Conditions," and "Special Conditions" sections of the specifications should be examined carefully by all parties involved in the project. These sections describe the items that have a direct bearing on the proposed project, but may not be part of the actual, physical installation. Temporary power, lighting, and water are examples of these kinds of items. Also included in these sections is information regarding completion dates, payment schedules (e.g., retainage), submittal requirements, allowances, alternates, and other important project requirements. Each of these conditions can have a significant bearing on the ultimate cost of the project. They must be read and understood prior to performing the estimate.

While analyzing the plans and specifications, the estimator should evaluate the different portions of the project to determine which areas warrant the most attention. The estimator should focus first on those items that represent the largest cost centers of the project or that entail the greatest risk. These cost centers are not always the portions of the job that require the most time to estimate but are those items that will have the most significant impact on the estimate.

Figure 3.1, from Division 17 of *Means Electrical Cost Data,* is a chart showing typical percentages of electrical and mechanical work relative to

171 | S.F., C.F. and % of Total Costs

171 000 | S.F. & C.F. Costs			UNIT COSTS			% OF TOTAL			
		UNIT	1/4	MEDIAN	3/4	1/4	MEDIAN	3/4	
010	0010	**APARTMENTS** Low Rise (1 to 3 story) R171 -100	S.F.	39.25	49.45	65.05				**010**
	0020	Total project cost	C.F.	3.52	4.62	5.75				
	0100	Site work R171 -200	S.F.	3.26	4.69	7.50	6.30%	10.50%	14%	
	0500	Masonry		.71	1.83	3.10	1.50%	3.90%	6.50%	
	1500	Finishes		4.12	5.30	6.95	8.90%	10.70%	12.90%	
	1800	Equipment		1.28	1.94	2.89	2.80%	4.40%	6.30%	
	2720	Plumbing		3.06	3.99	5.05	6.70%	9%	10.10%	
	2770	Heating, ventilating, air conditioning		1.94	2.36	3.48	4.20%	5.60%	7.60%	
	2900	Electrical		2.26	3.02	4.16	5.20%	6.70%	8.50%	
	3100	Total: Mechanical & Electrical		6.75	8.35	10.75	15.90%	18.20%	22.20%	
	9000	Per apartment unit, total cost	Apt.	30,200	45,300	67,200				
	9500	Total: Mechanical & Electrical	"	5,600	8,300	11,800				
020	0010	**APARTMENTS** Mid Rise (4 to 7 story)	S.F.	51.55	62.35	76				**020**
	0020	Total project costs	C.F.	4.04	5.55	7.65				
	0100	Site work	S.F.	2.01	3.93	7.30	5.20%	6.70%	9.10%	
	0500	Masonry		3.15	4.41	6.55	5.20%	7.30%	10.50%	
	1500	Finishes		6.40	8.10	10.60	10.40%	11.90%	16.90%	
	1800	Equipment		1.71	2.33	3.10	2.80%	3.50%	4.50%	
	2500	Conveying equipment		1.17	1.44	1.73	2%	2.20%	2.60%	
	2720	Plumbing		3.05	4.81	5.30	6.20%	7.40%	8.90%	
	2900	Electrical		3.50	4.66	5.70	6.60%	7.20%	8.90%	
	3100	Total: Mechanical & Electrical		9.60	12.05	15.50	17.90%	20.10%	22.30%	
	9000	Per apartment unit, total cost	Apt.	38,400	57,700	67,000				
	9500	Total: Mechanical & Electrical	"	11,900	13,400	21,000				
030	0010	**APARTMENTS** High Rise (8 to 24 story)	S.F.	59.10	71.25	87.10				**030**
	0020	Total project costs	C.F.	4.86	6.75	8.25				
	0100	Site work	S.F.	1.80	3.46	4.84	2.50%	4.80%	6.10%	
	0500	Masonry		3.34	6.05	7.65	4.70%	9.60%	10.70%	
	1500	Finishes		6.40	8.20	9.35	9.30%	11.70%	13.50%	
	1800	Equipment		1.88	2.31	3.09	2.70%	3.30%	4.30%	
	2500	Conveying equipment		1.19	1.97	2.81	2.20%	2.70%	3.30%	
	2720	Plumbing		3.77	5.12	6.45	6.70%	9.10%	10.60%	
	2900	Electrical		4.05	5.10	6.90	6.40%	7.60%	8.80%	
	3100	Total: Mechanical & Electrical		11.95	14.50	17.90	18.20%	21.80%	23.90%	
	9000	Per apartment unit, total cost	Apt.	55,200	65,000	70,100				
	9500	Total: Mechanical & Electrical	"	13,100	15,100	16,400				
040	0010	**AUDITORIUMS**	S.F.	60	83.25	109				**040**
	0020	Total project costs	C.F.	3.91	5.45	7.80				
	2720	Plumbing	S.F.	3.79	5.05	6.50	5.80%	7%	8.40%	
	2900	Electrical		4.85	6.85	8.95	6.70%	8.80%	11%	
	3100	Total: Mechanical & Electrical		10.05	13.30	23.10	14.70%	18.50%	23.60%	
050	0010	**AUTOMOTIVE SALES**	S.F.	41.40	49.55	74.75				**050**
	0020	Total project costs	C.F.	3.05	3.47	4.51				
	2720	Plumbing	S.F.	2.21	3.59	3.92	6.20%	6.40%	7%	
	2770	Heating, ventilating, air conditioning		3.18	4.87	5.27	6.30%	10%	10.30%	
	2900	Electrical		3.65	5.45	6.30	7.40%	9.90%	12.40%	
	3100	Total: Mechanical & Electrical		7.70	11.25	14.75	16.60%	19.10%	27%	
060	0010	**BANKS**	S.F.	89.40	111	143				**060**
	0020	Total project costs	C.F.	6.40	8.65	11.35				
	0100	Site work	S.F.	8.80	16.20	24.05	7%	13.80%	17.10%	
	0500	Masonry		4.49	7.45	16.45	2.90%	5.80%	11.30%	
	1500	Finishes		7.60	10.30	13.25	5.50%	7.60%	9.90%	
	1800	Equipment		3.54	7.40	16.80	3.20%	8.20%	12.50%	
	2720	Plumbing		2.84	4.05	5.95	2.80%	3.90%	4.90%	
	2770	Heating, ventilating, air conditioning		5.50	7.25	9.80	5%	7.20%	8.50%	

Figure 3.1

projects as a whole. These charts have been developed to represent the overall average percentages for new construction. Commonly used building types are included.

When the overall scope of the work has been identified, the drawings should be examined to confirm the information in the specifications. This is the time to clarify details while reviewing the general content. The estimator should note which sections, elevations, and detail drawings are for which plans. At this point and throughout the whole estimating process, the estimator should note and list any discrepancies between the plans and specifications, as well as any possible omissions. It is often stated in bid documents that bidders are obliged to notify the owner or architect/engineer of any such discrepancies. When so notified, the designer will most often issue an addendum to the contract documents to properly notify all parties concerned and to assure equal and competitive bidding. Competition can be fair only if the same information is provided for all bidders.

Once familiar with the contract documents, the estimator should solicit bids by notifying appropriate subcontractors, manufacturers, and vendors. Those whose work may be affected by the site conditions should accompany the estimator on a job site visit (especially in cases of renovation and remodeling, where existing conditions can have a significant effect on the cost of a project).

During a site visit, the estimator should take notes, and possibly photographs, of all situations pertinent to the construction and thus to the project estimate. If unusual site conditions exist, or if questions arise during the takeoff, a second site visit is recommended.

In some areas, questions are likely to arise that cannot be answered clearly by the plans and specifications. It is crucial that the owner or responsible party be notified quickly, preferably in writing, so that these questions may be resolved before unnecessary problems arise. Often such items involve more than one contractor and can be resolved only by the owner or construction manager. A proper estimate cannot be completed until all such questions are answered.

The Quantity Takeoff

The quantity takeoff is the cornerstone of construction bidding. The amount of detail shown on electrical drawings is perhaps the least of any for the major trades. As a result, the electrical estimator must not only count the items shown on the drawings but also envision the completed design, including fittings, hangers, fasteners, devices, and cover plates. To effectively cover all aspects of the project, certain steps must be followed.

The quantity takeoff should be organized so that the information gathered can be used to future advantage. Scheduling can be made easier if items are taken off and listed by construction phase or by floor. Material purchasing will similarly benefit.

Units for each item should be used consistently throughout the whole project—from takeoff to cost control. In this way, the original estimate can be equitably compared to progress reports and final cost reports. It will be easier to keep track of the job. (See Chapter 11: Cost Control and Analysis.)

Part II of this book is devoted to descriptions of 71 electrical components. In that section, a takeoff procedure is suggested for each component. Typical material and labor units are also given for each component installation. Each material and labor unit is comprised of a list of items that are generally included in the component. Also given are the units by which the component is measured or counted.

Traditionally, quantities are taken off from the drawings in the same sequence as they are erected or installed. Now, however, the sequence of takeoff and estimating is more often based on the systems or type of work. In this case, preference in the estimating process is given to certain items or components based on the relative costs.

Quantities should be taken off by one person if the project is not too large and if time allows. For larger projects, the plans are often split and the work assigned to two or more quantity surveyors. In this case, a project leader should be assigned to coordinate and assemble the estimate.

When working with the plans during the quantity takeoff, consistency is very important. If each job is approached in the same manner, a pattern will develop, such as moving from the lower floors to the top, clockwise, or counterclockwise. The choice of method is not important, but consistency is. The purpose of being consistent is to avoid duplications as well as omissions and errors. Pre-printed forms provide an excellent means for developing consistent patterns. Figures 4.1 and 4.3 are two examples of takeoff forms. The Quantity Sheet (Figure 4.1) is designed purely for quantity takeoff. Note that one list of materials can be used for up to four different areas or segments. Part III of this book (the sample estimate) contains examples of the use of quantity sheets. Figure 4.2 shows a Cost Analysis sheet, which can be used in conjunction with a Quantity Sheet. Totals of quantities are transferred to this sheet for pricing and extensions. Figure 4.3, a Consolidated Estimate sheet, is designed to be used for both quantity takeoff and pricing on one form. There are many other variations.

Every contractor can benefit from designing custom company forms. If all employees of a company use the same types of forms, then communications and coordination of the estimating process will proceed more smoothly. One estimator will be able to more easily understand the work of another. R.S. Means has published two books completely devoted to forms and their use, entitled *Means Forms for Building Construction Professionals* and *Means Forms for Contractors.* Scores of forms, examples, and instructions for use are included.

Appropriate and easy-to-use forms are the first, and most important, of the "tools of the trade" for estimators. Other tools useful to the estimator include scales, rotometers, mechanical counters, digitizers, and colored pencils.

A number of shortcuts can be used for the quantity takeoff. If approached logically and systematically, these techniques help to save time without sacrificing accuracy. Consistent use of accepted abbreviations saves the time of writing things out. An abbreviations list similar to the one that appears in the Appendix of this book might be posted in a conspicuous place for each estimator to provide a consistent pattern of definitions for use within an office.

All dimensions—whether printed, measured, or calculated—that can be used for determining quantities of more than one item should be listed on a separate sheet and posted for easy reference. Posted gross dimensions can also be used to quickly check for order of magnitude errors.

Rounding off, or decreasing the number of significant digits, should be done only when it will not statistically affect the resulting product. The estimator must use good judgment to determine instances when rounding is appropriate. An overall two- or three-percent variation in a competitive market can often be the difference between getting and losing a job, or between profit and no profit. The estimator should establish rules for rounding to achieve a consistent level of precision. In general, it is best not to round numbers until the final summary of quantities.

The final summary is also the time to convert units of measure into standards for practical use (linear feet of wire to one hundred linear foot units, for example). This is done to keep the numerical value of the unit cost manageable. The installation of type THW #14 wire requires .00615 labor-hours per linear foot, but this information is expressed as .615 L.H./C.L.F. (labor-hours per hundred linear feet). There is a glossary of common abbreviations in the Appendix section.

Be sure to quantify (count) and include "labor only" items that are not shown on plans. Such items may or may not be indicated in the specifications and might include cleanup, special labor for handling materials, testing, etc.

Means Forms
QUANTITY SHEET

SHEET NO.										
PROJECT								ESTIMATE NO.		
LOCATION				ARCHITECT				DATE		
TAKE OFF BY				EXTENSIONS BY:				CHECKED BY:		

DESCRIPTION	NO.	DIMENSIONS			UNIT	UNIT	UNIT	UNIT

Figure 4.1

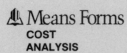

Means Forms

COST ANALYSIS

	SHEET NO.
PROJECT	ESTIMATE NO.
ARCHITECT	DATE

TAKE OFF BY:	QUANTITIES BY:	PRICES BY:	EXTENSIONS BY:	CHECKED BY:

DESCRIPTION	SOURCE/DIMENSIONS			QUANTITY	UNIT	MATERIAL		LABOR		EQ./TOTAL	
						UNIT COST	TOTAL	UNIT COST	TOTAL	UNIT COST	TOTAL

Figure 4.2

22

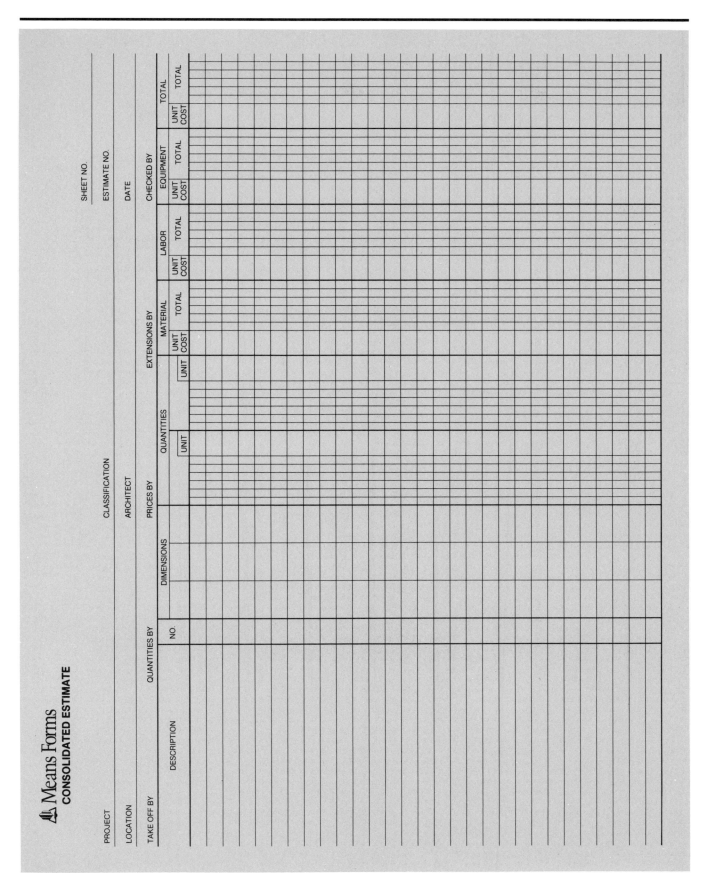

Figure 4.3

The following list is a summation of the suggestions mentioned in this chapter along with a few additional guidelines that will be helpful during the quantity takeoff:

- Use pre-printed forms.
- Transfer carefully when copying numbers from one sheet to the next.
- List dimensions (width, length) in a consistent order.
- Use printed measurements, if available.
- Verify the scale of drawings before using them as a basis for measurement.
- Convert feet and inches to decimal feet.
- Do not round off until the final summary of quantities.
- Mark drawings as quantities are counted.
- Be alert for changes in scale, or notes such as "N.T.S." (not to scale).
- Include required items that may not appear in the plans and specs.

And perhaps the four most important points:

- Write legibly.
- Be organized.
- Use common sense.
- Be consistent.

Pricing
the Estimate

When the quantities have been counted, then values, in the form of unit costs, must be applied and project burdens (overhead and profit) added to determine the total selling price (i.e., the quote). Depending on the chosen estimating method (based on the degree of accuracy required) and the level of detail, these unit costs may be direct or "bare," or may include overhead, profit, or contingencies. In Unit Price Estimating, the unit costs most commonly used are "bare," or "unburdened." Most contractors extend labor quantities as labor-hours and material quantities as dollars. When the total labor-hours are determined, it is necessary to multiply these figures by the appropriate hourly rate before adding markups. Items such as overhead and profit are usually added to the total direct costs at the estimate summary.

Sources of Cost Information

One of the most difficult aspects of the estimator's job is determining accurate and reliable bare cost data. Sources for such data are varied, but can be categorized in terms of their relative reliability. The most reliable of any cost information is the accurate, up-to-date, well-kept records of completed work by the estimator's own company. There is no better cost for a particular construction item than the *actual* cost to the contractor of that item from another recent job, modified (if necessary) to meet the requirements of the project being estimated.

Quotations by vendors for material costs are also reliable. In this case, however, the estimator must still apply the labor costs.

Whenever possible, all price quotations from vendors or subcontractors should be obtained in writing. Qualifications and exclusions should be clearly stated. The items quoted should be checked to be sure that they are complete and as specified. One way to ensure that these requirements are met is to prepare a form on which all subcontractors and vendors must submit their quotations. This form, generally called a "request for quote," can suggest all of the appropriate questions. It also provides a format to organize the information needed by the estimator and, later, the purchasing agent. This technique can be especially useful to the estimator in a smaller organization, since he or she must often act as purchasing agent as well.

The above procedures are ideal, but in the realistic haste of estimating and bidding, quotations are often received verbally, either in person or by telephone. The importance of gathering all pertinent information is heightened because omissions are more likely. A pre-printed form, such the Telephone Quotation form shown in Figure 5.1, can be extremely useful to ensure that all required information and qualifications are obtained and understood. How often has a subcontractor said, "I didn't know that I was supposed to include that"? With the help of such forms, the appropriate questions may be covered.

If the estimator has no cost records for a particular item and is unable to obtain a quotation, then the next most reliable source of price information is a current unit price cost book such as *Means Electrical Cost Data*. R.S. Means presents all such data in the form of national averages; these figures can be adjusted to local conditions with City Cost Indexes, a procedure that will be explained in Part III of this book. In addition to being a source of primary costs, unit price books can also be useful as a reference or cross-check for verifying costs obtained elsewhere.

Lacking cost information from any of the above-mentioned sources, the estimator may have to rely on experience and personal knowledge of the field to develop costs.

No matter which source of cost information is used, the system and sequence of pricing should be the same as that used for the quantity takeoff. This consistent approach should continue through both accounting and cost control during work on the project.

Types of Costs

Types of Costs in a Construction Estimate

Direct Costs	Indirect Costs
Material	Taxes and insurance
Labor	Overhead
Equipment	Profit
Subcontractors	Contingencies
Project overhead	
Sales tax	
Bonds	

All costs included in a Unit Price Estimate can be divided into two types: direct and indirect. Direct costs are those dedicated solely to the physical construction of a specific project. Material, labor, equipment, and subcontract costs, as well as project overhead costs, are all direct.

Indirect costs are usually added to the estimate at the summary stage and are most often calculated as a percentage of the direct costs. They include such items as taxes, insurance, overhead, profit, and contingencies. The indirect costs account for the great variation among different bidders' estimates.

A clear understanding of direct and indirect cost factors is a fundamental part of pricing the estimate. Chapters 6 and 7 address the components of direct and indirect costs in detail.

TELEPHONE QUOTATION

DATE _____

PROJECT _____

TIME _____

FIRM QUOTING _____

PHONE (_____) _____

ADDRESS _____

BY _____

ITEM QUOTED _____

RECEIVED BY _____

WORK INCLUDED	AMOUNT OF QUOTATION

DELIVERY TIME				**TOTAL BID**	
DOES QUOTATION INCLUDE THE FOLLOWING:			If ☐ NO is checked, determine the following:		
STATE & LOCAL SALES TAXES	☐ YES	☐ NO	MATERIAL VALUE		
DELIVERY TO THE JOB SITE	☐ YES	☐ NO	WEIGHT		
COMPLETE INSTALLATION	☐ YES	☐ NO	QUANTITY		
COMPLETE SECTION AS PER PLANS & SPECIFICATIONS	☐ YES	☐ NO	DESCRIBE BELOW		

EXCLUSIONS AND QUALIFICATIONS	

ADDENDA ACKNOWLEDGEMENT	**TOTAL ADJUSTMENTS**	
	ADJUSTED TOTAL BID	

ALTERNATES	
ALTERNATE NO.	
ALTERNATE NO.	
ALTERNATE NO.	
ALTERNATE NO.	
ALTERNATE NO.	
ALTERNATE NO.	
ALTERNATE NO.	

Figure 5.1

Chapter 6

Direct Costs

Direct costs can be defined as those necessary for the completion of the project — in other words, the hard costs. Material, labor, and equipment are among the more obvious items in this category. While subcontract costs include the overhead and profit (indirect costs) of the subcontractor, they are considered to be direct costs to the prime contractor. Also included are certain project overhead costs for items that are necessary for construction. Examples are a storage trailer, tools, and temporary power and lighting. Sales tax and bonds are additional direct costs, since they are essential for the performance of the project.

Material

When quantities have been carefully taken off, estimates of material costs can be very accurate. For a high level of accuracy, the material unit prices must be reliable and current. The most reliable source of material costs is a quotation from a vendor for the particular job in question. Ideally, the vendor should have access to the plans and specifications for verification of quantities and specified products. Providing quotes is a service that most suppliers will include on large, bulk procurements, such as lighting fixtures or switchgear.

Material pricing appears relatively simple and straightforward. There are, however, certain considerations that the estimator must address when analyzing material quotations. The reputation of the vendor is a significant factor. Can the vendor "deliver," both figuratively and literally? Estimators may choose not to rely on a "competitive" lower price from an unknown vendor, but will instead use a slightly higher price from a known, reliable vendor. Experience is the best judge for such decisions.

There are many other questions that the estimator should ask: How long is the price guaranteed? At the end of that period, is there an escalation clause? Does the price include delivery charges or sales tax, if required? Where is the point of FOB (Free On Board)? (With sensitive electronic or large electrical equipment, this can be an extremely important factor.) Are guarantees and warranties in compliance with the specification requirements? Will there be adequate and appropriate storage space available? If not, can staggered shipments be made? Note that most of these questions are addressed on the Telephone Quotation form in Figure 5.1. More information should be obtained, however, to ensure that a quoted price is accurate and competitive.

The estimator must be sure that the quotation or obtained price is for the materials as per plans and specifications. Architects and engineers may write into the specifications that: a) a particular type or brand of product must be used with no substitution; b) a particular type or brand of product is specified, but alternate brands of equal quality and performance may be accepted *upon approval;* or c) no particular type or brand is specified. Depending on the options, the estimator may be able to find an acceptable, less expensive alternative. In some cases, these substitutions can substantially lower the cost of a project. Note also that many specification packages will require that "catalog cuts" be submitted for certain materials as part of the bid proposal. In this case, there is pressure on the estimator to obtain the lowest possible price on materials that he or she believes will meet the specified criteria.

When the estimator has received material quotations, there are still other considerations that should influence the final choice of a vendor. Lead time—the amount of time between order and delivery—must be determined and considered. It does not matter how competitive or low a quote is if the material cannot be delivered to the job site on time to support the schedule. If a delivery date is promised, is there a guarantee, or a penalty clause for late delivery?

The estimator should also determine whether there are any unusual payment requirements. Cash flow for a company can be severely affected if a large material purchase, thought to be payable in 30 days or 90 days, is delivered C.O.D. (Cash On Delivery) or "site draft." Truck drivers may not allow unloading until payment has been received. Such requirements must be determined during the estimating stage so that the cost of borrowing money, if necessary, can be included.

If unable to obtain the quotation of a vendor from whom the material would be purchased, the estimator has other sources for obtaining material prices. These include, in order of reliability:

1. Current price lists from manufacturers' catalogs. Be sure to check that the list indicates any "contractor discounts."
2. Cost records from previous jobs. Historical costs must be updated for present market conditions.
3. Reputable and current annual unit price cost books, such as *Means Electrical Cost Data.* Such books usually represent national averages and must be factored to local markets.

No matter which price source is used, the estimator must be sure to include an allowance for any burdens, such as delivery or finance charges, over the actual cost of the material. (The same kinds of concerns that apply to vendor quotations should be taken into consideration when using these other price sources.)

Labor

To determine the installation cost for each item of construction, the estimator must know two pieces of information: first, the labor rate (hourly wage or salary) of the worker, and second, how much time a worker will need to complete a given unit of the installation—in other words, the productivity or labor units. Wage rates are known going into a project, but productivity may be very difficult to determine.

To estimators working for contractors, the construction labor rates that the contractor pays will be known, well-documented, and constantly updated. Estimators for owners, architects, or engineers must determine labor rates from outside sources. Unit price data books, such as *Means Electrical Cost Data,* provide national average labor wage rates. The unit costs for labor are based on these averages. Figure 6.1 shows national average *union* rates for the construction industry based on January 1, 1995. Figure 6.2 lists national average *open shop* rates, again based on January 1, 1995.

Note the column entitled "Workers' Compensation." Of all the trades, electricians have the lowest rate. This is an average number that varies from

		A		B	C	D	E	F	G	H	I
		Base Rate Incl. Fringes		Work-ers' Comp.	Average Fixed Over-head	Over-head	Profit	Total Overhead & Profit		Rate with O & P	
Abbr.	Trade	Hourly	Daily	Ins.				%	Amount	Hourly	Daily
Skwk	Skilled Workers Average (35 trades)	$25.35	$202.80	19.8%	16.8%	13.0%	10.0%	59.6%	$15.10	$40.45	$323.60
	Helpers Average (5 trades)	18.85	150.80	21.2		11.0		59.0	11.10	29.95	239.60
	Foreman Average, Inside ($.50 over trade)	25.85	206.80	19.8		13.0		59.6	15.40	41.25	330.00
	Foreman Average, Outside ($2.00 over trade)	27.35	218.80	19.8		13.0		59.6	16.30	43.65	349.20
Clab	Common Building Laborers	19.40	155.20	21.7		11.0		59.5	11.55	30.95	247.60
Asbe	Asbestos Workers	28.00	224.00	19.0		16.0		61.8	17.30	45.30	362.40
Boil	Boilermakers	29.30	234.40	12.1		16.0		54.9	16.10	45.40	363.20
Bric	Bricklayers	25.25	202.00	19.3		11.0		57.1	14.40	39.65	317.20
Brhe	Bricklayer Helpers	19.55	156.40	19.3		11.0		57.1	11.15	30.70	245.60
Carp	Carpenters	24.60	196.80	21.7		11.0		59.5	14.65	39.25	314.00
Cefi	Cement Finishers	23.90	191.20	12.4		11.0		50.2	12.00	35.90	287.20
Elec	Electricians	28.50	228.00	7.9		16.0		50.7	14.45	42.95	343.60
Elev	Elevator Constructors	29.05	232.40	9.2		16.0		52.0	15.10	44.15	353.20
Eqhv	Equipment Operators, Crane or Shovel	26.15	209.20	13.0		14.0		53.8	14.05	40.20	321.60
Eqmd	Equipment Operators, Medium Equipment	25.15	201.20	13.0		14.0		53.8	13.55	38.70	309.60
Eqlt	Equipment Operators, Light Equipment	24.15	193.20	13.0		14.0		53.8	13.00	37.15	297.20
Eqol	Equipment Operators, Oilers	21.40	171.20	13.0		14.0		53.8	11.50	32.90	263.20
Eqmm	Equipment Operators, Master Mechanics	26.85	214.80	13.0		14.0		53.8	14.45	41.30	330.40
Glaz	Glaziers	24.50	196.00	16.0		11.0		53.8	13.20	37.70	301.60
Lath	Lathers	24.30	194.40	13.9		11.0		51.7	12.55	36.85	294.80
Marb	Marble Setters	25.10	200.80	19.3		11.0		57.1	14.35	39.45	315.60
Mill	Millwrights	25.95	207.60	13.2		11.0		51.0	13.25	39.20	313.60
Mstz	Mosaic and Terrazzo Workers	24.55	196.40	11.0		11.0		48.8	12.00	36.55	292.40
Pord	Painters, Ordinary	22.60	180.80	16.4		11.0		54.2	12.25	34.85	278.80
Psst	Painters, Structural Steel	23.50	188.00	64.2		11.0		102.0	23.95	47.45	379.60
Pape	Paper Hangers	22.85	182.80	16.4		11.0		54.2	12.40	35.25	282.00
Pile	Pile Drivers	24.70	197.60	33.4		16.0		76.2	18.80	43.50	348.00
Plas	Plasterers	23.70	189.60	17.4		11.0		55.2	13.10	36.80	294.40
Plah	Plasterer Helpers	19.80	158.40	17.4		11.0		55.2	10.95	30.75	246.00
Plum	Plumbers	29.30	234.40	10.1		16.0		52.9	15.50	44.80	358.40
Rodm	Rodmen (Reinforcing)	27.10	216.80	36.1		14.0		76.9	20.85	47.95	383.60
Rofc	Roofers, Composition	22.05	176.40	36.4		11.0		74.2	16.35	38.40	307.20
Rots	Roofers, Tile and Slate	22.05	176.40	36.4		11.0		74.2	16.35	38.40	307.20
Rohe	Roofer Helpers (Composition)	15.60	124.80	36.4		11.0		74.2	11.60	27.20	217.60
Shee	Sheet Metal Workers	28.10	224.80	13.7		16.0		56.5	15.90	44.00	352.00
Spri	Sprinkler Installers	30.85	246.80	10.4		16.0		53.2	16.40	47.25	378.00
Stpi	Steamfitters or Pipefitters	29.25	234.00	10.1		16.0		52.9	15.45	44.70	357.60
Ston	Stone Masons	25.35	202.80	19.3		11.0		57.1	14.45	39.80	318.40
Sswk	Structural Steel Workers	27.15	217.20	44.4		14.0		85.2	23.15	50.30	402.40
Tilf	Tile Layers	24.45	195.60	11.0		11.0		48.8	11.95	36.40	291.20
Tilh	Tile Layer Helpers	19.95	159.60	11.0		11.0		48.8	9.75	29.70	237.60
Trlt	Truck Drivers, Light	20.00	160.00	16.9		11.0		54.7	10.95	30.95	247.60
Trhv	Truck Drivers, Heavy	20.35	162.80	16.9		11.0		54.7	11.15	31.50	252.00
Sswl	Welders, Structural Steel	27.15	217.20	44.4		14.0		85.2	23.15	50.30	402.40
Wrck	*Wrecking	19.40	155.20	44.4	↓	11.0	↓	82.2	15.95	35.35	282.80

*Not included in Averages.

Figure 6.1

state to state (and between crafts). See Figure 6.3. Workers' Compensation is a direct cost when applied to field labor.

If more accurate union labor rates are required, the estimator has a couple of options. Union locals can provide rates (as well as negotiated increases) for a particular location. Employer bargaining groups can usually provide labor cost data as well. R.S. Means Co., Inc. publishes *Labor Rates for the Construction Industry* on an annual basis. This book lists the union labor rates by trade for over 314 U.S. and Canadian cities.

Determination of non-union, or "open shop," rates is much more difficult. In larger cities, employer organizations often exist to represent open shop contractors. These organizations may have records of local pay scales, but ultimately, wage rates are determined by each contractor. The national average for electricians' open shop base rate is 64% of the union rate.

		A		B	C	D	E	F	G	H	I
		Base Rate Incl. Fringes		Work-ers' Comp. Ins.	Average Fixed Over-head	Over-head	Profit	Total Overhead & Profit		Rate with O & P	
Abbr.	Trade	Hourly	Daily					%	Amount	Hourly	Daily
Skwk	Skilled Workers Average (35 trades)	$16.65	$133.20	19.8%	16.8%	27.0%	10.0%	73.6%	$12.25	$28.90	$231.20
	Helpers Average (5 trades)	12.40	99.20	21.2		25.0		73.0	9.05	21.45	171.60
	Foreman Average, Inside ($.50 over trade)	17.15	137.20	19.8		27.0		73.6	12.60	29.75	238.00
	Foreman Average, Outside ($2.00 over trade)	18.65	149.20	19.8		27.0		73.6	13.75	32.40	259.20
Clab	Common Building Laborers	12.05	96.40	21.7		25.0		73.5	8.85	20.90	167.20
Asbe	Asbestos Workers	17.65	141.20	19.0		30.0		75.8	13.40	31.05	248.40
Boil	Boilermakers	18.45	147.60	12.1		30.0		68.9	12.70	31.15	249.20
Bric	Bricklayers	16.90	135.20	19.3		25.0		71.1	12.00	28.90	231.20
Brhe	Bricklayer Helpers	13.10	104.80	19.3		25.0		71.1	9.30	22.40	179.20
Carp	Carpenters	16.50	132.00	21.7		25.0		73.5	12.15	28.65	229.20
Cefi	Cement Finishers	16.00	128.00	12.4		25.0		64.2	10.25	26.25	210.00
Elec	Electricians	18.25	146.00	7.9		30.0		64.7	11.80	30.05	240.40
Elev	Elevator Constructors	18.60	148.80	9.2		30.0		66.0	12.30	30.90	247.20
Eqhv	Equipment Operators, Crane or Shovel	17.25	138.00	13.0		28.0		67.8	11.70	28.95	231.60
Eqmd	Equipment Operators, Medium Equipment	16.60	132.80	13.0		28.0		67.8	11.25	27.85	222.80
Eqlt	Equipment Operators, Light Equipment	15.95	127.60	13.0		28.0		67.8	10.80	26.75	214.00
Eqol	Equipment Operators, Oilers	14.10	112.80	13.0		28.0		67.8	9.55	23.65	189.20
Eqmm	Equipment Operators, Master Mechanics	17.70	141.60	13.0		28.0		67.8	12.00	29.70	237.60
Glaz	Glaziers	16.65	133.20	16.0		25.0		67.8	11.30	27.95	223.60
Lath	Lathers	16.30	130.40	13.9		25.0		65.7	10.70	27.00	216.00
Marb	Marble Setters	16.80	134.40	19.3		25.0		71.1	11.95	28.75	230.00
Mill	Millwrights	17.40	139.20	13.2		25.0		65.0	11.30	28.70	229.60
Mstz	Mosaic and Terrazzo Workers	16.45	131.60	11.0		25.0		62.8	10.35	26.80	214.40
Pord	Painters, Ordinary	15.35	122.80	16.4		25.0		68.2	10.45	25.80	206.40
Psst	Painters, Structural Steel	16.00	128.00	64.2		25.0		116.0	18.55	34.55	276.40
Pape	Paper Hangers	15.55	124.40	16.4		25.0		68.2	10.60	26.15	209.20
Pile	Pile Drivers	16.55	132.40	33.4		30.0		90.2	14.95	31.50	252.00
Plas	Plasterers	15.90	127.20	17.4		25.0		69.2	11.00	26.90	215.20
Plah	Plasterer Helpers	13.25	106.00	17.4		25.0		69.2	9.15	22.40	179.20
Plum	Plumbers	18.45	147.60	10.1		30.0		66.9	12.35	30.80	246.40
Rodm	Rodmen (Reinforcing)	17.35	138.80	36.1		28.0		90.9	15.75	33.10	264.80
Rofc	Roofers, Composition	14.55	116.40	36.4		25.0		88.2	12.85	27.40	219.20
Rots	Roofers, Tile and Slate	14.55	116.40	36.4		25.0		88.2	12.85	27.40	219.20
Rohe	Roofer Helpers (Composition)	10.30	82.40	36.4		25.0		88.2	9.10	19.40	155.20
Shee	Sheet Metal Workers	17.70	141.60	13.7		30.0		70.5	12.50	30.20	241.60
Spri	Sprinkler Installers	19.45	155.60	10.4		30.0		67.2	13.05	32.50	260.00
Stpi	Steamfitters or Pipefitters	18.45	147.60	10.1		30.0		66.9	12.35	30.80	246.40
Ston	Stone Masons	16.50	132.00	19.3		25.0		71.1	11.75	28.25	226.00
Sswk	Structural Steel Workers	17.40	139.20	44.4		28.0		99.2	17.25	34.65	277.20
Tilf	Tile Layers	16.40	131.20	11.0		25.0		62.8	10.30	26.70	213.60
Tilh	Tile Layer Helpers	13.35	106.80	11.0		25.0		62.8	8.40	21.75	174.00
Trlt	Truck Drivers, Light	13.60	108.80	16.9		25.0		68.7	9.35	22.95	183.60
Trhv	Truck Drivers, Heavy	13.85	110.80	16.9		25.0		68.7	9.50	23.35	186.80
Sswl	Welders, Structural Steel	17.40	139.20	44.4		28.0		99.2	17.25	34.65	277.20
Wrck	*Wrecking	12.40	99.20	44.4		25.0		96.2	11.95	24.35	194.80

*Not included in Averages.

Figure 6.2

R010-060 Worker's Compensation Insurance Rates by Trade and State (cont.)

State	Carpentry – 3 stories or less 5651	Carpentry – interior cab. work 5437	Carpentry – general 5403	Concrete Work – NOC 5213	Concrete Work – flat (flr., sdwk.) 5221	Electrical Wiring – inside 5190	Excavation – earth NOC 6217	Excavation – rock 6217	Glaziers 5462	Insulation Work 5479	Lathing 5443	Masonry 5022	Painting & Decorating 5474	Pile Driving 6003	Plastering 5480	Plumbing 5183	Roofing 5551	Sheet Metal Work (HVAC) 5538	Steel Erection – door & sash 5102	Steel Erection – inter., ornam. 5102	Steel Erection – structure 5040	Steel Erection – NOC 5057	Tile Work – (interior ceramic) 5348	Waterproofing 9014	Wrecking 5701
AL	27.81	15.56	26.44	16.88	10.75	8.86	15.62	15.62	16.59	22.10	15.35	16.84	17.10	63.77	16.07	12.67	37.77	21.80	14.82	14.82	39.13	41.37	14.86	6.10	39.13
AK	10.83	8.09	12.71	12.63	11.99	7.25	13.15	13.15	28.84	17.88	10.83	12.29	16.04	51.68	15.05	6.52	23.99	8.94	11.24	11.24	50.85	50.85	12.62	5.27	50.85
AZ	26.59	8.31	28.24	20.93	11.21	11.40	12.31	12.31	14.83	29.05	11.37	23.90	17.03	31.62	21.50	10.09	28.94	15.85	20.00	20.00	44.75	27.02	10.16	7.99	44.75
AR	15.01	10.40	14.82	21.37	6.55	5.55	9.85	9.85	9.85	12.81	10.52	12.41	12.12	22.41	11.94	6.35	17.87	11.62	9.85	9.85	37.54	31.54	5.59	7.43	37.54
CA	28.28	9.07	28.28	13.18	13.18	9.93	7.88	7.88	16.37	23.34	10.90	14.55	19.45	21.18	18.12	11.59	39.79	15.33	13.55	13.55	23.93	21.91	7.74	19.45	21.91
CO	32.22	13.54	20.95	20.96	15.13	9.20	15.99	15.99	15.98	21.31	14.68	31.06	21.85	41.53	37.40	14.50	59.10	12.54	11.83	11.83	73.46	43.49	15.04	12.26	73.46
CT	24.64	18.01	28.42	22.23	13.44	8.55	13.15	13.15	23.65	27.05	29.49	29.78	13.92	20.64	17.13	15.98	37.27	16.18	17.48	17.48	56.24	53.32	19.68	4.89	56.24
DE	13.83	13.83	11.56	9.28	6.29	5.82	8.54	8.54	11.18	11.56	10.51	9.85	13.41	11.64	10.51	5.41	22.89	10.29	10.21	10.21	26.69	25.69	10.21	7.54	25.69
DC	16.31	12.11	23.98	28.37	12.35	15.36	15.97	15.97	28.77	24.86	14.21	35.14	12.71	64.91	17.30	22.92	40.09	16.90	42.01	42.01	53.70	58.84	22.62	5.80	53.70
FL	35.29	20.09	34.27	36.70	17.79	12.38	15.26	15.26	22.94	29.18	26.21	27.64	32.18	54.46	28.65	14.16	48.53	21.35	23.16	23.16	38.22	45.13	10.84	9.59	38.22
GA	22.45	11.60	25.91	17.09	13.59	8.50	25.84	25.84	15.93	13.85	20.93	16.63	15.45	39.89	15.11	8.05	35.56	13.78	9.93	9.93	26.03	47.70	10.64	10.44	26.03
HI	11.66	9.32	39.81	13.93	9.03	8.89	10.81	10.81	14.80	20.18	9.51	17.35	7.68	28.43	19.16	5.36	40.64	8.32	14.10	14.10	27.94	26.82	7.72	10.50	27.94
ID	18.03	8.66	20.80	19.53	6.95	6.09	10.91	10.91	13.41	23.48	9.19	18.69	20.23	23.88	11.76	8.32	31.90	12.06	9.49	9.49	34.29	22.59	7.93	9.57	34.29
IL	24.60	16.08	24.80	39.19	15.57	11.59	13.22	13.22	38.55	30.89	15.67	24.67	18.15	48.11	20.80	17.25	42.95	20.10	26.79	26.79	90.05	123.28	15.02	8.13	90.05
IN	10.09	3.47	8.44	7.83	3.85	3.08	5.51	5.51	6.77	9.01	5.07	6.19	4.92	12.17	6.23	3.23	18.09	5.15	4.60	4.60	14.84	15.69	5.24	4.79	14.44
IA	9.50	7.13	16.03	16.11	6.54	5.94	6.28	6.28	12.51	13.45	7.43	16.85	11.74	21.21	9.49	8.20	24.37	9.72	16.04	16.04	30.97	28.88	6.56	6.13	22.77
KS	16.65	6.92	13.33	22.10	10.66	6.63	8.32	8.32	10.66	16.06	10.33	15.48	9.30	25.60	16.02	7.71	36.80	9.70	9.19	9.19	27.50	40.14	6.90	8.22	27.50
KY	16.93	13.73	20.53	19.03	10.35	9.01	11.26	11.26	13.70	15.58	13.27	21.92	21.28	33.15	13.19	11.05	25.26	16.71	11.79	11.79	41.08	29.55	10.52	8.34	41.80
LA	29.63	22.95	26.01	20.86	14.80	10.48	24.73	24.73	23.88	20.82	14.00	21.27	27.63	54.39	21.42	13.78	49.11	21.35	15.51	15.51	66.41	36.94	12.82	10.26	66.41
ME	13.43	10.42	43.59	24.29	11.12	10.02	14.75	14.75	13.35	15.39	14.03	17.26	16.07	31.44	17.95	11.12	32.07	17.70	15.08	15.08	37.84	61.81	11.66	9.37	37.84
MD	10.55	5.95	10.55	11.35	5.05	5.15	9.25	9.25	13.20	13.05	6.45	11.35	6.75	27.45	6.65	5.55	22.80	7.00	9.15	9.15	26.80	18.50	6.35	3.50	26.80
MA	18.14	14.71	37.91	45.04	24.08	7.52	13.48	13.48	26.31	26.43	23.40	33.79	19.43	41.16	19.58	11.73	85.62	19.82	24.66	24.66	85.62	76.27	20.73	8.20	85.62
MI	17.68	15.32	25.20	44.58	17.81	8.26	17.08	17.08	14.28	21.08	14.53	33.00	17.86	64.20	25.48	12.45	47.31	13.72	16.04	16.04	64.20	62.95	11.83	10.42	64.20
MN	30.24	31.00	50.60	29.04	29.88	11.28	22.80	22.80	30.13	46.25	32.72	40.45	27.47	80.14	32.72	22.91	103.79	20.95	20.43	20.43	134.74	47.55	35.31	11.68	134.74
MS	20.90	6.85	14.19	15.74	7.63	6.89	10.30	10.30	12.94	8.68	10.00	9.81	12.48	32.55	12.95	7.27	14.88	12.69	12.41	12.41	18.89	17.68	10.71	5.64	18.89
MO	16.36	7.42	10.15	13.20	9.50	5.53	8.76	8.76	8.91	15.76	10.24	11.45	10.74	18.16	12.40	6.43	22.56	8.41	11.43	11.43	37.81	25.20	6.27	5.41	37.81
MT	52.17	27.93	69.29	56.19	29.86	14.03	49.39	49.39	33.78	41.80	31.63	84.05	50.77	79.69	41.87	24.16	116.91	18.48	41.18	41.18	149.63	81.38	21.16	13.65	149.63
NE	13.06	10.47	14.72	18.35	11.18	4.78	13.09	13.09	12.47	19.96	10.72	16.30	11.19	26.27	13.81	8.57	31.30	14.85	12.36	12.36	28.89	31.65	8.07	7.49	28.89
NV	19.28	19.28	19.28	13.79	13.79	11.00	12.00	12.00	14.86	20.84	22.35	16.08	32.70	10.72	22.35	14.20	30.05	32.89	13.53	13.53	32.70	32.70	11.32	10.72	32.70
NH	22.33	13.20	27.91	25.25	14.23	7.51	16.31	16.31	16.49	23.49	15.87	17.52	16.14	46.91	20.48	9.60	58.35	15.89	15.30	15.30	57.01	30.34	12.57	9.99	57.01
NJ	9.76	7.48	9.76	10.02	7.59	4.58	7.74	7.74	8.14	10.78	9.18	9.65	10.20	16.60	9.18	5.23	25.99	6.25	12.43	12.43	24.73	12.97	4.25	4.79	31.33
NM	25.38	19.50	25.22	31.31	20.90	7.53	12.69	12.69	21.11	25.80	14.35	35.70	16.41	60.40	26.11	11.04	53.08	13.66	20.09	20.09	50.91	42.32	15.70	11.02	50.91
NY	15.56	8.76	16.56	19.77	14.11	8.16	11.78	11.78	19.19	17.96	20.82	23.62	13.36	39.69	12.53	13.04	35.38	25.55	15.56	15.56	47.74	47.44	11.35	8.03	25.31
NC	16.91	10.06	18.51	11.41	7.97	9.64	10.63	10.63	12.37	13.62	6.95	11.04	28.06	20.32	17.10	8.01	21.19	10.04	10.09	10.09	26.90	16.56	5.52	4.87	26.90
ND	12.75	12.75	12.75	14.88	14.88	5.45	10.04	10.04	10.01	13.05	12.54	12.01	14.01	28.99	12.54	7.54	25.23	7.54	12.75	12.75	28.99	28.99	9.30	25.23	28.99
OH	11.12	11.12	11.12	11.08	11.08	4.99	11.08	11.08	14.31	12.59	12.59	11.95	14.31	11.08	12.59	6.72	24.98	22.38	11.08	11.08	11.08	11.08	9.42	11.08	11.08
OK	26.16	11.79	19.33	15.51	11.50	7.41	18.45	18.45	13.55	18.00	12.05	16.80	17.10	36.26	18.29	8.72	42.26	12.45	11.17	11.17	69.45	46.76	11.42	8.20	69.45
OR	43.04	11.66	24.68	24.34	12.69	7.42	14.95	14.95	14.25	27.82	14.16	17.68	26.21	30.84	19.53	10.53	40.95	13.36	9.77	9.77	63.61	41.32	11.92	13.52	63.61
PA	15.80	15.80	19.85	28.18	11.84	7.80	12.74	12.74	15.69	19.85	18.94	18.96	22.05	32.12	18.94	11.57	43.30	12.58	24.71	24.71	59.05	24.71	11.83	18.96	81.34
RI	15.52	7.13	12.32	14.83	16.49	6.22	12.89	12.89	18.05	15.23	11.26	14.94	17.87	30.71	15.05	4.69	31.27	6.80	10.13	10.13	78.01	40.30	9.28	8.00	78.01
SC	19.09	10.31	25.02	15.30	8.48	8.37	9.70	9.70	15.93	10.37	9.10	9.40	9.92	22.00	16.81	7.24	27.15	12.42	10.03	10.03	24.28	37.11	6.55	4.93	24.28
SD	17.66	11.24	24.25	18.11	9.59	6.75	12.28	12.28	14.08	21.04	11.71	14.05	12.35	29.70	20.68	10.96	40.42	11.76	13.49	13.49	38.94	34.30	9.24	6.01	38.94
TN	19.66	6.72	14.98	13.67	9.30	6.37	10.27	10.27	10.68	15.65	8.34	11.32	11.35	28.76	13.21	7.89	25.29	11.98	11.26	11.26	34.83	25.87	5.58	5.81	34.83
TX	28.29	18.95	28.29	25.59	19.49	11.60	18.16	18.16	14.17	25.84	13.47	23.12	18.29	43.91	20.99	12.88	47.24	22.92	14.29	14.29	50.47	31.01	9.94	11.38	54.81
UT	11.17	11.17	11.17	17.68	7.99	7.05	6.38	6.38	9.55	10.95	12.32	13.75	15.29	17.24	10.60	6.41	26.27	6.30	8.99	8.99	23.51	23.51	6.06	5.83	26.53
VT	10.87	9.12	16.84	28.18	11.22	5.64	10.56	10.56	13.33	15.62	11.47	14.08	9.76	29.21	15.93	9.35	19.90	11.31	14.46	14.46	40.48	40.96	9.18	8.32	40.48
VA	11.01	9.60	11.88	17.06	7.35	5.92	7.52	7.52	7.71	14.09	7.19	10.61	9.50	28.31	12.88	7.19	26.94	10.08	10.27	10.27	22.55	23.32	7.59	4.23	22.55
WA	14.42	14.42	14.42	11.21	9.83	4.00	9.15	9.15	17.44	13.39	16.20	13.92	11.74	18.72	17.30	5.63	15.89	5.89	12.89	12.89	22.81	22.81	8.23	12.45	18.64
WV	13.34	13.34	13.34	17.69	17.69	5.01	9.14	9.14	6.36	6.36	15.65	13.58	15.65	8.95	15.65	6.61	12.04	6.36	14.98	14.98	13.27	14.98	13.58	4.13	13.27
WI	17.96	8.85	17.66	13.00	10.47	6.65	7.74	7.74	13.08	17.66	10.25	16.67	14.93	29.92	16.56	7.51	34.22	9.18	16.25	16.25	44.99	26.23	11.31	6.80	44.99
WY	9.52	9.52	9.52	9.52	9.52	9.52	9.52	9.52	9.52	9.52	9.52	9.52	9.52	9.52	9.52	9.52	9.52	9.52	9.52	9.52	9.52	9.52	9.52	9.52	9.52
AVG.	19.40	12.37	21.69	20.46	12.43	7.89	13.04	13.04	15.97	19.03	13.91	19.33	16.36	33.38	17.35	10.11	36.37	13.69	14.85	14.85	44.39	36.14	11.04	8.91	44.37

Figure 6.3

However, because of a higher overhead percentage, the rate with overhead and profit is 70% of union shop wages.

Labor units (or labor-hours) are the least predictable of all factors for building projects. It is important to determine, as accurately as possible, prevailing productivity. The best source of labor productivity or labor units (and, therefore, labor costs) is the estimator's well-kept records from previous projects. If there are no company records for productivity, cost data books such as *Means Electrical Cost Data,* and productivity reference books such as *Means Productivity Standards for Construction,* can be invaluable. Included with the listing for each individual construction item is the designation of a suggested crew make-up (one electrician in most cases). The crew is the minimum grouping of talent that can be expected to accomplish the task efficiently. Figure 6.4, a typical page from *Means Electrical Cost Data,* includes this data and indicates the required number of man-hours for each "unit" of work. When multiplied by the average union wage rate for electricians (see Figure 6.1), the result is the "bare" installed unit cost, which appears in the "INST." column.

The estimator who has neither company records nor the sources described above must put together the appropriate crews and determine the expected output or productivity. This type of estimating should be attempted only based on strong experience and considerable exposure to construction methods and practices. There are rare occasions when this approach is necessary to estimate a particular item or a new technique. Even then, the new labor units are often extrapolated from existing figures for similar work, rather than being created from scratch.

Equipment

In recent years, construction equipment has become more important, not only because of the incentive to reduce labor costs, but also as a response to new, high-technology construction methods and materials. As a result, equipment costs represent an increasing percentage of total project costs in construction. Estimators must carefully address the issue of equipment and related expenses. Equipment costs can be divided into the following two categories:

1. Rental, lease, or ownership costs. These costs may be determined based on hourly, daily, weekly, monthly, or annual increments. These fees or payments buy only the "right" to use the equipment (i.e., exclusive of operating costs).
2. Operating costs. Once the "right" of use is obtained, costs are incurred for actual use or operation. These costs may include fuel, lubrication, maintenance, and parts.

Equipment costs, as described above, do not include the labor expense of operators. However, some cost books and suppliers may include the operator in the quoted price for equipment as an "operated" rental cost. In other words, the equipment is priced as if it were a subcontract cost. In electrical construction, equipment is often procured in this way, via a contract with the general contractor on site. The advantage of this approach is that it can be used on an "as needed" basis and not carried as a weekly or monthly cost.

Equipment ownership costs apply to both leased and owned equipment. The operating costs of equipment, whether rented, leased, or owned, are available from the following sources (listed in order of reliability):

1. The company's own records

163 | Motors, Starters, Boards and Switches

163 200	Boards	CREW	DAILY OUTPUT	MAN-HOURS	UNIT	MAT.	LABOR	EQUIP.	TOTAL	TOTAL INCL O&P	
255 4800	3 pole, 15 to 60 amp, FA	1 Elec	5.30	1.509	Ea.	245	43		288	335	**255**
4900	70 to 100 amp, FA		4	2		295	57		352	410	
5000	15 to 60 amp, FH		5.30	1.509		365	43		408	465	
5100	70 to 100 amp, FH		4	2		415	57		472	540	
5200	125 to 225 amp, KA		3.20	2.500		685	71.50		756.50	860	
5300	125 to 225 amp, KH		3.20	2.500		1,550	71.50		1,621.50	1,800	
5400	125 to 400 amp, LA		2.30	3.478		1,250	99		1,349	1,525	
5500	125 to 600 amp, MA		1.60	5		2,075	143		2,218	2,500	
5600	700 & 800 amp, MA	▼	1.30	6.154	▼	2,675	175		2,850	3,225	
260 0010	**SWITCHBOARDS** Incoming main service section,	R163 -260									**260**
0100	Aluminum bus bars, not including CT's or PT's										
0200	No main disconnect, includes CT compartment										
0300	120/208 volt, 4 wire, 600 amp	1 Elec	.50	16	Ea.	2,350	455		2,805	3,250	
0400	800 amp		.44	18.182		2,575	520		3,095	3,600	
0500	1000 amp		.40	20		2,975	570		3,545	4,125	
0600	1200 amp		.36	22.222		3,175	635		3,810	4,450	
0700	1600 amp		.33	24.242		3,475	690		4,165	4,875	
0800	2000 amp		.31	25.806		3,725	735		4,460	5,200	
1000	3000 amp		.28	28.571		4,825	815		5,640	6,525	
1200	277/480 volt, 4 wire, 600 amp		.50	16		2,375	455		2,830	3,300	
1300	800 amp		.44	18.182		2,575	520		3,095	3,600	
1400	1000 amp		.40	20		2,975	570		3,545	4,125	
1500	1200 amp		.36	22.222		3,175	635		3,810	4,450	
1600	1600 amp		.33	24.242		3,450	690		4,140	4,850	
1700	2000 amp		.31	25.806		3,725	735		4,460	5,200	
1800	3000 amp		.28	28.571		4,775	815		5,590	6,475	
1900	4000 amp	▼	.26	30.769	▼	5,925	875		6,800	7,850	
2000	Fused switch & CT compartment										
2100	120/208 volt, 4 wire, 400 amp	1 Elec	.56	14.286	Ea.	3,275	405		3,680	4,225	
2200	600 amp		.47	17.021		3,825	485		4,310	4,925	
2300	800 amp		.42	19.048		5,150	545		5,695	6,500	
2400	1200 amp		.34	23.529		6,400	670		7,070	8,050	
2500	277/480 volt, 4 wire, 400 amp		.57	14.035		3,375	400		3,775	4,325	
2600	600 amp		.47	17.021		3,875	485		4,360	5,000	
2700	800 amp		.42	19.048		5,175	545		5,720	6,525	
2800	1200 amp	▼	.34	23.529	▼	6,450	670		7,120	8,100	
2900	Pressure switch & CT compartment										
3000	120/208 volt, 4 wire, 800 amp	1 Elec	.40	20	Ea.	7,075	570		7,645	8,625	
3100	1200 amp		.33	24.242		8,050	690		8,740	9,900	
3200	1600 amp		.31	25.806		8,950	735		9,685	11,000	
3300	2000 amp		.28	28.571		10,500	815		11,315	12,800	
3310	2500 amp		.25	32		11,900	910		12,810	14,500	
3320	3000 amp		.22	36.364		18,000	1,025		19,025	21,400	
3330	4000 amp		.20	40		23,800	1,150		24,950	27,900	
3400	277/480 volt, 4 wire, 800 amp		.40	20		10,300	570		10,870	12,200	
3600	1200 amp, with ground fault		.33	24.242		12,100	690		12,790	14,400	
4000	1600 amp, with ground fault		.31	25.806		13,000	735		13,735	15,400	
4200	2000 amp, with ground fault	▼	.28	28.571	▼	15,600	815		16,415	18,400	
4400	Circuit breaker, molded case & CT compartment										
4600	3 pole, 4 wire, 600 amp	1 Elec	.47	17.021	Ea.	5,275	485		5,760	6,525	
4800	800 amp		.42	19.048		5,650	545		6,195	7,050	
5000	1200 amp	▼	.34	23.529	▼	7,775	670		8,445	9,550	
5100	Copper bus bars, not incl. CT's or PT's, add, minimum					15%					
262 0010	**SWITCHBOARD** (in plant distribution)										**262**
0100	Main lugs only, to 600 volt, 3 pole, 3 wire, 200 amp	1 Elec	.60	13.333	Ea.	1,525	380		1,905	2,250	

Figure 6.4

2. Annual cost books containing equipment operating costs, such as *Means Electrical Cost Data*
3. Manufacturers' estimates
4. Textbooks dealing with equipment operating costs

These operating costs consist of fuel, lubrication, expendable parts replacement, minor maintenance, transportation, and mobilizing costs. For estimating purposes, the equipment ownership and operating costs should be listed separately. In this way, the decision to rent, lease, or purchase can be decided project by project.

There are two commonly used methods for including equipment costs in a construction estimate. The first is to include the equipment as a part of the construction task for which it is used. In this case, costs are included in each line item as a separate unit price. The advantage of this method is that costs are allocated to the division or task that actually incurs the expense. As a result, more accurate records can be kept for each installed component. A disadvantage of this method occurs in the pricing of equipment that may be used for many different tasks. Duplication of costs can occur in this instance. Another disadvantage is that the budget may be left short; for example, the estimate may reflect two hours for a crane truck, when the minimum availability of the truck involves a daily (eight-hour) rental charge.

The second method for including equipment costs in the estimate is to keep all such costs separate and to include them in Division 1 as a part of Project Overhead. The advantage of this method is that all equipment costs are grouped together, and that machines used for several tasks are included (without duplication). One disadvantage is that for future estimating purposes, equipment costs will be known only on a per-job basis and not per installed unit.

Whichever method is used, the estimator must be consistent, and must be sure that all equipment costs are included but not duplicated. The estimating method should be the same as that chosen for cost monitoring and accounting. In this way, the data will be available both for monitoring the project's costs and for bidding future projects.

A final word of caution about equipment is to consider its age and reliability. If an older item, such as a pick-up truck, needs frequent repair, it may cost far more in lost labor-hours to the project than is reflected in its calculated cost rate.

Subcontractors

On the occasions when subcontractors are used, quotations should be solicited and analyzed in the same way as material quotes. A primary concern is that the bid covers the work as per plans and specifications, and that all appropriate work alternates and allowances are included. Any exclusions should be clearly stated and explained. If the bid is received verbally, a form such as the Telephone Quotation form shown in Figure 5.1 will help to ensure that it is documented accurately. Any unique scheduling or payment requirements must be noted and evaluated prior to submission of your bid. Such requirements could affect (restrict or enhance) the normal progress of the project, so should be known in advance.

The estimator should note how long the subcontract bid will be honored. This time period usually varies from 30 to 90 days and is often included as a condition in complete bids.

The estimator should question and verify the bonding capability and capacity of unfamiliar subcontractors. Taking such action may be necessary when bidding in a new location. Other than word of mouth, these inquiries may be the only way to confirm subcontractor reliability.

Project Overhead

Project overhead represents those construction costs that are usually included in Division 1—General Requirements. Site management is covered in this section. Typical items are supervisory personnel, job engineers, daily and final cleanup, and temporary heat and power. While these items may not be directly part of the physical structure, they are a part of the project. Project overhead, like all other direct costs, can be separated into material, labor, and equipment components. Figure 6.5 is a Project Overhead Summary form, which can help ensure that all appropriate costs are included.

Some may not agree that certain items (such as equipment or scaffolding) should be included as project overhead, and might prefer to list such items in another division. Ultimately, it is not important *where* each item is incorporated into the estimate but that *every item is included somewhere.*

Project overhead often includes time-related items: for example, equipment rental, supervisory labor, and temporary utilities. The cost for these items depends on the duration of the project. A preliminary schedule should, therefore, be developed *prior* to completion of the estimate so that time-related items can be properly counted. This will be further discussed in Chapter 9: Pre-Bid Scheduling.

Bonds

Although bonds are really a type of "direct cost," they are priced and based on the total "bid" or "selling price." For that reason, they are generally figured after indirect costs have been added. Bonding requirements for a project will be specified in Division 1—General Requirements, and will be included in the construction contract. Various types of bonds may be required. Listed below are a few common types:

Bid Bond: A form of bid security executed by the bidder or principal and by a surety (bonding company) to guarantee that the bidder will enter into a contract within a specified time and furnish any required Performance or Labor and Material Payment Bonds.

Completion Bond: Also known as "Construction" or "Contract" Bond. The guarantee by a surety that the construction contract will be completed and that it will be clear of all liens and encumbrances.

Labor and Material Payment Bond: The guarantee by a surety to the owner that the contractor will pay for all labor and materials used in the performance of the contract as per the construction documents. The claimants under the bond are those having direct contracts with the contractor or any subcontractor.

Performance Bond: (1) A guarantee that a contractor will perform a job according to the terms of the contract. (2) A bond of the contractor in which a surety guarantees to the owner that the work will be performed in accordance with the contract documents. Except where prohibited by statute, the Performance Bond is frequently combined with the Labor and Material Payment Bond.

Surety Bond: A legal instrument under which one party agrees to answer to another party for the debt, default, or failure to perform of a third party.

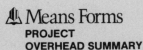

Means Forms

PROJECT
OVERHEAD SUMMARY

SHEET NO. _____

PROJECT _____

ESTIMATE NO. _____

LOCATION _____ ARCHITECT _____ DATE _____

QUANTITIES BY: _____ PRICES BY: _____ EXTENSIONS BY: _____ CHECKED BY: _____

DESCRIPTION	QUANTITY	UNIT	MATERIAL/EQUIPMENT		LABOR		TOTAL COST	
			UNIT	TOTAL	UNIT	TOTAL	UNIT	TOTAL
Job Organization: Superintendent								
Project Manager								
Timekeeper & Material Clerk								
Clerical								
Safety, Watchman & First Aid								
Travel Expense: Superintendent								
Project Manager								
Engineering: Layout								
Inspection/Quantities								
Drawings								
CPM Schedule								
Testing: Soil								
Materials								
Structural								
Equipment: Cranes								
Concrete Pump, Conveyor, Etc.								
Elevators, Hoists								
Freight & Hauling								
Loading, Unloading, Erecting, Etc.								
Maintenance								
Pumping								
Scaffolding								
Small Power Equipment/Tools								
Field Offices: Job Office								
Architect/Owner's Office								
Temporary Telephones								
Utilities								
Temporary Toilets								
Storage Areas & Sheds								
Temporary Utilities: Heat								
Light & Power								
Water								
PAGE TOTALS								

Page 1 of 2

Figure 6.5

⚓ Means Forms

DESCRIPTION	QUANTITY	UNIT	MATERIAL/EQUIPMENT		LABOR		TOTAL COST	
			UNIT	TOTAL	UNIT	TOTAL	UNIT	TOTAL
Total Brought Forward								
Winter Protection: Temp. Heat/Protection								
Snow Plowing								
Thawing Materials								
Temporary Roads								
Signs & Barricades: Site Sign								
Temporary Fences								
Temporary Stairs, Ladders & Floors								
Photographs								
Clean Up								
Dumpster								
Final Clean Up								
Punch List								
Permits: Building								
Misc.								
Insurance: Builders Risk								
Owner's Protective Liability								
Umbrella								
Unemployment Ins. & Social Security								
Taxes								
City Sales Tax								
State Sales Tax								
Bonds								
Performance								
Material & Equipment								
Main Office Expense								
Special Items								
TOTALS:								

Page 2 of 2

Figure 6.5 (continued)

Sales Tax

Sales tax varies from state to state and often from city to city within a state (see Figure 6.6). Larger cities may have a sales tax in addition to the state sales tax. Some localities also impose separate sales taxes on labor and equipment.

When bidding takes place in unfamiliar locations, the estimator should check with local agencies regarding the amount and the method of payment of sales tax. Local authorities may require owners to withhold payments to out-of-state contractors until payment of all required sales tax has been verified.

Sales tax is often taken for granted or even omitted and, as can be seen in Figure 6.6, can be as much as 7.25% of material costs. Indeed, this can represent a significant portion of the project's total cost. Conversely, some clients and/or their projects may be tax exempt. If this fact is unknown to the estimator, a large dollar amount for sales tax might be needlessly included in a bid.

Sales Tax Percentages on Materials by State

State	Tax (%)	State	Tax (%)	State	Tax (%)	State	Tax (%)
Alabama	4	Illinois	6.25	Montana	0	Rhode Island	7
Alaska	0	Indiana	5	Nebraska	5	South Carolina	5
Arizona	5.5	Iowa	5	Nevada	6.75	South Dakota	4
Arkansas	4.5	Kansas	4.9	New Hampshire	0	Tennessee	6
California	7.25	Kentucky	6	New Jersey	6	Texas	6.25
Colorado	3	Louisiana	4	New Mexico	5	Utah	5
Connecticut	6	Maine	6	New York	4	Vermont	5
Delaware	0	Maryland	5	North Carolina	4	Virginia	4.5
District of Columbia	7	Massachusetts	5	North Dakota	5	Washington	6.5
Florida	6	Michigan	4.6	Ohio	5	West Virginia	6
Georgia	4	Minnesota	6.5	Oklahoma	4.5	Wisconsin	5
Hawaii	4	Mississippi	7	Oregon	0	Wyoming	4
Idaho	5	Missouri	4.225	Pennsylvania	6	Average	4.73%

Figure 6.6

Chapter 7

Indirect Costs

Indirect costs are those "costs of doing business" that are incurred by the general staff. These expenses are sometimes referred to as a "burden" to the project. Indirect costs may include certain fixed, or known, expenses and percentages, as well as costs that can be variable and subjectively determined. Government authorities require payment of certain taxes and insurance, usually based on labor costs and determined by trade. These are a type of fixed indirect cost. Office overhead, if well understood and established, can also be considered as a relatively fixed percentage. Profit and contingencies, however, are more of a variable subjective cost. These figures are often determined based on the judgment and discretion of the person responsible for the company's growth and success.

If the direct costs for the same project have been carefully determined, they should not vary significantly from one estimator to another. The indirect costs are often responsible for variations between bids.

The direct costs of a project must be itemized, tabulated, and totalled before the indirect costs can be applied to the estimate. Indirect costs include:

1. Taxes and insurance (on office staff)
2. Office or operating overhead (vs. project overhead)
3. Profit
4. Contingencies

Taxes and Insurance

The taxes and insurance included as indirect costs are most often related to the costs of management and/or type of work. This category may include workers' compensation, builder's risk, and public liability insurance, as well as employer-paid Social Security and unemployment insurance. By law, the employer must pay these expenses. Rates are based on the type and salary of the employees, as well as the location and/or type of business. These are "home office expenses."

Office or Operating Overhead

Office overhead, or the cost of doing business, is perhaps one of the main reasons why so many contractors are unable to realize a profit or even stay in business. This effect is manifested in two ways. Either a company does not know its true overhead cost and, therefore, fails to mark up its costs enough to recover them; or management does not restrain or control overhead costs effectively and fails to remain competitive.

If a contractor does not know the costs of operating the business, then these costs will probably not be recovered. Many companies survive, and even turn a profit, by simply adding an arbitrary percentage for overhead to each job, without knowing how the percentage is derived or what is included. When annual volume changes significantly, whether by increase or decrease, the previously used percentage for overhead may no longer be valid. When such a volume change occurs, the owner often finds that the company is not doing as well as before and cannot determine the reasons. Chances are, overhead costs are not being fully recovered. As an example, Figure 7.1 lists annual office costs and expenses for a typical electrical

Annual Main Office Expenses

Assume: $1,500,000 Annual Volume in the Field
       30% Material, 70% Labor

Office/Operating Expenses:

Owner	$ 60,000
Engineer/Estimator	44,000
Secretary/Receptionist	18,000
Personnel Insurance & Taxes	44,030
Physical Plant Expenses:	
Office Rent	10,000
Utilities	1,800
Telephone	6,000
Vehicles (2)	13,000
Office Equipment	2,400
Legal/Accounting Services	5,000
Miscellaneous:	
Advertising	1,750
Seminars	3,000
Travel & Entertainment	8,000
Uncollected Receivables	18,000
Total	$234,980

$$\frac{\text{Expenses}}{\text{Labor Volume}} = \frac{\$234,980}{\$1,050,000} = 22.4\%$$

To support this overhead, job site staffing would have to average approximately 23 workers throughout the year.

Figure 7.1

contractor. It is assumed that the anticipated annual volume of the company is $1,500,000. Each of the items is described briefly below:

Owner: This includes only a reasonable base salary and does not include profits. An owner's salary is *not* a company's profit.

Engineer/Estimator: Since the owner is primarily on the road getting business, the engineer/estimator is the person who runs the daily operation of the company and is responsible for estimating. In some operations, the estimator successfully wins a bid, then becomes the "project manager" and is responsible to the owner for the project's profitability.

Secretary/Receptionist: This person manages office operations and handles paperwork. A talented individual in this position can be a tremendous asset.

Personnel Insurance & Taxes: These costs are for main office personnel only and, for this example, are calculated as 40.95% of the total salaries based on the following breakdown:

Workers' Compensation	6.00%
FICA	7.65%
Unemployment	7.30%
Medical & other insurance	10.00%
Profit sharing, pension, etc.	10.00%
	40.95%

Physical Plant Expenses: Whether the office, warehouse, and yard are rented or owned, roughly the same costs are incurred. Telephone and utility costs will vary depending on the size of the building and the type of business. Office equipment includes items such as the rental of a copy machine and typewriters.

Legal/Accounting Services: Accountant fees are primarily for quarterly audits. Legal fees go toward collecting and contract disputes. In addition, a prudent contractor will have every contract read by a lawyer prior to signing.

Miscellaneous: There are many expenses that could be placed in this category. Included in the example in Figure 7.1 are just a few of the possibilities. Advertising includes the Yellow Pages and promotional materials.

Uncollected Receivables: This amount can vary greatly, and is often affected by the overall economic climate. Depending on the timing of "uncollectables," cash flow can be severely restricted and can cause serious financial problems, even for large companies. Sound cash planning and anticipation of such possibilities can help to prevent severe repercussions.

While the office example used here is feasible within the industry, keep in mind that it is hypothetical and that conditions and costs vary widely from company to company.

For the example company in Figure 7.1 to stay in business without losses (profit is not yet a factor), not only must all direct construction costs be paid, but an additional $234,980 must be recovered during the year (as a percentage of volume) to operate the office. The percentage may be calculated and applied in two ways:

    1. Office overhead applied as a percentage of labor costs only.
       This method requires that labor and material costs be estimated separately.

2. Office overhead applied as a percentage of total project costs. This is appropriate where material and labor costs are not estimated separately.

Remember that the anticipated volume is $1,500,000 for the year, 70% of which is expected to be labor. Office overhead costs, therefore, will be approximately 22.4% of the labor cost, or 15.7% of annual volume for this example. The most common method for recovering these costs is to apply this percentage to each job over the course of the year.

The estimator must also remember that, if volume changes significantly, then the percentage for office overhead should be recalculated for current conditions. The same is true if there are changes in office staff. Salaries are the major portion of office overhead costs. It should be noted that a percentage is commonly applied to material costs for handling, regardless of the method of recovering office overhead costs. This percentage is more easily calculated if material costs are estimated and listed separately.

Profit

Determining a fair and reasonable percentage to be included for profit is not an easy task. This responsibility is usually left to the owner or chief estimator. Experience is crucial in anticipating what profit the market will bear. The economic climate, competition, knowledge of the project, and familiarity with the architect, engineer, or owner all affect the way in which profit is determined.

Chapter 10 includes a method to mathematically determine the profit margin based on historical bidding information. As with all facets of estimating, experience is the key to success.

Contingencies

Like profit, contingencies can be difficult to quantify. Especially appropriate in preliminary budgets, the addition of a contingency is meant to protect the contractor as well as to give the owner a realistic estimate of potential project costs.

A contingency percentage should be based on the number of "unknowns" in a project, or the level of risk involved. This percentage should be inversely proportional to the amount of planning detail that has been done for the project. If complete plans and specifications are supplied, and the estimate is thorough and precise, then there is little need for a contingency. Figure 7.2, from *Means Electrical Cost Data,* lists suggested contingency percentages that may be added to an estimate based on the stage of planning and development.

If an estimate is priced and each individual item is rounded up or "padded," this is, in essence, adding a contingency. This method can cause problems, however, because the estimator can never be quite sure of what is the actual cost and what is the "padding," or safety margin, for each item.

In summary, the estimator cannot determine exactly how much has been included as a contingency factor for the project as a whole. A much more accurate and controllable approach is to price the estimate precisely and then add one contingency amount at the bottom line.

010 | Overhead and Miscellaneous Data

		010 000	Overhead	CREW	DAILY OUTPUT	MAN-HOURS	UNIT	1995 BARE COSTS				TOTAL INCL O&P	
								MAT.	LABOR	EQUIP.	TOTAL		
008	0011	BOND, PERFORMANCE See 010-068											008
012	0011	CONSTRUCTION COST INDEX For 209 major U.S. and											012
	0020	Canadian cities, total cost, min. (Charlotte, NC)					%					77.50%	
	0050	Average										100%	
	0100	Maximum (New York, NY)										133.90%	
020	0010	CONTINGENCIES Allowance to add at conceptual stage					Project					15%	020
	0050	Schematic stage										10%	
	0100	Preliminary working drawing stage										7%	
	0150	Final working drawing stage										2%	
022	0010	CONTRACTOR EQUIPMENT See division 016 R016-410											022
024	0010	CREWS For building construction, see How To Use This Book											024
028	0010	ENGINEERING FEES Educational planning consultant, minimum					Project					.50%	028
	0100	Maximum					"					2.50%	
	0200	Electrical, minimum					Contrct					4.10%	
	0300	Maximum										10.10%	
	0400	Elevator & conveying systems, minimum										2.50%	
	0500	Maximum										5%	
	0600	Food service & kitchen equipment, minimum										8%	
	0700	Maximum										12%	
	1000	Mechanical (plumbing & HVAC), minimum										4.10%	
	1100	Maximum										10.10%	
032	0010	FACTORS To be added to construction costs for particular job											032
	0200												
	0500	Cut & patch to match existing construction, add, minimum					Costs	2%	3%				
	0550	Maximum						5%	9%				
	0800	Dust protection, add, minimum						1%	2%				
	0850	Maximum						4%	11%				
	1100	Equipment usage curtailment, add, minimum						1%	1%				
	1150	Maximum						3%	10%				
	1400	Material handling & storage limitation, add, minimum						1%	1%				
	1450	Maximum						6%	7%				
	1700	Protection of existing work, add, minimum						2%	2%				
	1750	Maximum						5%	7%				
	2000	Shift work requirements, add, minimum							5%				
	2050	Maximum							30%				
	2300	Temporary shoring and bracing, add, minimum						2%	5%				
	2350	Maximum						5%	12%				
034	0010	FIELD OFFICE EXPENSE											034
	0100	Office equipment rental, average					Month	147			147	162	
	0120	Office supplies, average					"	263			263	289	
	0125	Office trailer rental, see division 015-904											
	0140	Telephone bill; avg. bill/month incl. long dist.					Month	247			247	271	
	0160	Field office lights & HVAC					"	82			82	90	
038	0010	HISTORICAL COST INDEXES (Reference) Back to 1945											038
040	0010	INSURANCE Builders risk, standard, minimum R010-040					Job					.22%	040
	0050	Maximum										.59%	
	0200	All-risk type, minimum R010-060										.25%	
	0250	Maximum										.62%	
	0400	Contractor's equipment floater, minimum					Value					.50%	
	0450	Maximum					"					1.50%	
	0600	Public liability, average					Job					1.55%	
	0800	Workers' compensation & employer's liability, average											

Figure 7.2

The Estimate Summary

At the pricing stage of the estimate, there is typically a significant amount of paperwork that must be assembled, analyzed, and tabulated. Generally, the information contained in this paperwork is covered by the following major categories:

- Quantity Sheets for all electrical work items (see Figure 8.1)
- Material suppliers' written quotations (see note below)
- Material suppliers' Telephone Quotations (see Figure 8.2)
- Subcontractors' written quotations
- Equipment suppliers' quotations
- Cost Analysis or Consolidated Estimate sheets (pricing sheets) (see Figures 8.3 and 8.4)
- Recap Summary Sheets

Note: Additional forms, such as Request for Quote forms, are often prepared by the individual electrical contractor.

In the "real world" of estimating, many quotations, especially for bulk materials and for subcontracts, are not received until the last minute before the bidding deadline. Therefore, a system is needed to efficiently handle the paperwork and to ensure that everything will get transferred once (and only once) from the quantity takeoff to the cost analysis sheets. Some general rules for this process are as follows:

- Write on only one side of any document, whenever possible.
- Code each sheet with a large division number in a consistent place, preferably near one of the upper corners.
- Use Telephone Quotation forms for uniformity in recording prices received by phone.
- Document the source of every quantity and price.
- Keep each type of document in its "pile" (Quantities, Material, Subcontractors, Equipment) filed in order by division number.
- Keep the entire estimate in one or more compartmentalized folders.
- When an item is transferred to the Cost Analysis sheet, check it off.
- Most importantly, number and code each takeoff sheet and each pricing extension sheet as it is created. At the same time, keep an index list of each sheet by number. If a sheet is to be

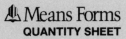

QUANTITY SHEET

SHEET NO.							
PROJECT						ESTIMATE NO.	
LOCATION		ARCHITECT			DATE		
TAKE OFF BY		EXTENSIONS BY:			CHECKED BY:		

DESCRIPTION	NO.	DIMENSIONS			UNIT	UNIT	UNIT	UNIT

Figure 8.1

Means Forms
**TELEPHONE
QUOTATION**

		DATE
PROJECT		TIME
FIRM QUOTING		PHONE ( )
ADDRESS		BY
ITEM QUOTED		RECEIVED BY

WORK INCLUDED	AMOUNT OF QUOTATION

DELIVERY TIME			**TOTAL BID**	
DOES QUOTATION INCLUDE THE FOLLOWING:			If ☐ NO is checked, determine the following:	
STATE & LOCAL SALES TAXES	☐ YES	☐ NO	MATERIAL VALUE	
DELIVERY TO THE JOB SITE	☐ YES	☐ NO	WEIGHT	
COMPLETE INSTALLATION	☐ YES	☐ NO	QUANTITY	
COMPLETE SECTION AS PER PLANS & SPECIFICATIONS	☐ YES	☐ NO	DESCRIBE BELOW	

EXCLUSIONS AND QUALIFICATIONS	

ADDENDA ACKNOWLEDGEMENT	**TOTAL ADJUSTMENTS**	
	ADJUSTED TOTAL BID	

ALTERNATES	
ALTERNATE NO.	
ALTERNATE NO.	
ALTERNATE NO.	
ALTERNATE NO.	
ALTERNATE NO.	
ALTERNATE NO.	
ALTERNATE NO.	

Figure 8.2

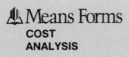

COST
ANALYSIS

							MATERIAL		LABOR		EQ./TOTAL	

SHEET NO.

PROJECT

ESTIMATE NO.

ARCHITECT

DATE

TAKE OFF BY: QUANTITIES BY: PRICES BY: EXTENSIONS BY: CHECKED BY:

DESCRIPTION	SOURCE/DIMENSIONS			QUANTITY	UNIT	MATERIAL		LABOR		EQ./TOTAL	
						UNIT COST	TOTAL	UNIT COST	TOTAL	UNIT COST	TOTAL

Figure 8.3

50

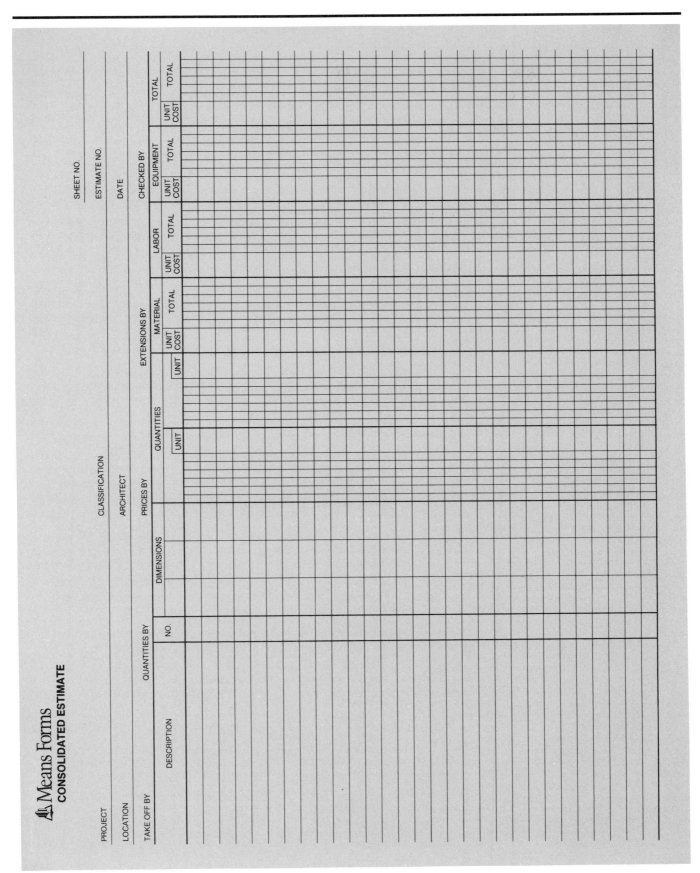

Figure 8.4

abandoned, write "VOID" on it, but do not discard it. Keep it until the bid is accepted to be able to account for all pages and sheets.

Note: A helpful technique for organizing these sheets and forms involves the use of colors to code each category of cost sheets. This system makes locating and revising sheets both easier and quicker.

All subcontract costs should be properly noted and listed separately. These costs contain the subcontractor's markups and may be treated differently from other direct costs when the estimator calculates the general contractor's overhead, profit, and contingency allowance.

After all the unit prices, subcontractor prices, and allowances have been entered on the pricing sheets, the costs are extended. In making the extensions, ignore the cents column and round all totals to the nearest dollar. In a column of figures, the cents will average out and will not be of consequence. Finally, each subdivision is added and the results checked, preferably by someone other than the person doing the extensions.

It is important to check the larger items for order of magnitude errors. If the total subdivision costs are divided by the building area, the resulting square foot cost figures can be used to quickly pinpoint areas that are out of line with expected square foot costs. These cost figures should be recorded for comparison to past projects and as a resource for future estimating.

The takeoff and pricing method, as discussed, has been to utilize a Quantity Sheet for the material takeoff (see Figure 8.1) and to transfer the data to an analysis form for pricing the material, labor, and subcontractor items (see Figure 8.3).

An alternative to this method is a consolidation of the takeoff task and pricing on a single form. This approach works well for smaller bids and for change orders. An example, the Consolidated Estimate Form, is shown in Figure 8.4. The same sequences and recommendations used to complete the Quantity Sheet and Cost Analysis form are to be followed when using the Consolidated Estimate form to price the estimate.

When the pricing of all direct costs is complete, the estimator has two choices: 1) to make all further price changes and adjustments on the Cost Analysis or Consolidated Estimate sheets, or 2) to transfer the total costs for each subdivision to an Estimate Summary sheet so that all further price changes, until bid time, will be done on one sheet. Any indirect markups and burdens will be figured on this sheet.

Unless the estimate has a limited number of items, it is recommended that costs be transferred to an Estimate Summary sheet. This step should be double-checked since an error of transposition may easily occur. Preprinted terms can be useful, although a plain columnar form may suffice. This summary, with page numbers from each extension sheet, can also serve as an index.

A company that repeatedly uses certain standard listings can save valuable time by having a custom Estimate Summary sheet printed with these items listed. The printed MasterFormat division and subdivision headings serve as another type of checklist, ensuring that all required costs are included. Appropriate column headings or categories for any Estimate Summary form could be as follows:

1. Material
2. Labor
3. Equipment

4. Subcontractor

5. Total

As items are listed in the proper columns, each category is added and appropriate markups applied to the total dollar values. Different percentages may be added to the sum of each column at the estimate summary. These percentages may include the following items, as discussed in Chapter 7:

1. Taxes and insurance

2. Overhead

3. Profit

4. Contingencies

Chapter 9

Pre-Bid Scheduling

The need for planning and scheduling is clear once the contract is signed and work commences on the project. However, some scheduling is also important during the bidding stage for the following reasons:

1. To determine if the project can be completed in the allotted or specified time using normal crew sizes.
2. To identify potential overtime requirements.
3. To determine the time requirements for supervision.
4. To anticipate possible temporary heat and power requirements.
5. To price certain general requirement items and overhead costs.
6. To budget for equipment usage.
7. To anticipate and justify material and equipment delivery requirements. (An awareness of these requirements may, for example, justify using a more expensive vendor quote with better delivery terms.)

The schedule produced prior to bidding may be a simple bar chart or network diagram that includes overall quantities, probable delivery times, and available manpower. Network scheduling methods, such as the Critical Path Method (CPM) and the Precedence Diagram, simplify pre-bid scheduling because they do not require time-scaled line diagrams.

In the CPM Diagram, the activity is represented by an arrow. Nodes indicate start/stop between activities. The Precedence Diagram, on the other hand, shows the activity as a node with arrows used to denote precedence relationships between the activities. The precedence arrows may be used in different configurations to represent the sequential relationships between activities. Examples of CPM and Precedence Diagrams are shown in Figures 9.1 and 9.2, respectively. In both systems, duration times are indicated along each path. The sequence (path) of activities requiring the most total time represents the shortest possible time (critical path) in which those activities may be completed.

For example, in both Figure 9.1 and Figure 9.2, activities A, B, and C require 20 successive days for completion before activity G can begin. Activity paths for D and E (15 days), and for F (12 days), are shorter and can easily be completed during the 20-day sequence. Therefore, this 20-day sequence is the shortest possible time (i.e., the "critical path") for the completion of these activities before activity G can begin. Past experience or a prepared

Figure 9.1

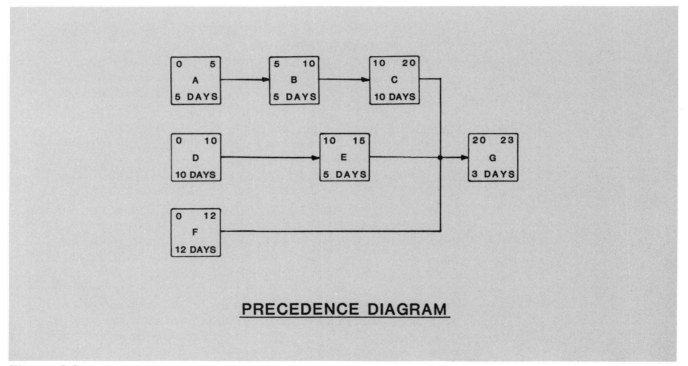

Figure 9.2

rough schedule may suggest that the time specified in the bidding documents is insufficient to complete the required work. In such cases, a more comprehensive schedule should be produced prior to bidding; this schedule will help to determine the added overtime or premium time work costs required to meet the completion date.

A three-story office building project is used for the Sample Estimate in Part III of this book. A preliminary schedule is needed to determine the supervision and manning requirements of the job. The specifications state that the building must be completed within one year. Normally, the excavation, foundations, and superstructure can be completed in approximately one-half of the construction period. Therefore, the major portion of the electrical work (assuming exposed conduit and undercarpet power and phone systems) is restricted to the last six months of the one year allotted. The service and distribution equipment installation might be restrained by the delivery of the equipment.

A rough schedule for the electrical work might be produced as shown in Figure 9.3. The labor-days used to develop this schedule are derived from the labor-hour figures in the estimate. Labor-hours can be determined based on the figures in *Means Electrical Cost Data*. Labor-days can also be figured by dividing the total labor cost shown on the estimate by the cost per labor-day for an electrician.

As shown, the preliminary schedule can be used to determine supervision requirements, to develop appropriate crew sizes, and as a basis for ordering materials. All of these factors must be considered at this preliminary stage to determine how to meet the required one-year completion date.

A pre-bid schedule can provide much more information than simple job duration. It can be used to refine the estimate by introducing realistic manpower projections. The schedule may also help the contractor to adjust the structure and size of the company based on projected requirements for months, even years, ahead. A schedule can also become an effective tool for negotiating contracts.

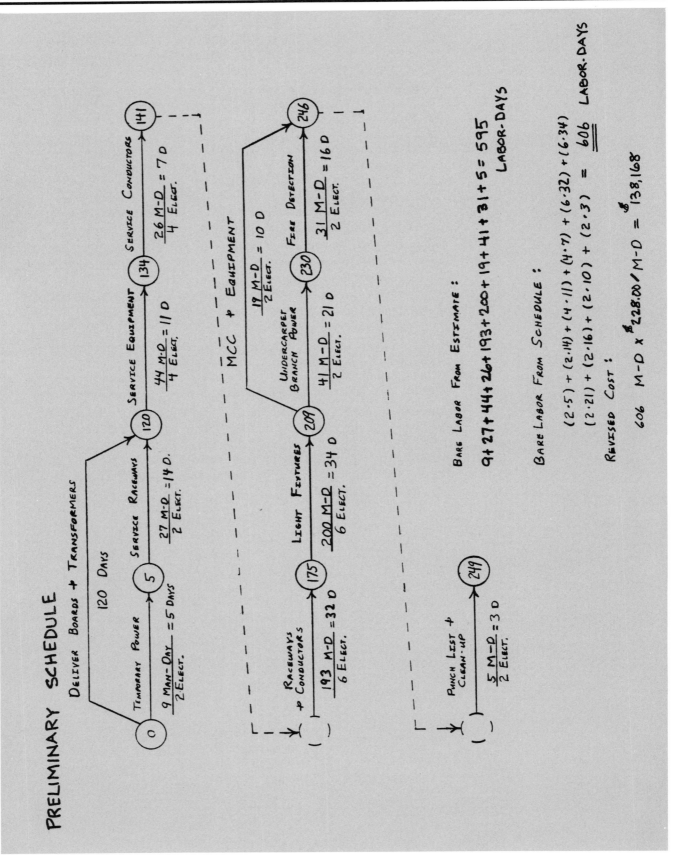

Figure 9.3

Chapter 10

Bidding Strategies

The goal of most contractors is to make as much money as possible on each job and, more importantly, to maximize return on investment on an annual basis. Often, this can be done by taking *fewer* jobs at a *higher* profit and by limiting bidding to the jobs that are most likely to be successful for the company.

Resource Analysis

Since a contractor cannot physically bid every job in a geographic area, a selection process must determine which projects to bid. This process should begin with an analysis of the strengths and weaknesses of the contractor. The following items must be considered as objectively as possible:

- Individual strengths of the company's top management
- Management experience with the type of construction involved, from top management to project superintendents
- Cost records adequate for the appropriate type of construction
- Bonding capability and capacity
- Size of projects with which the company is "comfortable"
- Geographic area that can be managed effectively
- Unusual corporate assets such as:
  - Specialized equipment availability
  - Reliable and timely cost control systems
  - Strong balance sheet

Market Analysis

Most contractors tend to concentrate on a few particular types of projects. From time to time, the company should step back and examine the portion of the industry they are serving. During this process, the following items should be carefully analyzed:

- Historical trend of the market segment
- Expected future trend of the market segment
- Geographic expectations of the market segment
- Historical and expected competition from other contractors
- Risk involved in the particular market segment
- Typical size of projects in this market
- Expected return on investment from the market segment

If several of these areas are experiencing a downturn, then it is definitely appropriate to examine an alternate market. On the other hand, many managers may feel that "bad times" are the times when they should consolidate and narrow their market. These managers are likely to expand or broaden their market only when current activities are especially strong.

Bidding Analysis

Certain steps should be taken to develop a bid strategy within a particular market. The first is to obtain the bid results of jobs in the prospective geographic area. These results should be set up on a tabular basis. This is fairly easy to do in the case of public jobs, since the bid results are normally published (or at least available) from the agency responsible for the project. In private work, this step is more difficult, since the bid results are not normally divulged by the owner.

Determining Risk in a New Market Area

One way to measure success in bidding is how much money is "left on the table" — the difference between the low bid and next lowest bid. The contractor who consistently takes jobs by a wide margin below the next bidder is clearly not making as much money as possible. Information on competitive public bidding is used to determine the amount of money left on the table; this information serves as the basis for fine-tuning a future bidding strategy.

For example, assume a public market where all bid prices and the total number of bidders are known. For each "type" of market sector, create a chart showing the percentage left on the table versus the total number of bidders. When the median figure (percent left on the table) for each number of bidders is connected with a smooth curve, the usual shape of the curve is like the one shown in Figure 10.1.

The exact shape and magnitude of the amounts left on the table will depend on how much risk is involved with that type of work. If the percentages left on the table are high, then the work can be assumed to be very

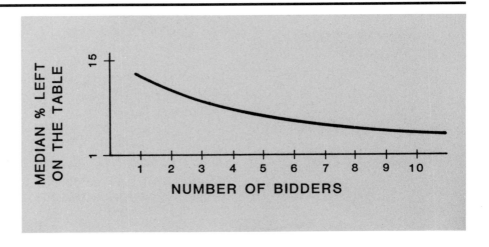

Figure 10.1

risky—with a high profit or loss potential if the award is won. If the percentages are low, the work is probably neither as risky nor as potentially profitable.

Analyzing the Bid's Risk

If a company has been bidding in a particular market, certain information should be collected and recorded as a basis for a bidding analysis. First, the percentage left on the table should be tabulated (as shown in Figure 10.1), along with the number of bidders for the projects in that market on which the company was the low bidder. By probability, half the bids should be above the median line and half below. If more than half are below the line, the company is doing well; if more than half are above, the bidding strategy should be examined.

Maximizing the Profit-to-Volume Ratio

Once the bidding track record for the company has been established, the next step is to reduce the historical percentage left on the table. One method is to create a chart showing, for instance, the last ten jobs on which the company was low bidder, and the dollar spread between the low and second-lowest bid. Next, rank the percentage differences from one to ten (one being the smallest and ten being the largest left on the table). An example is shown in Figure 10.2. This example is for a larger general contractor, but the principles apply to any size or type of contractor involved in bidding.

The company's "cost" ($17,170,000) is derived from the company's low bids ($18,887,000) assuming a 10% profit ($1,717,000). The "second bid" is the next lowest bid. The "difference" is the dollar amount between the low bid and the second bid (money "left on the table"). The differences are

Job No.	"Cost"	Low Bid	Second Bid	Difference	% Diff	% Rank	Profit (Assumed at 10%)
1	$ 918,000	$ 1,009,800	$1,095,000	$ 85,200	9.28	10	$ 91,800
2	1,955,000	2,150,500	2,238,000	87,500	4.48	3	195,500
3	2,141,000	2,355,100	2,493,000	137,900	6.44	6	214,100
4	1,005,000	1,105,500	1,118,000	12,500	1.24	1	100,500
5	2,391,000	2,630,100	2,805,000	174,900	7.31	8	239,100
6	2,782,000	3,060,200	3,188,000	127,800	4.59	4	278,200
7	1,093,000	1,202,300	1,282,000	79,700	7.29	7	109,300
8	832,000	915,200	926,000	10,800	1.30	2	83,200
9	2,372,000	2,609,200	2,745,000	135,800	5.73	5	237,200
10	1,681,000	1,849,100	2,005,000	155,900	9.27	9	168,100
	$17,170,000	$18,887,000		$1,008,000			$1,717,000 = 10% of Cost

Figure 10.2

then ranked based on the percentage of job "costs" left on the table for each. Figure the median difference by averaging the two middle percentages — that is, the fifth and sixth ranked numbers.

$$\text{Median \% Difference} = \frac{5.73 + 6.44}{2} = 6.09\%$$

From Figure 10.2, the median percentage left on the table is 6.09%. To maximize the potential returns on a series of competitive bids, a useful formula is needed for pricing profit. The following formula has proven effective.

$$\text{Normal Profit \%} + \frac{\text{Median \% Difference}}{2} = \text{Adjusted Profit \%}$$

$$10.00 \quad + \quad \frac{6.09}{2} \quad = 13.05\%$$

Now apply this adjusted profit percentage to the same list of ten jobs as shown in Figure 10.3.

Note that the job "costs" remain the same, but that the low bids have been revised. Compare the bottom line results of Figure 10.2 to those of Figure 10.3 based on the two profit margins, 10% and 13.05%, respectively.

Total volume *drops* from $18,887,000 to $17,333,900.

Net profits *rise* from $1,717,000 to $2,000,900.

Profits rise while volume drops! If the original volume is maintained or even increased, profits rise even further. Note how this occurs. By determining a reasonable increase in profit margin, the company has, in effect, raised all bids. By doing so, the company loses two jobs to the second bidder (Jobs 4 and 8 in Figure 10.3).

Job No.	Company's "Cost"	Revised Low Bid	Second Bid	Adj. Diff.	Profit [10% + 3.05%]		Total
1	$ 918,000	$ 1,037,800	$1,095,000	$ 57,200	$ 91,800 +	$28,000	$ 119,800
2	1,955,000	2,210,100	2,238,000	$ 27,900	$195,500 +	59,600	255,100
3	2,141,000	2,420,400	2,493,000	$ 72,600	214,100 +	65,300	279,400
4	(1,005,000)	(1,136,100)	1,118,000 (L)	—	100,500 +	30,600	0
5	2,391,000	2,703,000	2,805,000	102,000	239,100 +	72,900	312,000
6	2,782,000	3,145,100	3,188,000	42,900	278,200 +	84,900	363,100
7	1,093,000	1,235,600	1,282,000	46,400	109,300 +	33,300	142,600
8	(832,000)	(940,600)	926,000 (L)	—	83,200 +	25,400	0
9	2,372,000	2,681,500	2,745,000	63,500	237,200 +	72,300	309,500
10	1,681,000	1,900,400	2,005,000	104,600	168,100 +	51,300	219,400
	$15,333,000	$17,333,900		$517,100			$2,000,900

Figure 10.3

A positive effect of this volume loss is reduced exposure to risk. Since the profit margin is higher, the remaining eight jobs collectively produce more profit than the ten jobs based on the original, lower profit margin. From where did this money come? The money "left on the table" has been reduced from $1,008,000 to $517,100. The whole purpose is to systematically decrease the dollar amount difference between the low bids and the second low bids.

Caution: This is a hypothetical approach based on the following assumptions:

- Profit must be assumed to be the bid or estimated profit, not the actual profit when the job is over.
- Bidding must be done in the same market in which data for the analysis was gathered.
- Economic conditions should be stable from the time the data is gathered until the analysis is used in bidding. If conditions change, use of such an analysis should be reviewed.
- Each contractor must make roughly the same number of bidding mistakes. For higher numbers of jobs in the sample, this requirement becomes more probable.
- The company must bid additional jobs if total annual volume is to be maintained or increased. Likewise, if the net total profit margin is to remain constant, even fewer jobs need to be won.
- Finally, the basic cost numbers and sources must remain constant. If a new estimator is hired or a better cost source is found, this technique cannot work effectively until a new track record has been established.

The accuracy of this strategy depends on the criteria listed above. Nevertheless, it is a valid concept that can be applied, with appropriate and reasonable judgment, to many bidding situations.

Chapter 11

Cost Control and Analysis

An internal accounting system should be used by contractors and construction managers to logically gather and track the costs of a construction project. With this information, a cost analysis can be performed for each activity—both during the installation process and at its conclusion. This information or "feedback" becomes the basis for management decisions throughout the duration of the project. This cost data is also helpful for future bid proposals.

The categories for an electrical project are major items of construction (e.g., lighting), which can be subdivided into component activities (e.g., wire, conduit, fixtures). These activities should coincide with the system and methods of the quantity takeoff. Uniformity is important in the units of measure and in the grouping of components into cost centers. For instance, cost centers for an electrical project might include categories such as lighting, switchgear, branch power, MCC's and motors, and alarm systems. Activities within one of these categories—branch power, for example— might include such items as receptacles, boxes, conduit, and wire.

The major purposes of cost control and analysis are as follows:
- To provide management with a system to monitor costs and progress
- To provide cost feedback to the estimator(s)
- To determine the costs of change orders
- To be used as a basis for progress payment requisitions to the owner, the general contractor, or his or her representative
- To manage cash flow
- To identify areas of potential cost overruns to management for corrective action

It is important to establish a cost control system that is uniform—both throughout the company and from job to job. Such a system might begin with a uniform Chart of Accounts, which is a listing of code numbers for work activities. The Chart of Accounts is used to assign time and cost against work activities for the purpose of creating cost reports. A Chart of Accounts should have enough scope and detail so that it can be used for any of the projects that the company may win. Naturally, an effective Chart of Accounts will also be flexible enough to incorporate new activities as the company takes on new or different kinds of projects. Using a cost control system, the various costs can be consistently allocated. The following information should be recorded for each cost component:

- Labor charges in dollars and labor-hours, summarized from weekly time cards and distributed by code
- Quantities completed to date, to determine unit costs
- Equipment rental costs derived from purchase orders or from weekly charges issued by an equipment company
- Material charges determined from purchase orders
- Allocation of appropriate subcontractor charges
- Job overhead items, listed separately or by component

Each component of costs—labor, materials, and equipment—is now calculated on a unit basis by dividing the quantity installed to date into the cost to date. This procedure establishes the actual installed unit costs to date.

At this point, it is also useful to calculate the percent complete to date. This is done in two steps, or levels. First, the percent complete for each activity is calculated based on the actual quantity installed to date divided by the total quantity estimated for the activity. Second, the project total percent complete is calculated. To arrive at this number, multiply the percent complete of each activity times the total estimated cost for that activity. Then add these results for a total (sometimes called "earned" dollars) and divide this sum by the estimated total. The result is the project's overall percent complete.

The quantities that remain to be installed for each activity should be estimated based on the actual unit cost to date. This is the projected cost to complete each activity. Because of inefficiencies and mobilization costs as the work begins, it is not practical to use the actual units for projecting costs until an activity is 20% complete. Below 20%, the costs as originally estimated should be used. The actual costs to date are added to the projected costs to obtain the anticipated costs at the end of the project.

Typical forms that may be used to develop a cost control system are shown in Figures 11.1 to 11.6.

The analysis of categories serves as a useful management tool, providing information on a constant, up-to-date basis. Immediate attention is attracted to any center that is projecting a loss. Management can concentrate on this item in an attempt to make it profitable or to minimize the expected loss.

The estimating department can use the unit costs developed in the field as background information for future bidding purposes. Particularly useful are unit labor costs and unit labor-hours productivity for the separate activities. This information should be integrated into the accumulated historical data. A particular advantage of unit labor-hour records is that they tend to be constant over time. Current unit labor costs can be figured simply by multiplying these labor-hour standards times the current labor rate per hour.

Frequently, items are added to or deleted from the contract via either field change orders or contract amendments. Accurate cost records are an excellent basis for determining the cost changes that will result.

As discussed above, the determination of completed quantities is necessary to calculate unit costs. These quantities are used to figure the percent complete in each category. These percentages can, in turn, be used to calculate the billing for progress payment requisitions (invoices).

Means Forms

DAILY TIME SHEET

PROJECT _____

FOREMAN _____

WEATHER CONDITIONS _____

TEMPERATURE _____

DATE _____

SHEET NO. _____

DESCRIPTION OF WORK

NO.	NAME									TOTALS HOURS REG-ULAR	OVER-TIME	COST INFORMATION RATE	TOTAL	UNIT COST
		HOURS												
		UNITS												
		HOURS												
		UNITS												
		HOURS												
		UNITS												
		HOURS												
		UNITS												
		HOURS												
		UNITS												
		HOURS												
		UNITS												
		HOURS												
		UNITS												
		HOURS												
		UNITS												
		HOURS												
		UNITS												
		HOURS												
		UNITS												
		HOURS												
		UNITS												
		HOURS												
		UNITS												
		HOURS												
		UNITS												
		HOURS												
		UNITS												
	TOTALS	HOURS												
		UNITS												
	EQUIPMENT													

Figure 11.1

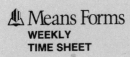

**WEEKLY
TIME SHEET**

EMPLOYEE	EMPLOYEE NUMBER	WEEK ENDING
FOREMAN	HOURLY RATE	PIECE WORK RATE

PROJECT	NO.	DESCRIPTION OF WORK	DAY						TOTAL	HOURS	RATE	TOTAL COST	UNIT COST
			HOURS							REG.			
			UNITS							O.T.			
			HOURS							REG.			
			UNITS							O.T.			
			HOURS							REG.			
			UNITS							O.T.			
			HOURS							REG.			
			UNITS							O.T.			
			HOURS							REG.			
			UNITS							O.T.			
			HOURS							REG.			
			UNITS							O.T.			
			HOURS							REG.			
			UNITS							O.T.			
		TOTAL	HOURS							REG.			
			UNITS							O.T.			

PAYROLL DEDUCTIONS	F.I.C.A.	INCOME TAXES			HOSPITAL-IZATION			TOTAL DEDUCTIONS			LESS DEDUCTIONS
		FEDERAL	STATE	CITY/COUNTY							
	$	$	$	$	$	$	$	$			NET PAY

Figure 11.2

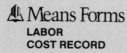

Means Forms

**LABOR
COST RECORD**

SHEET NO.

DATE FROM:

PROJECT

DATE TO:

LOCATION

BY:

DATE	CHARGE NO.	DESCRIPTION	HOURS	RATE	AMOUNT	HOURS	RATE	AMOUNT	HOURS	RATE	AMOUNT

Figure 11.3

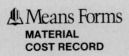 Means Forms

**MATERIAL
COST RECORD**

SHEET NO. _____

DATE FROM _____

DATE TO _____

PROJECT _____

LOCATION _____   BY _____

DATE	NUMBER	VENDOR/DESCRIPTION	QTY.	UNIT PRICE		QTY.	UNIT PRICE		QTY.	UNIT PRICE	

Figure 11.4

Figure 11.5

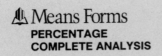

**PERCENTAGE
COMPLETE ANALYSIS**

PAGE _____

PROJECT _____

DATE _____

ARCHITECT _____

BY _____ FROM _____ TO _____

NO.	DESCRIPTION	ACTUAL OR ESTIMATED	TOTAL PROJECT	THIS PERIOD		PERCENT TOTAL TO DATE										
				QUANTITY	%	QUANTITY	10	20	30	40	50	60	70	80	90	100
		ACTUAL														
		ESTIMATED														
		ACTUAL														
		ESTIMATED														
		ACTUAL														
		ESTIMATED														
		ACTUAL														
		ESTIMATED														
		ACTUAL														
		ESTIMATED														
		ACTUAL														
		ESTIMATED														
		ACTUAL														
		ESTIMATED														
		ACTUAL														
		ESTIMATED														
		ACTUAL														
		ESTIMATED														
		ACTUAL														
		ESTIMATED														
		ACTUAL														
		ESTIMATED														
		ACTUAL														
		ESTIMATED														
		ACTUAL														
		ESTIMATED														
		ACTUAL														
		ESTIMATED														
		ACTUAL														
		ESTIMATED														
		ACTUAL														
		ESTIMATED														
		ACTUAL														
		ESTIMATED														
		ACTUAL														
		ESTIMATED														
		ACTUAL														
		ESTIMATED														
		ACTUAL														
		ESTIMATED														
		ACTUAL														
		ESTIMATED														

Figure 11.6

A cost system is only as good as the people responsible for coding and recording the required information. Simplicity is the key word. Do not try to break down the code into very small items unless there is a specific need.

Continuous updating of reports is important so that operations that are not in control can be immediately brought to the attention of management.

Finally, be sure to draft clear directions and instructions for each phase of the process. Adequate time must be spent to ensure that all who are involved (especially the foremen and supervisors) clearly understand the program.

Productivity and Efficiency

When using a cost control system such as the one described here, the unit costs should reflect standard practices. Productivity should be based on a five-day, eight-hour-per-day (during daylight hours) work week. Exceptions can be made if a company's requirements are unique. Installation costs should be derived using normal minimum crew sizes, under normal weather conditions, during the normal construction season.

All unusual costs incurred or expected should be recorded separately for each category of work. For example, an overtime situation might occur on every job and in the same proportion. In this case, it would make sense to carry the unit price adjusted for the added cost of premium time. Likewise, unusual weather delays, strike activity, owner/architect delays, or contractor interference should have separate, identifiable cost contributions; these are applied as isolated costs to the activities affected by the delays. This procedure serves two purposes:

- To identify and separate the cost contribution of the delay so that future job estimates will not automatically include an allowance for these "non-typical" delays.
- To serve as a basis for an extra compensation claim and/or as justification for reasonable extension of the job.

Overtime Impact

The use of long-term overtime is counter-productive on almost any construction job; that is, the longer the period of overtime, the lower the actual production rate. There have been numerous studies conducted that come up with slightly different numbers, but all reach the same conclusion. Figure 11.7 tabulates the effects of overtime work on efficiency.

As illustrated in Figure 11.7, there can be a difference between the *actual* payroll cost per hour and the *effective* cost per hour for overtime work. This is because of the reduced production efficiency with the increase in weekly hours beyond 40. This difference between actual and effective costs results from overtime work over a prolonged period. Short-term overtime work does not result in as great a reduction in efficiency and, in such cases, effective cost may not vary significantly from the actual payroll cost. As the total hours per week are increased on a regular basis, more time is lost because of fatigue, lowered morale, and an increased accident rate.

As an example, assume a project where workers are working 6 days a week, 10 hours per day. From Figure 11.7 (based on productivity studies), the effective productive hours are 52.5 hours (87.5% of 60 hours). This represents a theoretical production efficiency of 52.5/60 or 87.5%.

Depending on the locale and day of week, overtime hours may be paid at time and a half or double time. For time and a half, the overall (average) actual payroll cost (including regular and overtime hours) is determined as follows:

For time and a half:

$$\frac{40 \text{ reg. hrs.} + (20 \text{ overtime hrs.} \times 1.5)}{60 \text{ hrs.}} = 1.167$$

Based on 60 hours, the payroll cost per hour will be (on average) 116.7% of the normal rate at 40 hours per week. However, because the effective production (efficiency) for 60 hours is reduced to the equivalent of 52.5 hours, the effective cost of overtime is calculated as shown below:

For time and a half:

$$\frac{40 \text{ reg. hrs.} + (20 \text{ overtime hrs.} \times 1.5)}{52.5 \text{ hrs.}} = 1.33$$

Installed cost will be 133% of the normal rate (for labor).

Therefore, when figuring overtime, the actual cost per unit of work will be higher than the apparent overtime payroll dollar increases, because of the reduced productivity of the longer work week. These calculations are true only for those cost factors determined by hours worked. Costs that are applied weekly or monthly, such as equipment rentals, will not be similarly affected.

Days per Week	Hours per Day	Production Efficiency					Payroll Cost Factors	
		1 Week	2 Weeks	3 Weeks	4 Weeks	Average 4 Weeks	@ 1-1/2 times	@ 2 times
	8	100%	100%	100%	100%	100%	100%	100%
	9	100	100	95	90	96.25	105.6	111.1
5	10	100	95	90	85	91.25	110.0	120.0
	11	95	90	75	65	81.25	113.6	127.3
	12	90	85	70	60	76.25	116.7	133.3
	8	100	100	95	90	96.25	108.3	116.7
	9	100	95	90	85	92.50	113.0	125.9
6	10	95	90	85	80	87.50	116.7	133.3
	11	95	85	70	65	78.75	119.7	139.4
	12	90	80	65	60	73.75	122.2	144.4
	8	100	95	85	75	88.75	114.3	128.6
	9	95	90	80	70	83.75	118.3	136.5
7	10	90	85	75	65	78.75	121.4	142.9
	11	85	80	65	60	72.50	124.0	148.1
	12	85	75	60	55	68.75	126.2	152.4

Figure 11.7

Retainage and Cash Flow

The majority of construction projects have some percentage of retainage held back by the owner until the job is complete. This retainage can range from 5% to as high as 15% or 20% in unusual cases. The most typical retainage is 10%. Since the profit on a given job may be less than the amount of withheld retainage, the contractor must wait longer before a positive cash flow is achieved than if there were no retainage.

Figures 11.8 and 11.9 are graphic and tabular representations of the projected cash flow for a small project. With this kind of projection, the contractor is able to anticipate cash needs throughout the course of the job. Note that at the eleventh of May, before the second payment is received, the contractor has paid out about $25,000 more than has been received. This is the maximum amount of cash (on hand or financed) that is required for the whole project. At an early stage of planning, the contractor can determine if there will be adequate cash available or if a loan is needed. In the latter case, the expense of interest could be anticipated and included in the estimate. On larger projects, the projection of cash flow becomes crucial, because unexpected interest expense can quickly erode profit margin.

A note on the subject of financing may be helpful here. In the above example, assume that the contractor has adequate cash resources to finance the project. Does this mean that the project need not bear any interest charges? No. At the very least, money withdrawn from savings or investments will result in unrealized interest (effective losses). These "losses" should be included in the project records for the purpose of determining actual job profit. For this reason, many companies assign interest charges to their jobs for negative cash flow. Likewise, the project is credited if a positive cash flow is realized. In this way, an owner or manager can readily assess the contribution (or liability) of each job to the company's "financial health." For example, if a project has a 5% profit at completion but has incurred 10% in finance charges, it certainly has not helped the company to stay in business.

The General Conditions section of the specifications usually explains the responsibilities of both the owner and the contractor with regard to billing and payments. Even the best planning and projections are contingent upon the owner paying requisitions as anticipated. There is an almost unavoidable adversarial relationship between contractor and owner regarding payment during the construction process. However, it is in the best interest of the owner that the contractor be solvent so that delays, complications, and financial difficulties can be avoided prior to final completion of the project. The interest of both parties is best served if information is shared and communication is open. Both are working toward the same goal: the timely and successful completion of the project.

Life-Cycle Costs

Life-cycle costing is a valuable method of evaluating the total costs of an economic unit during its entire life. Regardless of whether the unit is a piece of excavating machinery or a manufacturing building, life-cycle costing gives the owner an opportunity to look at the economic consequences of a decision. Today, the initial cost of a unit is often not the most important cost factor; the operation and maintenance costs of some building types far exceed the initial outlay. Hospitals, for example, may have operating costs within a three-year period that exceed the original construction costs.

Estimators are in the business of initial costs. But what about the other costs that affect any owner: taxes, fuel, inflation, borrowing, estimated salvage at the end of the facility's lifespan, and expected repair or remodeling costs?

Figure 11.8

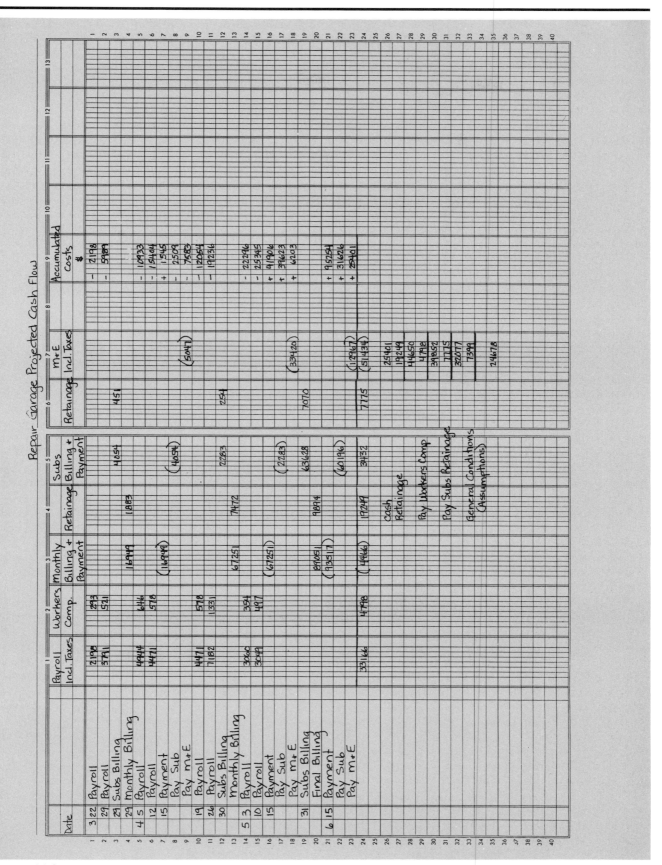

Figure 11.9

These costs that may occur at a later date need to be evaluated in advance. The thread that ties all of these costs together is the time-value of money. The value of money today is quite different from what it will be tomorrow. One thousand dollars placed in a savings bank at 5% interest will, in four years, have increased to $1,215.50. Conversely, if $1,000 is needed four years from now, then $822.70 should be placed in an account today. Another way of saying the same thing is that at 5% interest, the value of $1,000 four years from now is worth only $822.70 today.

Using interest and time, future costs are equated to the present by means of a present worth formula. Standard texts in engineering economics have outlined different methods for handling interest and time. A present worth evaluation could be used, or all costs might be converted into an equivalent, uniform annual cost method.

The present worth of a piece of equipment (such as a trenching machine) can be figured, based on a given lifespan, anticipated maintenance cost, operating costs, and money borrowed at the current rate. Having these figures can help in determining whether to rent or purchase. The costs between two different machines can also be analyzed in this manner to determine which is a better investment.

Part 2

Components of Electrical Systems

Chapter 12

Raceways

Raceways are channels constructed to house and protect electrical conductors. This chapter contains descriptions of 11 different types of raceways, fittings, and associated installation activities. The appropriate units for measure are provided for each of these components, along with material and labor requirements and a step-by-step takeoff procedure. Cost modification factors are given when economy of scale or difficult working conditions may affect the cost of the project.

Cable Tray

A cable tray system is a prefabricated metal raceway structure consisting of lengths of tray with associated fittings. Together, these components form a continuous rigid open support for cables. Cable tray is usually made of aluminum or galvanized steel but is also available in PVC-coated steel, fiberglass, and stainless steel.

There are three basic types of tray: ladder, trough, and solid bottom. Trays have an overall nominal depth of 4 through 7 inches and are supplied in standard lengths of 12 and 24 feet. Standard widths are 6, 9, 12, 18, 24, 30, and 36 inches.

Fittings are the components that provide changes of both direction and size that are needed to bypass obstructions and vary run direction, while providing a continuous support path. Horizontal and vertical bends are offered with a selection of radii from 12″ to 48″ to match the bending capability of the cable being supported.

Horizontal fittings: Horizontal bends are tray fittings that provide a change of direction in a horizontal plane (i.e., left or right). Bends are offered in 30, 45, 60, and 90 degree configurations.

Vertical fittings: Vertical bends are tray fittings that provide a change in direction in a vertical plane (i.e., up or down). Bends are offered in 30, 45, 60, and 90 degree configurations.

Miscellaneous fittings: T's, Y's, and X's are examples of other fittings available in both vertical and horizontal configurations.

Cable tray is used for many types of power and control needs. Accessories make the tray system adaptable to various situations. The linear foot cost of cable tray and fittings, in most estimating standards, does not include accessories, since including them would limit cost flexibility. Accessories should be thought of as providing the following functions: a means of exit, a means of dividing, and a means of support.

Exit accessories:
   Trough drop-out bushings
   Drop-out fittings
   Cable ties and clamps
   Conduit to tray clamps
   Cable grips

Dividing accessories:
   Barrier strips
   Straight
   Vertical inside and outside
   Horizontal

Support accessories:
   Cable tray brackets
   Trapeze hangers
   Hold down clamps and hanger clamps
   Threaded rod
   Beam clamps

Accessories are, in most cases, not shown on the electrical print. Usually, however, a reference is made to a detail that shows a typical configuration.

There are two basic types of cable tray covers—solid and vented. Solid covers are used when maximum protection of cables is required and no accumulation of heat is expected. Vented covers provide cable protection while allowing heat to dissipate from the cables. Both ventilated and solid covers protect cables from damage. In many instances, however, protection is required only in certain areas or on vertical risers subject to physical damage, or for personnel protection.

Covers are available in either aluminum or steel, and finishes are offered to match the tray construction. Aluminum and pregalvanized covers 24″ wide or less come in 6′ and 12′ lengths. Covers wider than 24″ come in 6′ lengths only.

For straight cover, the material cost per unit includes the cover in 6′ lengths, each one including 4 cover clamps. The material cost for cable tray covers for horizontal and vertical bends includes 4 cover clamps; for tees, 6 cover clamps; and for crosses, 8 cover clamps. Fitting covers come in sizes and widths that conform to the arrangements of the fittings.

Units for Measure: Cable tray is normally measured in linear feet (L.F.). The total linear feet must be figured for each size and depth of tray. Each unique fitting (EA.) must be counted and tabulated. The same applies to each hanger style and/or support (EA.). Related items, such as welded joints or field fabrication, must be identified and listed (EA.).

Material Units: Various assumptions are made in all estimating standards as to what is included per unit (L.F., EA., etc.) Being familiar with these assumptions and the standard being used will help you to adjust material and labor prices to suit your own project. In turn, estimates will be both more reliable and competitive.

The following items are generally included per L.F. of cable tray:
    Tray in standard lengths (i.e., 12 feet)
    One pair of connector plates every 12 L.F. (including bolts and
        nuts)
    One pair of clamp-type hangers every 12 L.F.
    One pair of 3/8″ threaded rods

Labor Units: The following procedures are generally included per L.F. of cable tray:
    Receiving and uncrating
    Measuring and marking
    Installing one pair of beam clamp hangers every 12 L.F.
    Installing cable tray straight sections, using and including the setting
        up of rolling stages
    Bolting sections of tray together
    Adjusting and leveling of tray

These additional procedures are listed and extended:
    Fittings
    Field fabrication
    Hanger supports
    Welded joints
    Cable

Labor adjustments are made for work over 15′ high.

Typical Job Conditions: Productivity is based on the following conditions:
    New installation
    Work plane to 15′ using rolling staging
    Unrestricted area
    Material storage within 100′ of the installation
    Installation on the first three floors
    Minimum of 100 L.F. to be installed

Takeoff Procedure: First, consult architectural prints for area construction, marking on the electrical print this information: height of ceiling, size of area, construction type. Note on the print the typical hanger arrangement for each area being taken off: clamp type or beam type, trapeze, etc. Mark the parameters of like types and sizes of cable tray.

Next, set up the quantity takeoff sheet — typical for straight sections only. Note the scale, and be careful of reduced prints. Using a scale or rotometer, work from the origin of service out to the end or point of use. Mark each section of tray measured with a colored pencil. For better results and to leave an audit trail, mark different sizes with different colors.

Transfer each section measured to the takeoff sheet, noting the height on the right hand corner. Go back over the print and mark any changes in elevation or risers. Transfer the riser quantities to the takeoff sheet.

The previous procedure should show how to take off straight lengths. Now go back to the print and list all fittings by their respective sizes and types on the worksheet. Mark all fittings on the print to complete the audit trail.

Cost Modifications: When tray is installed at heights over 15', add the following percentages to labor:

15'	to	20'	high	+10%
20'		25'		+20%
25'		30'		+25%
30'		35'		+30%
35'		40'		+35%
Over		40'		+40%

Check the prints for hole-cutting requirements in walls to allow the tray to go through. Adjust the estimates according to the following figures:

Up to 4 S.F. opening:

2" Gypsum block	=	.50 L.H. EA.
4"	=	.57
8"	=	.73
12" Brick wall	=	4.00
12" Concrete block	=	1.67
8" Brick wall	=	2.22
5/8" Thick drywall	=	.33

Note: On masonry walls, use a minimum charge of 2 L.H. (Long Span High Strength Bar Joists).

To substitute the hanger type (if included in L.F. cost of cable tray) with a particular type as specified for the project, deduct the cost of the hangers used and add the type required. For example: Deduct the following from the L.F. material cost and labor-hours for the price of cable tray without hangers or supports.

Description	Material	Labor-hours
6" Tray	−12%	−17%
9"	−17%	−17%
12"	−17%	−17%
18"	−16%	−17%
24"	−17%	−17%
30"	−15%	−16%
36"	−16%	−16%

Add the cost of each new type of hanger selected.

Conduit (to 15' High)

Conduit should be divided into the following three categories: power distribution, branch lighting, and branch power. Using these distinctions, the estimator does not take off all quantities of conduit at one time. Instead, he or she can concentrate on the quantities in one particular system. In this way, the estimator can associate the conduit with the other components in the system to arrive at the appropriate labor-hours.

The most common types of overhead conduit systems are as follows:

Aluminum
Rigid galvanized steel
Steel intermediate metallic conduit (IMC)
Rigid steel, plastic coated
Electrical metallic tubing (EMT)

In many instances, architectural prints are simply marked "conduit," with a given size. It is important that the estimator find out the type of conduit specified, as the costs can vary widely.

Fittings are used to connect, change direction, or support conduit runs. The complexity and time required to perform particular conduit installations increase by the number of fittings required. A certain number of fittings is assumed for each 100 L.F. of conduit installed. If the quantities exceed those in the linear foot models, then the excess material and labor units must be included.

An alternative method of conduit pricing does not include fittings, terminations, or hangers. It is designed to give the estimator greater flexibility when adapting an estimate to unique needs.

For example, if hangers to be used support multiple conduit runs, the estimator can estimate the cost of each hanger and not have to bother "backing out" the cost of hangers included in the L.F. cost of the previous section.

This method is also useful when there are many straight conduit runs. The estimator does not have to pay attention to terminations, bushings, locknuts, etc., that are built into the cost per 100 L.F. of conduit in the first method.

Units for Measure: Conduit is measured in linear feet (L.F.). Fittings, hangers, supports, and racks are counted as each (EA.).

Material Units: The estimator must be aware of what is included in the L.F. cost of conduit before taking it off. The following materials are normally included per L.F. of aluminum, rigid galvanized, steel-intermediate, and steel-plastic coated conduit on a per-100-linear-foot basis.

    11 Threaded steel couplings
    11 Beam hangers
    2 Elbows (factory sweeps)
    4 Locknuts and 2 fiber bushings
    2 Field thread pipe terminations
    2 Concentric knockouts removed

For EMT:

    11 Set screw steel couplings
    11 Beam clamps
    2 Field bends on 1/2″ and 3/4″
    2 Elbows (factory sweeps) for 1″ and above
    2 Set screw steel box connectors
    2 Concentric knockouts removed

Note: For congested areas or complex runs, it will be necessary to augment these basic assumptions by adding items on a unit basis.

Labor Units: The following procedures are generally included per L.F. of conduit:

    Unloading, uncrating, and hauling
    Set up of rolling stage
    Laying out
    Installing conduit and fittings

These additional procedures are listed and extended:

    Staging (rental or purchase)
    Structural modifications
    Wire
    Junction boxes
    Additional fittings
    Painting of conduit

Takeoff Procedure: Set up the quantity takeoff sheet by size and type of conduit. Use a rotometer and start from the panel or source, working out to the point of use. Mark each run with a colored pencil. Then mark changes of level and drops. Measure each size before going to another stage. Transfer the measurements to a cost sheet and price.

Cost Modifications: Add the following percentages to labor according to the height of these elevated installations:

15'	to	20'	high	+10%
20'		25'		+20%
25'		30'		+25%
30'		35'		+30%
35'		40'		+35%
40' and over				+40%

Add these percentages to the L.F. labor cost, but not to the material cost of the fittings. Add these percentages only to the quantities exceeding the different height levels, not to the total conduit quantities.

Where conduit runs through walls of different types of material, add appropriate cutting costs. Figure the cost of each penetration by the size of conduit, type of wall, and thickness of wall. (See "Cutting and Drilling" later in this chapter.)

Conduit Fittings

For estimating purposes, we will define fittings as any material item that must be added to our 100 L.F. cost models (as described in the previous chapter). By adding the appropriate fittings, we are also beginning to define the complexity of the conduit. For example, a run requiring the installation of four LB's and one T fitting per 100 L.F. can certainly be considered a more complex installation than one containing only two field bends.

Our approach will be to analyze some common fittings and to explain the logic behind each type. The estimator can apply this logic to any type of fitting, including those that are not listed in any standard, but follow the same installation procedure. In such cases, the estimator must still find out the material price but will be able to figure reasonable labor-hours.

Locknuts are used to terminate and secure conduit endings. This procedure involves screwing the locknuts onto an existing conduit thread. Only a material price is needed. Note: Some locknuts also have a sealing ring insert for wet areas.

Bushings are used to protect wires from damage when a conduit terminates in an enclosure. There are several material variations for bushings. Among them are plastic, steel, and steel grounding bushings. Although the installation method is the same as for a locknut, several labor assumptions have been added for estimating ease. Since it is unlikely that a 10′ conduit length will end at an exact location, the labor-hour cost includes field cutting and threading one conduit end.

When field threading is not practical, threadless couplings are used to join two pieces of galvanized steel conduit, and threadless connectors are used to terminate a rigid galvanized steel conduit run into an enclosure. Threaded LB's and T's are used to change the direction or split a conduit run when field bends are not practical or allowed by code.

Nipples (manufactured type) are used to join electrical enclosures or raceway where there is not enough room for standard conduit techniques. There are many variations of nipples, such as chase and offset types. Nipples are available in the same diameters as conduit. Generally, nipples are under 6″ in length.

Expansion couplings are used when the expansion and contraction of a building (or bridge) will cause damage or a loss of continuity in the conduit run. They are also used when a run exceeds a certain length — to compensate for the thermal expansion and contraction of the conduit material.

Units for Measure: Fittings are counted as each (EA.) and listed by size and type.

Material Units: There is a great variety of fittings available for each type of conduit. The most common include:

> Locknuts
> Bushings
> Threadless couplings
> Threadless connectors
> Threaded LB's and T's
> Nipples of various lengths
> Expansion couplings
> Unions

Note: Fittings are manufactured in several types, such as explosion-proof, PVC-coated, and malleable iron. Be sure your fittings conform to the installation.

Labor Units: Different fitting types require different types of labor units:

Bushings: Generally include installing locknuts, installing bushings, and cutting and threading one conduit end.

Threadless couplings: Generally include cutting to fit two ends of rigid galvanized steel conduit (when field threading is not practical) and installing the coupling.

Threadless connectors: Generally include cutting to fit one end of a galvanized steel conduit and installing the connector.

Threaded LB's and T's: Generally include cutting and threading two ends of a conduit for LB's and three ends for T's, installing the fitting, and installing the fitting cover.

Nipples: Generally include removing two concentric KO's and installing the nipple (including locknuts).

Expansion couplings: Generally include field threading of one conduit end, installing a bushing on one conduit end, and installing the fitting.

These basic operations can be assumed for all fittings. Explosion-proof, seal-off fittings, for example, will include the above approach plus time for packing and pouring the sealing compound.

Takeoff Procedure: In most instances, a fitting will not be shown on a print for standard conduit installations. Many of the applications of particular fittings are dictated by legal and national codes, and/or by the project's own specifications. An estimator must be aware of these electrical codes as well as the location of restrictions requiring the use of fittings instead of field bends.

If possible, list the fittings on the same quantity sheet as the conduit. List by type and size of fitting. Count each fitting and put a check mark on the print. (It is easy to lose track of changes in direction of conduit runs.) Transfer the quantities to a cost analysis sheet and extend.

Conduit in Concrete Slab

Conduit in concrete slab is used for both branch circuit and power distribution when the locations of end use will not change. Embedded conduit is usually a very cost-effective method of raceway installation because of savings in support costs and reduced run lengths. The most common types of conduit used in "slab work" are PVC schedule 40 (plastic), rigid galvanized steel, and intermediate metallic conduit (IMC). These types of conduit are most resistant to corrosion and oxidation. Aluminum conduit is not recommended for use in concrete that contains chlorides, because it has the potential for oxidation and expansion.

Units for Measure: Conduit in slab is measured in linear feet (L.F.) for estimating. (Do not combine these footages with exposed raceways.) Special fittings, such as union-type (Erickson) couplings, are counted as each (EA.).

Material Units: The following items are generally included per L.F. of rigid galvanized conduit, IMC conduit, or PVC conduit:

> Conduit
> Ties to slab reinforcing
> Couplings
> Elbows (factory sweeps)
> Locknuts and two fiber bushings
> Removal of concentric knockouts

Labor Units: The following procedures are generally included per L.F. of conduit:

> Unloading, uncrating, and hauling from the loading dock
> Laying out
> Installing conduit (including the material items above)

These additional procedures are listed and extended:

> Wire
> Additional bends (over two per 100 ft.)

Takeoff Procedure: Set up the quantity takeoff sheet by size and type of conduit. Start from the panel or source and work out to the point of use. Mark each run with colored pencil. Measure each size before going to another stage.

Cost Modifications: When multiple conduits are run parallel in slab at the same time, apply the following percentage deductions to the labor-hours:

2 runs	− 5%
3	−10%
4	−15%
5	−20%
Over 5	−25%

Example #1:

6 runs of 100′ long 2″ PVC, run parallel at the same time by the same crew:

600 L.F. x .067 L.H./L.F.	40.20 L.H.
Less 25%	−10.05
	30.15 L.H.

Example #2:

PVC conduit run in slab involves "stub ups" in five locations for equipment, etc. The total length of the runs is 100′. To adjust material and labor, it is important to remember what was included in the linear foot estimate explained in the material and labor assumptions. Next, take off the number of additional field bends or factory sweeps. Add the resulting figures to the labor-hours and material.

> Total length involving "stub ups" is 100 L.F.
> 5 stubs require 10 manufactured elbows
> Total 2″ conduit runs = 100 L.F.

Conduit 100 L.F. × .067 L.H./L.F.	6.70 L.H.
Elbows 8 EA. × .444 L.H/EA.	+ 3.55 L.H.
	10.25 L.H.

Note: Although there are 10 elbows in the model, only 8 are included in the adjustment calculation. This is because 2 elbows were previously listed in the material per 100' of conduit. When an elbow is added, a coupling must also be added.

Conduit in Trench

Conduit in trench is used for power distribution and for communications. It is also commonly used for outdoor lighting applications, such as roadways or parking lots. In this case, the conduit installation may be either direct burial or concrete encased. Rigid galvanized steel and rigid PVC conduit are usually used in trenches. For corrosive soil applications, PVC-coated rigid steel may be specified. Fiber duct or PVC (plastic) conduit may also be used for the installation of a concrete duct bank. Transite duct (asbestos cement) is no longer used.

Units for Measure: Direct burial conduit is measured in linear feet (L.F.). Bends, fittings, spacers, etc. are counted as units (EA.). Trenching, sand, backfill, and concrete are all calculated separately—usually per cubic yard (C.Y.). Manholes are not included in the conduit units and must also be counted as units (EA.).

Material Units: The following items are generally included for rigid galvanized steel conduit:

Conduit
Threaded steel couplings
Elbows (factory sweeps)
Pipe terminations
Locknuts and fiber bushings

For PVC conduit, include these items:
    Conduit
    Field cemented couplings
    Elbows (factory sweeps)
    Terminal adapters (male)

Labor Units: The following procedures are generally included per L.F. of conduit:
    Unloading, uncrating, and hauling
    Laying out
    Installing conduit

These additional procedures are listed and extended:
    Excavation
    Bedding
    Concrete
    Backfill
    Wire

Typical Job Conditions: Productivity is based on a new installation in a dry prepared trench to 4' deep. Material staging area within 200' of installation.

Takeoff Procedure: Set up the quantity takeoff sheet by size and type of conduit. Start from the source and work out to the point of use. Mark each run with colored pencil. Measure each size before going to another stage.

Cutting and Drilling

Cutting and core drilling are required in certain restrictive situations. The most practical approach to this kind of work is to identify the physical restriction and price it as if it were part of the installation.

Walls are the most common restriction. The types that hinder conduit runs are usually concrete or masonry unit walls. Their thickness ranges from 8" to 24". Since the penetration must accommodate conduit sizes from 1/2" to 6", the core drill must be sized larger than the conduit's O.D. (outside diameter).

Units for Measure: Penetration holes (EA.) are taken off by the size of the penetration and for each different wall thickness. Also itemize for elevations over 10'.

Material and Labor Units: The following items are generally included per hole:

Measuring and marking
Set up of drill equipment with available power
Core drilling
Clean up

These additional items are listed and extended:

Cost of drill bits
Dust protection
Patching and grouting

Typical Job Conditions: Productivity is usually based on an unrestricted area, drilling to a height of 10' using a rotary drill.

Takeoff Procedure: Set up the work sheet by the type of wall. Mark each penetration on the print. Transfer the quantities to the work sheet.

Cost Modifications: When drilling at a level above 10', add the following percentages to the labor-hours:

10'	to	15' high – add	5%
16'		20'	10%
21'		25'	15%
26'		30'	20%
Over 30'			30%

Example: Twenty 2" holes are needed in an 8" thick concrete wall. Five conduits are at a height of 12', 10 are at 24', and 5 are at 35'. Adjust the labor accordingly.

5 holes	2" @ 12'	=	1.8 L.H. x 1.05	=	9.45 L.H.
10	2" @ 24'	=	1.8 L.H. x 1.15	=	20.70
5	2" @ 35'	=	1.8 L.H. x 1.3	=	12.15
				Total	42.30 L.H.

Note: If only one hole is to be drilled, a two-hour minimum charge should be applied for setting up, mobilization, etc.

Wire Duct — Plastic

Wire duct is designed to organize both branch and control wires within panels and enclosures. Slotted sides for wire ins/outs make this raceway accessible at 1/2″ intervals, and snap-on covers make it easy to add or change wire. Wire duct is available in standard 6′ lengths; its cross-sectional dimensions range from .5″ x .5″ to 4″ x 5″. Most wire duct is PVC and has an adhesive backing. This backing is used to hold the duct temporarily in place until it is riveted or screwed to a panel mounting plate.

Units for Measure: Wire duct is tabulated on a linear foot (L.F.) basis for each size of duct.

Material and Labor Units: The following items are generally included per L.F. of wire duct:

    Measuring and marking
    Duct
    Mounting screws, drilled and tapped
    Cutting to length
    Field installation

These additional items are listed and extended:

    Cover
    Wire
    Marking or labeling duct
    Panel or enclosure

Takeoff Procedure: First set up the work sheet by the dimensions of the wire duct. Include the duct cover on the work sheet. Measure the total linear footage and round to the next 6 L.F. Mark the different sizes of duct with a colored pencil. Transfer the lengths to a quantity sheet.

Cost Modifications: If wire duct is not field-installed in cabinets after setting, but is instead field-installed assembly-line fashion before the cabinets are mounted, then deduct the percentages below from the total labor-hours, according to the number of cabinets being worked.

1	to	3	− 0%
4		6	−15%
7		9	−30%
10		15	−25%
Over 16			−30%

For example, 18 boxes are to be fabricated at benches. Thirty feet of 4″ W x 5″ H duct and cover are to be installed in each cabinet:

18 boxes · × 30 L.F. duct/box	=	540 L.F. of 4″ W x 5″ H duct	
	=	540 L.F. of cover	
.160 L.H. × 540 L.F.	=	86 L.H. duct	
.08 L.H. × 540 L.F.	=	43 L.H. cover	
		129 L.H. Total	
		129 × .70 = 90.3	
			Adjusted L.H.

Trench Duct

Trench duct is a steel trough system set into a concrete floor, with a top cover fitted flush with the finished floor. Trench duct is used as a raceway system in concrete slabs and to feed underfloor raceways. It is also used as a flush raceway for such places as computer rooms, language labs, shop areas, and x-ray rooms. A trench duct system is made up of individual components that allow flexibility for specific needs. The basic components are as follows:

   U-trough
   Side rail assembly (standard 10′ lengths)
   Bottom plates (standard 5′ long by cover plate width)
   Cover plate of 1/4″ steel

Standard widths are 9″, 12″, 18″, 24″, 30″, and 36″, with standard depths of 2-3/8″ to 3-3/8″. All fittings come in standard duct widths. Changes in direction are made by an assortment of fittings, such as horizontal elbows, vertical elbows, crosses, and tees. The start and end accessories are end closures, risers, and cabinet connectors. All fittings must be added to material and labor calculations.

Units for Measure: Trench duct is measured on a linear foot (L.F.) basis. Fittings, supports, boxes, etc. are counted as each (EA.).

Material and Labor Units: Rather than pricing each individual component, most estimating standards have put the required components together to come up with a per L.F. cost rate. For example, the following items are generally included per single compartment, 36″ wide trench duct:

   Two side rails
   One 36″ wide bottom plate
   One 36″ wide cover plate
   Two tack welds to a cellular steel floor
   Adjusting and leveling

These additional items are listed and extended:

Wire
Fittings
Access holes from duct to cellular grid
Cutting and patching

Takeoff Procedure: Set up the quantity takeoff sheet by width and number of compartments of duct. Measure from the source of power to the end, rounding the measurement to the next 5′. Transfer quantities from the print to the work sheet. Go back over the print and mark the fittings, identifying by type of fitting, width, and number of compartments. Take off these accessories by type and width.

Cost Modifications: If labor-hours are based on the installation of up to 100 L.F. of trench duct, you can adjust for quantities over 100′. This can be done by decreasing the labor-hours by the following percentages. For lengths of:

100′	to	200′	−10%
200′		300′	−20%
Over 300′			−30%

Deduct for these labor factors only if the lengths are located in the same general area on the same floor, and are being installed by the same crew. This applies to the labor for linear feet (L.F.) of trench duct and associated fittings.

For example, 350 L.F. of 24″ wide trench duct is to be installed on a first-floor area. There are 5 horizontal elbows within this system. Adjust the labor-hours for these quantities:

$$350 \text{ L.F.} \times .727 \text{ L.H./L.F.} = 254 \text{ L.H.}$$
$$5 \text{ EA.} \times 5 \text{ L.H./EA.} = \underline{25}$$
$$279 \text{ L.H.}$$

Adjustment:

$$279 \text{ L.H. } (1.00 - .30) = 279 \text{ L.H. } (.70) = 195 \text{ L.H.}$$

Underfloor Duct

The purpose of underfloor duct is to make power and communication wiring available at numerous locations within a room. Used almost exclusively in office areas, the duct system is set before the concrete floor is poured. Wire or cable is accessed by hand holes spaced 24″ O.C. There are two standard types of ducts; both come blank or with hand holes and are manufactured in 10′ lengths. The sizes are standard duct and, for larger wire capacities, super duct. Underfloor duct systems are available in two basic designs, single-level and two-level.

The *single-level duct system* involves ducts that are all mounted at the same elevation. Special junction boxes are required that accommodate one, two, or three ducts on each side. If power and communication cables run through a common junction box, a divider system must be installed to separate the two types of cables.

In the *two-level duct system,* feeder ducts are run below branch distribution ducts. Power and communication wiring can be separated more easily with this system, and junction boxes are less crowded.

Units for Measure: Underfloor duct is estimated per linear foot (L.F.) and rounded up to the next 10′ length. All fittings, junction boxes, supports, etc. are listed as each (EA.).

Material Units: The following items are generally included per 10 L.F. of underfloor duct:

> One section duct
> One coupling

These additional items are listed and extended:

> Fittings and junction boxes
> Supports
> Adapters
> Outlets
> Wire and cable

Labor Units: The following procedures are generally included per 10 L.F. of underfloor duct:

> Unloading and uncrating
> Hauling from the loading dock
> Measuring and marking
> Setting the raceway and fittings in slab or on grade
> Leveling the raceway

These additional procedures are listed and extended:

> Floor cutting
> Excavation or backfill
> Concrete pour
> Grouting or patching
> Wire pulls
> Conduit

Takeoff Procedure: Because underfloor duct systems can vary from simple to complex, most standards require the estimator to list all components, and to price material and labor individually. Because of the wide range and cost of fittings, junctions, and accessories, it is not safe to assume that there will be a certain number of fittings or junction boxes per 100 L.F. of underfloor duct.

To take off underfloor duct, first set up the work sheet by type of duct (super or standard). Note whether or not the duct is insert type, and set it up by the on-center distance between inserts. Record the fittings separately from straight lengths of underfloor duct. Identify junction boxes as single-level or two-level. Rather than try to describe all the different types, sizes, and partition arrangements of each junction box, list them by the manufacturer's catalog number. Most underfloor duct systems are pre-engineered and contain a schedule of part numbers and descriptions.

Set up a third quantity sheet heading for "Accessories." This sheet will be used to list such items as 90-degree bends, cabinet connectors, supports, offset elbows, and conduit adapters.

Measure all straight lengths of underfloor duct and mark each type with a colored pencil. Transfer the lengths to a quantity sheet and round to the next 10′ length. Go back over the prints and list and mark all junction boxes and associated fittings; then count and transfer this information to the quantity sheet. Total the quantities on all sheets and transfer these figures to the cost analysis sheet.

Cost Modifications: Labor-hours are based on the installation of up to 100 L.F. of underfloor duct. Decrease the labor-hours by the following percentages to adjust for higher quantities.

100′	to	200′	− 5%
200′		500′	−10%
Over 500′			−15%

For example, 1500 L.F. of 1-3/8″ x 7-1/4″ blank super duct is to be installed in the same area of an office building; adjust the labor-hours for this installation:

$$\frac{\text{Total length}}{1500} \times \frac{\text{L.H. per L.F.}}{.133} \times \frac{\text{Modifier}}{.85} = 169.6 \text{ L.H.}$$

Use these percentages for straight lengths only; do not deduct from the labor-hours for junctions, fittings, or accessories.

Note: It is prudent to get material costs from a vendor or manufacturer whenever possible.

Surface Metal Raceways

Surface metal raceway (wiremold) is installed on walls or floors in existing buildings. It is used in situations where it would be too costly or difficult to install raceway within the wall. Surface metal raceway is available in many sizes and configurations. The smaller sizes are one-piece units and fasten to a surface with snap-on clips or straps. Wire must then be pulled in. The larger raceway consists of a base with a separate cover. The base is attached to the surface, and the cover snaps over the wires after they are put into place. Some larger sizes can be used with a divider, allowing power and telephone or other signal systems to share the same raceway.

Certain types of raceway are prewired with receptacles at regular spaces; in others, an assembled harness of prewired receptacles is installed in the raceway to match pre-cut holes in the cover.

A special type of raceway is available for use on floors. It is shallow, flat on top, and slanted on the sides to minimize tripping. Most raceway is available in 5′ or 10′ lengths, while most covers come in 5′ lengths. One-piece raceways are sold with couplings included.

Many different types of elbows, bushings, couplings, clips, adapters, boxes, and other fittings are manufactured. A catalog, readily available at most electrical supply stores, is helpful for both takeoff and installation.

Units for Measure: Wiremold is taken off in linear feet (L.F.) and rounded upward to the nearest 10′. Fittings, clips, boxes, adapters, etc. are counted as each (EA.).

Material Units: The following items are generally included per 10' of raceway:

Section(s) of straight raceway and covers
Coupling(s)
Supporting clip(s)

These additional items must be listed and extended:

All other fittings and boxes

Labor Units: The following procedures are generally included in the labor-hours:

Unloading and uncrating
Hauling from the loading dock
Installing raceway and fastening every 10'
Measuring and marking

These additional procedures must be listed and extended:

Installing wire, fittings, and boxes
Installing device covers
Installing on walls, floors, or ceilings over 10' high

Takeoff Procedure: First, label the work sheet according to style and size, fittings, and boxes. Then, take off the straight lengths of raceway for each size.

Next, take off the fittings for each size and run, being careful to note the correct elbow designation — horizontal, vertical, or offset. Finally, boxes are taken off. All of the above information is then transferred to a pricing sheet.

Wireways

Wireways are sheet-metal troughs with hinged or removable covers. Wireways are used to house and protect electrical wires and cable. Conductors are placed after the wireway system is completed. There are two basic types of wireway. The first is "NEMA 1," which provides protection for wiring installations where oil, water, or dust is not a problem. The second is "oiltight." This latter type ("NEMA 12"), with flanged, gasketed ends and hinged, gasketed covers, is used in areas that are exposed to oil, dust, coolants, and water.

Generally, wireway must be supported every five feet. However, supports every ten feet are permitted for wireway that is designed specifically for that purpose. (Vertical runs may be supported at 15′ intervals.) Wireways can be used only for exposed situations.

NEMA 1 lay-in systems come in standard sizes of 2-1/2″, 4″, 6″, 8″, 10″, and 12″ square. Standard lengths are 1′ through 5′, and 10′. Ten-foot lengths are the most common and can be assumed for estimating purposes unless otherwise specified. Oiltight wireways come in standard sizes of 2-1/2″, 4″, 6″, and 8″ square. Standard lengths are 1′ through 5′, and 10′.

For both NEMA 1 and oiltight wireway, fittings come in the same standard widths as the tray itself. Fittings allow changes of direction for straight lengths of wireway and are grouped into four classes:

Couplings
Elbows
Crosses and "T" boxes
Reducers

Wireway accessories are used to terminate or support wireway installations and include items such as:

End caps
Panel connectors
U connectors
Special hangers

Units for Measure: Wireway is measured in linear feet (L.F.). Standard lengths are 10′, but lengths of 1′ to 5′ are available to suit the installation. Fittings, brackets, reducers, and panel connectors must be listed as each (EA.).

Material Units: The following items are generally included per 10 L.F. of wireway:

One section straight raceway
One coupling or flange kit
Two wall bracket hangers
One section cover

These additional items are listed and extended:

Wire
Fittings
Accessories

Labor Units: The following procedures are generally included per 10 L.F. of wireway:

Receiving
Material handling
Installing raceway on wall-mounted hangers up to 10′ high and
    spaced every 5 L.F.
Installing cover

Takeoff Procedure: To take off wireway, first set up the work sheet by type and size of tray. List the fittings below straight sections of raceway and identify by type, size, and configuration. Measure from the source and work to the termination point. Many estimators like to measure total runs and transfer size quantities as they go. Because of short sections (manufactured sizes other than 10′ long) and different sizes and types, it may be best to measure all of one size first before proceeding to another. This is not a dramatic change of approach, since most wireway sizes remain constant or decline in size from source to termination. Go back over the print and list all fittings; be especially careful to distinguish between vertical and horizontal fittings. Review the print once more and list the accessories (hangers, etc.). Many areas require a variety of support or hanger arrangements. Transfer the totals to the cost analysis sheet.

Cost Modifications: If the specs call for fabricated hanger and support systems, the estimator must make an adjustment. To do so, deduct the following percentages from the linear foot cost for material and labor to arrive at a cost for wireway without hangers. Then add the cost of the hanger system specified.

Standard wireway		**Oiltight**	
Material	−8%	Material	−4%
Labor	−4%	Labor	−4%

For example: Adjust material and labor for 1000 L.F. of 6″ x 6″ standard type wireway so that hangers are not included.

	L.F.	x	Material $	x	Adjustment Factor	= Price without hangers
Material:	1000	x	$12.95	x	.92	= $11,914.00
			Unit L.H.			Labor-Hours
Labor:	1000	x	.267	x	.96	= 256.32

Labor-hours are based on installing wireway to a height of 10′. To adjust labor-hours for installations over 10′, add these percentages:

11′	to	15′ high	+10%
16′		20′	+15%
21′		25′	+20%
Over 25′			+25%

Add these percentages to labor only for those lengths that are installed at the specified heights; do not add to the material price.

Conductors and Grounding

A conductor is a wire or metal bar with a low resistance to the flow of electric current. Grounding is accomplished by a conductor connected between electrical equipment or a circuit and the earth. In this chapter, there are eleven sections on various types of wiring and terminations, and a section on grounding. Each section begins with a definition of the component, followed by units for measure, material and labor requirements, and a takeoff procedure.

Flexible Metallic Conduit

Flexible metallic conduit, sometimes referred to as "Greenfield" or "Flex," is a single strip of aluminum or galvanized steel, spiral wound and interlocked to provide a circular cross section of high strength and flexibility. Its flexibility, together with a continuous length, make it more cost effective than rigid conduit for use in finished frame buildings. Flexible metallic conduit can be purchased in lengths ranging from 25' to 250', depending on its diameter. It requires no elbow fittings or field bends for changes in direction.

Flexible metallic conduit does have restrictions. It cannot be used in wet locations, hoistways, acid storage areas, hazardous locations, under ground, or embedded in concrete. Sizes of flexible metallic conduit range from 3/8" to 4" diameter. The minimum size allowed by the N.E.C. (National Electrical Code) is 1/2" diameter except in the case of motor wiring, or for a run of less than 72". Flexible metallic conduit must be secured at intervals not exceeding 4-1/2', as well as within 12" of every outlet or fitting.

Conductors are pulled into flexible conduit with fish tape in much the same manner as rigid conduit.

"Liquidtight" ("Sealtight") is similar to flexible metallic conduit except that it is covered with a liquid-tight, plastic covering. It is used most often for conduit connections to motors and raceways in machines where protection from liquids is required.

Because of the flexibility of Greenfield and Sealtite, only a limited selection of fittings is necessary. The most common fittings are box connectors with either non-insulated or insulated throats. Both are available in straight and 90-degree versions. Rigid to flexible conduit couplings are also very common. Forty-five degree connectors and swivel adapters are also available for Sealtite.

Units for Measure: Flexible metallic conduit is measured in linear feet (L.F.) and the connectors are counted as units (EA.).

Material Units: The following items are generally included in the material cost per linear foot (L.F.) of Greenfield and Sealtite:

> The flexible metallic conduit
> The cost of a one-hole strap every 4-1/2 feet

These additional items must be listed and extended:

> Flex fittings and connectors
> Wire

Labor Units: The following procedures are generally included per linear foot (L.F.) of flexible metallic conduit:

> Material handling on site
> Installing conduit
> Securing conduit every 4-1/2 linear feet on masonry wall

Material and labor are based on an average of 50′ runs.

These additional items are listed and extended:

> Installing wire
> Installing fittings

Takeoff Procedure: To take off, first set up the work sheet by type and size of flexible metallic conduit. List the fittings on the same work sheet. There are many installation methods for flexible conduit. For example, flex used to feed branch circuits involves a takeoff procedure similar to that for rigid conduit.

This is a good time to calculate the wire quantity, since wire is not included in the installation price of flex. This tabulation is done by multiplying the quantities of conduit times the number of conductors. Add 10% for waste. Transfer the quantities from the takeoff sheet to the cost analysis sheet and extend.

Cost Modifications: If the installation is done above suspended ceilings, the conduits may be tied in place rather than fastened with straps. This method results in a savings of both material and labor costs. Deduct 7% from the material cost and 35% from the labor in this instance.

Wire

Wire is used to conduct current from electrical source to electrical use. Wire is made of either copper or aluminum conductors with an insulating jacket. Copper is normally used for sizes smaller than #6, while copper or aluminum is used on #6 and larger. Wire comes with various voltage ratings and insulation materials. Some types of insulation are thicker than others and require a larger-size conduit. Aluminum conductors of equal ampacity are larger in diameter than copper and may require larger conduit.

The cost impact of using different types of wire goes beyond the cost of the wire itself. For example, typical installed costs (including the installing contractor's overhead and profit) of several common wire types (of 600V wire per C.L.F.) are as follows:

#6 type THW copper stranded	$80.00
#6 THW aluminum stranded	58.00
#6 THHN-THWN copper	80.00
#6 XHHW copper	83.50
#6 XHHW aluminum	58.00
#4 XHHW aluminum	72.50
#4 THW aluminum	71.50

#6 copper wire is rated at 65 A. #6 aluminum is rated at 50 A. #4 aluminum is rated at 65 A. #6 THHN-THWN and XHHW, 4 wires, require 3/4" conduit. #6 THW, 4 wires, requires 1" conduit. #4 THHN-THWN, 4 wires, requires 1". #4 THW, 4 wires, requires 1-1/4". *Thus, both the cost of the wire and the installation must be considered in arriving at the true cost.*

Units for Measure: Wire quantity is usually expressed in units of 100 linear feet (C.L.F.). Care must be taken to multiply the run length by the total number of individual wires to get the total length. The ground wire is not always shown on the drawings, but it may be required by specification or code.

Note: Cable and wire are not always treated the same way. Cable is an assembly of two or more insulated wires laid up together, usually with an overall jacket. While some cables are estimated in C.L.F. units, heavier types may be measured in linear feet (L.F.) The estimator must be vigilant to avoid costly errors.

Material Units: Generally, the material costs include only the wire and cable. Such items as dunnage and deposits for reels must be figured separately.

Labor Units: The price per C.L.F. of wire generally includes these procedures:

Setting up wire coils or spools on racks
Attaching wire to pulling line
Measuring and cutting wire
Pulling wire into raceway
Identifying and tagging

These additional items are listed and extended:

Terminations to breakers, panelboards, or equipment
Splices
Reel storage and handling

Takeoff Procedure: Wire should be taken off in the following categories:

Feeders and service entrance
Branch lighting
Branch power

Feeder wire is usually taken off from the conduit feeder schedule sheet, using conduit lengths and an additional allowance for terminations at each end. As an example, switchboard-to-distribution panel would add 12 L.F. to each wire. Feeders are considered to be wire size #6 or larger. Branch circuits are #8, #10, or #12 wire size.

Wire quantities are taken off in one of two ways: by measuring each cable run, or by extending the conduit and raceway quantities times the number of conductors in the raceway. Ten percent should be added for waste and tie-ins. Keep in mind that the unit of measure for wire is C.L.F., not L.F. as in raceways. The formula reads:

$$\frac{\text{L.F. Raceway} \times \text{No. of Conductors} \times 1.10}{100} = \text{C.L.F.}$$

Cost Modifications: If more than three wires are being pulled at one time, the following percentages can be deducted from labor for that grouping:

4-5 wires	−25%
6-10	−30%
10-15	−35%
Over 15	−40%

If wire pull is less than 100′ in length and is interrupted several times by boxes, lighting outlets, etc., it may be necessary to add the following lengths to each wire being pulled:

Junction box to junction box	2 L.F.
Lighting panel to junction box	6 L.F.
Distribution panel to sub panel	8 L.F.
Switchboard to distribution panel	12 L.F.
Switchboard to motor control center	20 L.F.
Switchboard to cable tray	40 L.F.

Measure of Drops and Risers: When taking off wire quantities, it is important to include the wire for drops to electrical equipment. If the heights of various electrical equipment items are not clearly stated, use the following guide:

	Riser (Bottom Feed)	Drop (Top Feed)
Safety switch to 100 A	5'	6'
Safety switch 400 to 600 A	4'	6'
100 A panel 12 to 30 circuit	4'	6'
42 circuit panel	3'	6'
Switch box	3'	3'-6"
Switchgear	0'	8'
Motor control centers	0'	8'
1-35 KVA transformers	0'	2'
45 KVA transformers	0'	4'

Armored Cable

Armored cable is a fabricated assembly of approved cable with an aluminum or galvanized metal enclosure. Type AC (also called BX) available in wire sizes from #12 aluminum or #14 copper through A.W.G. Type AC is rated for 600V or less. Type MC (metal clad) allowed for applications at 5,000V or less: It may have a plastic overall jacket.

Both types of armored cable are used in applications where physical protection is needed and conduit is not practical. Armored cable is not installed in conduit, underground, or in wet locations.

One of the advantages of armored cable is protection against vermin.

Units for Measure: Armored cable is measured in linear feet (L.F.) of cable.

Material Units: Only the cable itself is included in the takeoff.

For large-size armored cable, box connectors must be added. When using BX, the cable is connected to boxes with built-in clamps designed to hold BX. No connectors are required in this case, and labor is included in the box installation.

Labor Units: These procedures are generally included for installation of BX cable:

> Field preparation
> Pulling cable
> Identification and tagging of the wire

These additional procedures must be listed and extended:

> Drilling of studs
> Wire terminations to equipment and breakers

Takeoff Procedure: First, measure the linear feet (L.F.) of each cable run, and tabulate according to size and type. Be sure to measure drops and risers. Total each column. Allow 10% for waste. Then transfer to a cost analysis sheet and extend. Refer to "Shielded Power Cables" (later in this chapter) for special notes.

Cable Terminations (to 600 Volt)

Any point at which a wire or cable starts or ends can be described as a "termination." The estimator must determine the number of individual cable runs and provide terminations for each conductor at each end. When equipment is of a nature that it must be set prior to pulling wire, cable terminations are not included. Switchgear, MCC's, control panels, etc., do not include terminations in their installation cost.

When working with lighting and wiring devices, such as switches and receptacles, the wires and cables are in place before the fixture or device is installed. Therefore, the installation price of a receptacle, for example, includes stripping, marking, and installing wire to the terminals on the receptacle. The installation of breakers, panels, and load centers all include terminations for branch wiring.

Units for Measure: Cable terminations are counted for each conductor of a cable at each end (EA.).

Material Units: The following items are generally included per unit:

> Termination lug
> Split bolt connector and tape (splice)

Two-way connector and tape (splice)
Tape (if required)

Labor Units: The following procedures are generally included per unit:
Stripping of insulation from cable
Cleaning and application of deoxidizing compound on aluminum
cable
Installation of terminal lug or connector on wire
Installation of terminal lug to equipment
Taping as required

Takeoff Procedure: First, list each cable size and type of lug. Provide for conductors for each cable end. Tabulate and add to get totals. Then transfer to cost analysis sheets and extend.

Note: Do not figure terminations for lighting and branch wiring devices, but do provide terminations for splices and jumpers as needed.

Shielded Power Cables

Shielded power cables are required in systems where the voltage is 5 kV or above. In the range of 2 kV to 5 kV, the use of shielded cables is a design option that depends on the intended use or application (such as in damp conduits). Below 2 kV, shielded power cable is not required.

Shielding is the practice of wrapping semiconducting layers — either closely fitting or bonded to the inner insulation layers with no voids. The purpose is to equalize the stress within the insulation and to confine the dielectric field within the cable. Shielding extends the life of the cable, limits electromagnetic interference, minimizes surface discharges, and reduces the hazard of shock.

Voltage ratings may be from 5 kV to 69 kV, and conductor sizes range from #6 to 1250 MCM with copper, or to 2000 MCM with aluminum.

As with any cable, shielded cable must be handled carefully. Particular attention must be paid to the manufacturer's specified minimum bending radius to avoid damaging the shield layers. Such damage would lead to premature cable failure.

Units for Measure: Shielded cable is measured in units of 100 linear feet (C.L.F.).

Material Units: The following items are generally included per C.L.F. of cable:
Cable
Wire ties

These additional items must also be listed and extended:

Terminations

Labor Units: The following procedures are generally included for the installation of shielded cable:

Receiving
Material handling
Setting up pulling equipment
Measuring and cutting cable
Pulling cable into conduit
Preparation of conduit for wire

These additional procedures must be listed and extended:

Conduit or cable tray
Wire terminations and splices

Takeoff Procedure: First, list the sizes, voltage rating, and types of cables on a takeoff sheet. Then measure the length of each run and list in the appropriate column. Total each column and add 10% for waste and contingency. Finally, transfer to the cost analysis sheets and extend.

When taking off the cable for procurement purposes, pay particular attention to the shipping lengths ordered. Most engineers will not permit splices. For example, a standard reel length is 1000 feet. If a cable run of 400 feet and three conductors is needed (i.e., 1200 feet total), it cannot be made from two reels, one with 1000 feet and the other with 200 feet. In this case, it is necessary to order 800 feet on one reel and 400 feet on another, or, better still, three reels with 400 feet on each.

Another option is to order the cable from the factory as three parallel 400-foot lengths on one reel. This reduces labor costs for handling in the field.

Whenever possible, order cable based on actual field-measured lengths of raceways. If the length measured from a drawing turns out to be five feet short, then the cable ordered in that too-short length would probably be scrap, and a new length would have to be ordered.

Cable Terminations (High Voltage)

A cable termination fastens the conductor of a wire to the devices or equipment it serves. Many low-voltage (600 V and less) devices have wire attachment terminals with built-in lugs. A screw, nut, bolt, or compression device may be used to firmly and directly attach the wire. Other equipment (motors, for example) must be terminated by attaching a termination lug to the wire, usually by crimping it to the wire. The lug is then bolted or screwed to the device's terminal. Tape or other insulation may be required. Splices are made in a similar manner.

For cables rated at 5 kV and above, the termination process is more complex. A termination lug is compressed onto the conductor, but special attention must be paid to the insulation. If the conductor's shield insulation was abruptly stopped, an electrostatic field would concentrate at the spot and, in time, cause the cable to fail. By tapering the insulation for several inches and applying layers of tape and other insulating materials, a "stress cone" is formed, which gradually equalizes the electrostatic potential over a long surface area.

In addition to stress cones, a series of skirts may be used for outdoor applications. The skirts are intended to prevent leakage from the termination along the damp surface of the cable terminations by effectively increasing the surface distance or length. Splices in high-voltage cables involve the same concerns and precautions as stress cones.

Both splices and terminations require a great deal of time and careful attention. A number of manufacturers supply kits for preforming terminations.

Units for Measure: Each end of each conductor is counted as one termination (EA.).

Material Units: The following items are generally included per unit:
    The termination lug
    A prepackaged kit to form a stress cone

Labor Units: The following procedures are generally included per unit:
> Cutting the cable to length
> Stripping the insulation
> Forming and shaping the stress cone
> Attaching the completed lug

This additional procedure must be listed and extended:
> Testing

Takeoff Procedure: The cable size, as well as the type of insulation and jacket, must be carefully noted when doing the takeoff. Also allow time for coordinating with others and checking phase. Take into account the possibility of overtime. (When a stress cone is started, it should be completed without interruption). Count each cable by size and multiply by the number of conductors, allowing for waste. List under the appropriate heading. Total and transfer the information to the cost analysis form and extend.

For low-voltage (under 600V) devices that have built-in terminals, such as outlets and switches, the labor for termination is included with the device's installation unit.

When purchasing termination lugs, it is important to ensure that they are compatible with the conductor material. Although some lugs are made to be suitable for either copper (CU) conductors or aluminum (AL) conductors, many are not and must be purchased accordingly.

Mineral Insulated Cable

Mineral insulated cable, type "M.I.," is an assembly of one or more bare copper conductors, insulated with a highly compressed refractory mineral insulation and enclosed in a seamless metallic sheath (which is both liquid- and gas-tight). The mineral insulation is magnesium oxide, and the sheath is phosphorous deoxidized copper. This type of cable can be used in hot or cold, wet or dry locations, and in hazardous areas. It can be exposed, embedded in concrete, or buried.

Mineral insulated cable is rated for 600V. Sizes range from #16 to 500 MCM (kcmil) single conductor, up to #4-3 conductor, to #6-4 conductor, and #10-7 conductor. M.I. cable is also available in heating versions, in stainless steel jackets, or in #16 wire rated at a maximum of 300V. Special fittings are used to terminate, a procedure that requires particular care. When M.I. cable is stripped, it must be sealed immediately with an adaptor to prevent moisture from entering the insulation. Special tools are available for use with mineral insulated cable. While M.I. cable *does not* need to be installed in conduit, conduit is sometimes used as a sleeve to protect the cable where it comes out of a slab. M.I. cable must be supported every six feet.

Units for Measure: Count M.I. cable in units of 100 linear feet (C.L.F.). Count each type of end termination (EA.).

Material Units: The following items are generally included per C.L.F. of M.I. cable:

Cable (with clips and fasteners every six feet)

This additional item must be listed and extended:

Each terminal

Labor Units: The following procedures are generally included per C.L.F. of M.I. cable:

Installing the M.I. wire
Fastening with bolts and clips

This additional procedure must be listed and extended:

Terminal kits

Takeoff Procedure: Cable should be taken off by size and number of conductors and by type of termination (hazardous or nonhazardous). Allow 10″ or more for making terminations and connections at each end of run. Supports must be installed at intervals of not more than six feet, per National Electrical Code. Keep in mind that the unit of measure of cable is C.L.F. List the lengths of each type of cable on the takeoff sheets. Total and add 10% for waste. Count the terminations required. Transfer the figures to a cost analysis sheet and extend.

Nonmetallic Sheathed Cable

Nonmetallic sheathed cable is factory-constructed of two, three, or four insulated conductors enclosed in an outer sheath. This covering is a plastic or fibrous material. Nonmetallic sheathed cable comes with or without a bare ground wire and is made with either aluminum or copper conductors. The conductor sizes range from #14 to 4/0.

Nonmetallic sheathed cable is a category that includes a variety of individual types. Each has specific uses and code restrictions. Some types of nonmetallic sheathed cable are listed below:

Type NM: Nonmetallic sheathed cable used for dry areas in residential wiring and in certain commercial buildings up to three stories high.

Type NMC: Similar to type NM but with a corrosion-resistant sheath. It can be used in damp areas.

Type SNM: Shielded type NM cable. It is used in cable trays and raceways.

Type SE: Service entrance cable. It has a flame-retardant, moisture-resistant covering.

Type USE: Underground service entrance cable. Its covering is moisture-resistant but not flame-retardant.

Units for Measure: Nonmetallic cable is measured in units of 100 linear feet (C.L.F.).

Material Units: The following items are generally included when taking off nonmetallic sheathed cable:

Cable

Staples, clips, or fasteners

These additional items must be listed and extended:

Box connectors

Labor Units: The following procedures are generally included in the labor-hours for nonmetallic cable:

Drilling wood (or bushings in metal) studs

Measuring

Running the cable

Staples and clips as required

These additional procedures must be listed and extended:

Knock-outs

Box connections

Terminations

Takeoff Procedure: When measuring, allow for drops, risers, and the amount used within boxes. List each type and size to be used. Measure and list under the appropriate column. Next, count the box connectors, grommets, etc. Total and add 10% for waste. Transfer the quantities to a cost analysis sheet and extend.

Fiber Optic Cable Systems

Fiber optic systems use optical fiber such as plastic, glass, or fused silica, a transparent material, to transmit radiant power (i.e., light) for control, communication, and signaling applications. The types of fiber optic cables can be nonconductive, conductive, or composite. The composite cables contain fiber optics and current-carrying electrical conductors. The configuration for one of the fiber optic systems is as follows:

The transceiver module acts as transmitting and receiving equipment in a common house, which converts electrical energy to light energy or vice-versa.

Pricing the fiber optic system is not an easy task. The performance of the whole system will affect the cost significantly. New specialized tools and techniques decrease the installing cost tremendously. In the fiber optic section of *Means Electrical Cost Data,* a benchmark for labor-hours and material costs is set up so that users can adjust their costs according to unique project conditions.

Units for Measure: Fiber optic cable is measured in hundred linear feet (C.L.F.) or in industry units of measure—meter (m) or kilometer (km). The connectors are counted as units (EA.).

Material Units: Generally, the material costs include only the cable. All the accessories shall be priced separately.

Labor Units: The following procedures are generally included for the installation of fiber optic cables:

> Receiving
> Material handling
> Setting up pulling equipment
> Measuring and cutting cable
> Pulling cable

These additional items are listed and extended:

> Terminations

Takeoff Procedure: Cable should be taken off by type, size, number of fibers, and number of terminations required. List the lengths of each type of cable on the takeoff sheets. Total and add 10% for waste. Transfer the figures to a cost analysis sheet and extend.

Special Wires

This category includes a number of distinct wire types, such as fixture wires, low-voltage instrumentation wire, signal cables, telephone cables, tray cables, high-performance unshielded twisted pair (UTP) communication cables, and coaxial cables. Each of these cables is designed to meet unique performance criteria for specific applications. Fixture wire, for example, has insulation rated for the high temperatures created in lighting fixtures. Coaxial cables are designed to have specific impedances that will match the input and output equipment's impedance; this arrangement results in the maximum energy transfer of signals.

Units for Measure: These wires are measured in linear feet (L.F.) and extended in units of 100 linear feet (C.L.F.). Special connectors for these cable(s), when required, are counted as one for each cable end (EA.).

Material Units: Wire only is generally included for special wires.

These additional items must be listed and extended:

    Special terminators (such as coaxial cable connectors)

    Strain relief grips, etc.

    Special tools for connectors or stripping

Labor Units: The following procedures are generally included for special wires:

    Cable pulled and supported as needed

These additional procedures must be listed and extended:

    Coax connector installed on cable with special crimp tool

    Strain relief

    Terminations

Takeoff Procedure: List the cables by type and size on the takeoff sheet. Then carefully measure cable runs for one system at a time (include drop and riser lengths). Mark runs with a colored pencil as they are taken off. Count fittings, terminators, or special support devices and list them on the same sheet. Next, total the columns and allow an extra 10% for wire footages for waste. Finally, transfer the totals to a cost analysis sheet, paying attention to the unit of measure, and extend.

Grounding

In most distribution systems, one conductor of the supply is grounded. This conductor is called the "neutral wire." In addition, the N.E.C. requires that a grounding conductor be supplied to connect non-current-carrying, conductive parts to ground. This distinction between the "grounded conductor" and the "grounding conductor" is important.

Grounding protects persons from injury in the event of an insulation failure within equipment. It also stabilizes the voltage with respect to ground and prevents surface potentials between equipment — which could harm both people and equipment (in a hospital, for example).

Lightning protection systems are a separate concern but are closely related to grounding in intent and practice. Lightning poses two kinds of danger. The first is the lightning strike itself. This can damage structures and distribution systems by passing a very high current for a brief time — causing heat, fire, and/or equipment failure. The second danger is from induced voltages in lines running close to the lightning's path. These pulses can be very high and can damage electrical equipment or cause injury to people.

In both systems, it is essential that a good, low-resistance ground path be provided. This can be accomplished via the use of ground rods, a ground grid, or attachment to metal pipes in contact with the earth (such as water pipes). Note: In communities where plastic water pipes are used between the street main and a building, this grounding method is not suitable — even though copper pipes may be used for the building's interior.

Connections between ground wires and pipes, conduits, or boxes are often made with cable clamps. Permanent connections between heavy ground wires and ground rods, building structural steel, other ground wires, or lightning rods are usually made with an exothermic weld process.

Units for Measure: Ground wire is measured in linear feet (L.F.) and extended in units of 100 linear feet (C.L.F.). Ground clamps and exothermic welds are counted as individual units (EA.).

Material Units: The following items are generally listed in the grounding takeoff:

Ground rods
Bare or insulated ground wire
Ground clamps
Exothermic weld metal (less molds and accessories)

Note: A different type of mold is necessary for each different type of connection.

These additional items must be listed and extended:

Sleeves or raceways to protect ground wires
Lightning rods and devices

Labor Units: The following procedures are generally listed for grounding takeoffs:

Running ground wire and supports as required
Ground clamps or lugs
Exothermic weld

These additional procedures must be listed and extended:

Excavation
Backfill
Sleeves or raceways used to protect grounding wires
Wall penetrations
Floor cutting
Core drilling

Takeoff Procedure: First, list the sizes and types of ground wires on the takeoff sheets. List ground rods by diameter and length. Identify and list each unique type of ground connection. Each shape and size of exothermic weld connection will require a separate mold. List each mold required on the takeoff sheet for material only. Next, measure the length of the cables by size and allow for drops and risers. Count the ground rods, clamps, and exothermic welds. Total and add 10% to wire for waste. Also, for estimating purposes, add 5-10% to exothermic welds. Finally, transfer the quantities to a cost analysis sheet and extend.

Undercarpet Wiring

Branch circuits are the conductors used between the circuit protection (fuse or breaker) and plug outlets for power and lighting. Flat Conductor Cable—type FCC (also referred to as "Undercarpet Power Systems")—is designed to be an accessible, flexible system for branch circuits.

Flat Conductor Cable is comprised of three or more flat copper conductors assembled edge-to-edge in an insulating jacket. Both a top and a bottom shield are required. All components must be firmly anchored (usually with adhesives). Crossings of two types of FCC, such as telephone (cable), are permitted, provided metal shield is placed between them. Transition assemblies are used to connect the Flat Conductor Cable to conventional wiring for the home run to a breaker panel.

Type FCC cable may be used in existing buildings to rework obsolete wiring systems, and in new buildings to allow customizing fit to the tenants and users of office areas.

As the FCC cable system gained popularity, a wide spectrum of complementary products also became available. These products include telephone systems, flat coaxial data cable systems, and fiber optic data link systems.

Type FCC cable must be installed under carpet squares not larger than 30″ by 30″. It is permitted on hard, smooth, continuous floor surfaces and on wall surfaces in metal raceways. It is not permitted outdoors or in wet locations; in corrosive atmospheres; or in residential, school, or hospital buildings.

The use of undercarpet wiring systems is decreasing because of many factors—the trend toward company downsizing, the resulting reorganization of communication channels within a company, and rapid new technology turnover in many organizations. For these types of changes, undercarpet wiring systems are inflexible for remodeling work and have therefore often been replaced by access floor wiring systems, poke-through systems, or modular furniture systems.

Units for Measure: The cable and shield are measured per linear foot (L.F.). Fittings, taps, splices, bends, etc. are counted as each unit (EA.).

Material Units: The following items are generally included for installation of undercarpet power systems:

Cable: Includes flat conductor cable with bottom shield, top shield, adhesive and tape.

Transition fitting: Includes one base, one cover, and one transition block.

Floor fitting: Includes one frame base kit, one transition block, and two covers (duplex/blank).

Tap: Includes one tap connector for each conductor, two insulating patches, and two top shield connectors.

Splice: Includes one splice connector for each conductor, two insulating patches, and two top shield connectors.

Cable bend: Includes two top shield connectors.

Cable dead end (outside of transition block): Includes two insulating patches.

A special connecting tool is also required.

Labor Units: The following procedures are generally included in the installation of undercarpet power systems:

Flat conductor cable: Includes placing the cable only. These additional procedures must be listed and extended:

Top shield
Mark floor
Tape primer
Hold down tape
Patching or leveling uneven floors
Filling in holes or removing projections from concrete slabs
Sealing porous floors
Sweeping and vacuuming floors
Removing existing carpeting, cutting carpet squares, and
installing carpet squares

Transition fitting: Includes assembling the transition block and attaching wires. These additional procedures must be listed and extended:

Wall outlet box for the transition fitting with cover
Home run wires and conduit

Floor fitting: Includes placing the receptacle device and terminating to the cable.

Tap: Includes terminating the conductors with connectors. These additional procedures must be listed and extended:

Insulating patches
Top shield

Splice: Includes terminating the conductors with connectors. These additional procedures must be listed and extended:

    Insulating patches
    Top shield

Cable bend: Includes folding the cable at 90 degrees to change direction. This additional item must be listed and extended:

    Top shield

Cable dead end: Includes cutting the cable to length and insulating patches.

Takeoff Procedure: List the cable by number of conductors. List components for each fitting type, tap, splice, and bend on your quantity takeoff sheet. Each component must be priced separately.

Start at the power supply transition fittings and survey each circuit for the components needed. Tabulate the quantities of each component under a specific circuit number. Use the floor plan layout scale to get the cable footage. Combine the count for each component in each circuit and list the total quantity in the last column.

Allow approximately 5% waste on items such as cable, top shield, tape, and spray adhesive.

Suggested guidelines:

    Equal amounts of cable and top shield should be included.
    For each roll of cable, include a set of cable splices.
    For every 1' of cable, include 2-1/2' of hold down tape.
    For every three rolls of hold down tape, include one can of spray
        adhesive.

Adjust the final figures wherever possible to accommodate standard packaging of the product. (This information is available from the distributor.)

Undercarpet Telephone Systems

An undercarpet telephone system is designed to connect telephone devices to a distribution closet using undercarpet cabling. This method provides flexibility in open office situations.

Units for Measure: The cable is measured per linear foot (L.F.). Fittings, taps, splices, bends, etc. are counted as each unit (EA.).

Material Units: The following items are generally included:

Cable runs: Include cable as with power systems. These additional items must be listed and extended:

    Tape
    Adhesive

Transition fittings: Include one base plate, one cover, and one transition block.

Floor fittings: Include one frame base kit, two covers, and modular jacks.

Labor Units: The following procedures are generally included:

Cable runs: Include cable only. These additional procedures must be listed and extended:

    Floor marking
    Floor preparation

Top shield
Tape
Spray adhesive
Cable folds
Conduit or raceways to transition floor boxes
Telephone cable to transition boxes
Terminations before transition boxes
Floor preparation as described in power section

Transition fittings: Include assembly of the transition block and terminating wires. These additional procedures must be listed and extended:

Wall outlet box with cover
Home run wires
Conduit

Floor fittings: Include placing the device, covers, modular jacks, and fastening in place. This additional procedure must be listed and extended:

Cutting carpet holes

Be sure to include all cable folds when pricing labor.

Takeoff Procedure: After reviewing floor plans, identify each transition. Number or letter each cable run from that fitting.

Start at the transition fitting and survey each circuit for the components needed. List the cable type, terminations, cable length, and floor fitting type under the specific circuit number.

Use the floor plan layout scale to get the cable footage. Add some extra length (next higher increment of 5′) to cable quantities.

Combine the list of components in each circuit and figure the total quantity in the last column. Calculate the necessary 5% allowance for such items as wire, tape, bottom shield, and spray adhesive.

Adjust the final figures whenever possible to accommodate standard packaging. Check that items such as transition fittings, floor boxes, and floor fittings—which are to be used for both power and telephone—have been priced as combination fittings, thereby avoiding duplication.

Be sure to include the marking of floors and drilling of fasteners if the fittings specified are not the adhesive type.

Undercarpet Data Systems

An undercarpet data system is designed to interconnect remote data processing terminals to the main computer by means of undercarpet wiring.

Units for Measure: As above, for telephone systems.

Material Units: The following items are generally included:

Cable: Includes the cable only. These additional items must be listed and extended:

Tape
Adhesive

Transition fittings: Include one base plate, one cover, and one transition block.

Floor fittings: Include one frame base kit, two covers, and modular jacks. This additional item must be listed and extended:

Connectors

Labor Units: The following procedures are generally included:

As telephone cable, but without shields

Additional procedures to be listed and extended include:

Conduit or raceways to transition or floor boxes
Data cable to transition boxes
Terminations before transition boxes
Floor preparation, as described in the power section
Notching cable sides to make turns

Takeoff Procedure: Start at the transition fittings and take off quantities in the same manner as the telephone system, keeping in mind that data cable does not require top or bottom shields. The data cable is simply cross-taped on the cable run to the floor fitting.

Data cable can be purchased in either bulk form or in precut lengths with connectors. If it is obtained in bulk, coaxial connector material and related labor must be priced.

Data cable cannot be folded and must be notched at 1″ intervals. A count of all turns must be added to the labor portion of the estimate. Notching requires:

90 degree turn	8 notches per side
180 degree turn	16 notches per side

Floor boxes, transition boxes and fittings are the same as described in the power and telephone procedures.

Since undercarpet systems require special hand tools, be sure to include this cost in proportion to the number of crews involved in the installation.

Chapter 14

Boxes and Wiring Devices

A box is used in electrical wiring—at each junction point, outlet, and switch. Boxes provide access to electric connections and serve as a mounting for fixtures and switches. They may also be used as pull points for wire in long runs or conduit. A wiring device is a switch or receptacle that controls, but does not consume, electricity. This chapter has five sections that cover various types of boxes, cabinets, wiring devices, and the appropriate fasteners and hangers. Descriptions, units for measure, material and labor requirements, and a takeoff procedure are given for each.

Pull Boxes & Cabinets

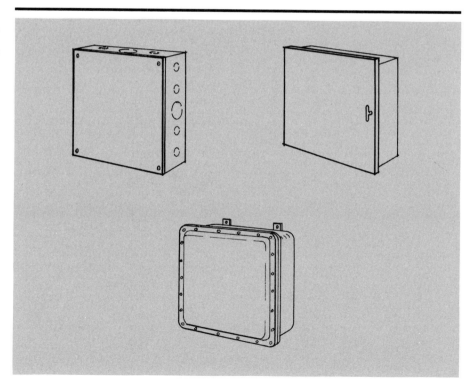

Pull boxes are inserted in a long run of conduit to facilitate the pulling of wire. They are also used where conduit changes direction or wires divide into different directions. Cabinets are used where wire terminates. Both come in various NEMA types to match the requirements of a given environment.

Boxes are usually made of galvanized steel, epoxy-painted steel, stainless steel, or aluminum. Less common materials include malleable iron, cast iron, cast aluminum, and high-density plastic.

Units for Measure: Boxes and cabinets are counted in terms of each (EA.) and are tabulated by size and type.

Material Units: The following items are generally included per unit:
Boxes
Covers
Fasteners

These additional items are listed and extended:
Support racks
Wire terminations

Labor Units: Different types of installations require different types of labor units:

Wall mount (indoor or outdoor) installations: Includes unloading and uncrating; hauling of enclosures from the loading dock; measuring and marking; and mounting and leveling boxes. Note: A plywood backboard is not included.

Ceiling mounting: Includes unloading and uncrating; hauling boxes from the loading dock; measuring and marking; drilling four lead anchor-type fasteners using a hammer drill; and installing and leveling boxes using rolling staging.

Freestanding cabinets: Includes unloading and uncrating; hauling cabinets from the loading dock; marking of floor; drilling four lead anchor-type fasteners using a hammer drill; and leveling and shimming.

Telephone cabinets: Includes unloading and uncrating; hauling cabinets; measuring and marking; and mounting and leveling, using four lead anchor-type fasteners.

These additional items must be listed and extended:
Punching or drilling holes for conduit
Wire and terminations

Takeoff Procedure: Verify the box requirements per the specifications. List cabinets and pull boxes by NEMA type and size.

Example:	Quantity	Type	Size
	3	NEMA 1	6"W x 6"H x 4"D
	2	NEMA 3R	6"W x 6"H x 4"D

Itemize and detail any special support or hanger requirements.

Outlet Boxes

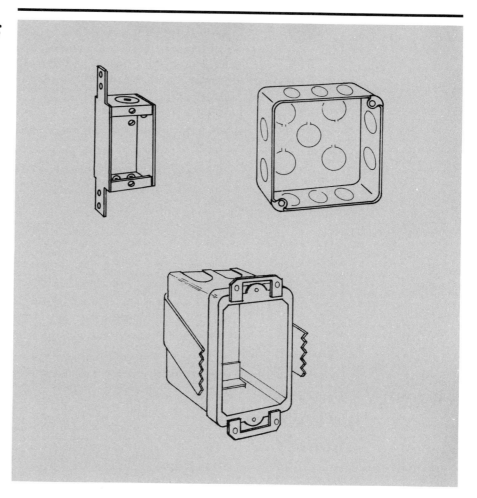

Outlet boxes made of steel or plastic are used to hold wiring devices, such as switches and receptacles. They are also used as a mount for lighting fixtures. Some outlet boxes are ready for flush mounting; others require a plaster frame. Some have plain knockouts for pipe up to 1-1/4″, while others have built-in brackets for Romex or BX wire. The capacity of outlet boxes ranges from one to six devices. They may have brackets for direct stud mounting or plaster ears for mounting in existing walls.

Units for Measure: Outlet boxes are counted as each (EA.). Related accessories, such as plaster rings and covers, are also counted individually.

Material Units: The following items are generally included per unit:

Box and fastener

Labor Units: The following procedures are generally included per outlet box:

Marking the box location
Mounting the box
Material handling

Takeoff Procedure: Outlet boxes should be included on the same takeoff sheet as branch wiring or devices to better explain what is included in each circuit. Each unit price in this section is a stand-alone item and contains no other component unless specified. To estimate a duplex outlet, for example, the following components may be listed:

Outlet box
Plaster ring
Duplex receptacle from Div. 162-300
Device cover

Cost Modifications: For large concentrations of plastic boxes in the same area, the following percentages can be deducted from labor-hours totals:

1	to	25	− 0%
26		50	−15%
51		75	−20%
76		100	−25%
Over 100			−30%

Note: It is important to understand that these percentages are not used on the total job quantities, but only in areas where concentrations reach the levels specified.

Wiring Devices and Low-Voltage Switching

A device is, by N.E.C. definition, "a unit of an electrical system which is intended to carry but not to utilize electric energy." Wiring devices include receptacles, wall switches, pilot lights, and wall plates. Low-voltage switching includes the above plus relays, transformers, rectifiers and controls.

Receptacles are a convenient means of connecting portable equipment and appliances to power. Receptacles are available in voltage ratings ranging from 125 to 600, and in amperages from 10 to 400. A wide variety of configurations is used to avoid having a plug or cap with a certain voltage and ampere rating inserted into a receptacle of another rating. Switches, used to turn off power to lights and receptacles, are also rated for different voltages and amperages. Low-voltage switching operates at 24V through a transformer and uses relays to control 120V lighting and above. Operating at a low voltage allows the use of multiconductor #18 wire—a size much smaller than regular wire. A master control can be used to operate all lighting from one location.

Units for Measure: Wiring devices are counted as each (EA.). It is important to list and quantify all associated items with each device, such as plates, boxes, and plaster rings.

Material Units: The following items are generally included per unit:
> Receptacles
> Wall switches
> Pilot lights

Low-voltage switching should include a count of the above plus these items:
> Relays
> Transformers
> Rectifiers
> Controls

Labor Units: The following procedures are generally included per unit:
> Stripping of wire insulation
> Attaching wire to device using terminals on the device itself
> Mounting of device in box

These additional items are listed and extended:
> Conduit
> Wire
> Boxes
> Cover plates
> Wire splices

Takeoff Procedure: Wiring devices should be priced on a takeoff form that includes associated boxes, covers, conduit, and wire. List the device as indicated on the drawings and note the legend symbol beside it. Then list all associated items necessary to complete the installation (i.e., box, cover plate, etc.). Count each device, marking the drawing as you go. Total and transfer to a cost analysis sheet for pricing and extension. When practical, get vendor quotes for the material portions.

Cost Modifications: For large concentrations of devices in the same area, deduct the following percentages from labor-hours:

1	to	10	− 0%
11		25	−20%
25		50	−25%
51		100	−35%
Over 100			−35%

Fasteners

Fasteners include various types of anchors, bolts, screws, nails, rivets, and studs. These are included to provide a reasonable guide to costs. However, conditions vary so greatly that one cost cannot be applied to all situations. Thought must be given to the particulars of each installation and costs adjusted accordingly.

Units for Measure: Fasteners are counted as units (EA.).

Material Units: A material unit generally is an assembly of the bolt, nut, washer, and anchor (as required).

Labor Units: The following procedures are generally included per unit:
  Drilling an appropriate mounting hole for the bolt (no holes are
    drilled in the device being mounted)
  Inserting and setting the anchor (when appropriate)
  Threading on and tightening the fastener

These additional items are listed and extended:
  Torquing and testing

Takeoff Procedure: As devices, boxes, panels, etc. are taken off, be cognizant of the assumptions made for mounting. If these allowances are inadequate, add fasteners accordingly. Also, when developing new installation costs, include fastener costs.

This takeoff is performed on the same sheet as that for the device being mounted. Transfer the quantities to a cost analysis sheet and extend.

Cost Modifications: Most installation costs include anchors, with several installed at one time in one area. Labor costs must be added for unusually difficult situations, or reduced for a large quantity installed at one time in the same area. These judgments must be left to the discretion of the estimator.

A fairly accurate count is important at this time so that quantities of specified or specialty fasteners can be ordered. (It is costly to waste field labor for lack of enough bolts!)

Hangers

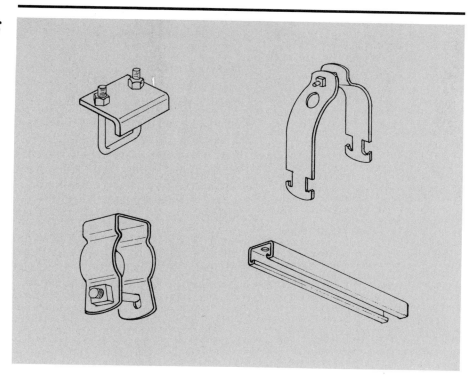

For our purposes, a hanger is a means of suspending or supporting electrical raceway installations. As mentioned in previous chapters, hangers are often included in the linear foot cost of a raceway at predetermined intervals. Variations from these standard assumptions become cost considerations for the estimator.

Hangers can be grouped into two distinct categories — those that are shop-manufactured and those that are field-fabricated. Manufactured hangers are designed to support by attaching to an existing building structure without modification. Examples are one- or two-hole straps, beam clamps, or riser clamps. A field-fabricated hanger is the manual combination of two or more components to provide support. A trapeze-type hanger is a typical example. To assemble a trapeze-type hanger, the following components are required:

> Channel steel ("Unistrut")
> Threaded rod
> Nuts, bolts, and washers
> Support steel
> Beam clamps or fasteners
> Conduit straps

Each of these items involves a material and labor cost. These must be combined for an accurate cost assessment. It can be costly to disregard the cost of hangers (or to assume that the linear foot cost of raceways will be accurate enough). This is particularly true on projects such as process piping, where whole networks of conduit racking systems are used.

Units for Measure: Unique hangers must first be estimated as mini-systems — to arrive at a cost for material and labor for each specific configuration. The hangers are then counted as each (EA.).

Material Units: The material price for hangers generally includes only the hanger itself (with the particular components required to assemble it).

Labor Units: The assembly of each component and installation of the completed unit are generally the only items included in the labor-hours.

Takeoff Procedure: Check the prints and specs for details on hanger arrangements. If the arrangement is similar to those priced into the linear foot quantities of raceway, then only a count for material procurement may be necessary. This count is the L.F. total for each size of raceway, divided by the specified distance between supports. If the hangers and supports are field fabricated, price them out as subassemblies to get the total cost of each fabricated hanger. Then divide the L.F. total of raceway by the specified distance between supports.

If the hangers are supporting groups of conduits, then count each hanger individually. Set up the work sheet by the type and size of hanger. Take off the quantities, including risers and clamps if required. Transfer the quantities to a cost analysis sheet and extend.

Chapter 15

Starters, Boards, and Switches

Starters are electric controllers that accelerate a motor from rest to running speed; they are also used to step the motor. Boards serve as a mounting for electric components and/or controls. Switches are devices used to open, close, or change the connection of an electric circuit. This chapter contains 18 sections and includes components ranging from panelboards and circuit breakers to motor control centers and meter sockets. Each of these components is first defined, then supplied with the appropriate units for measure. Following are material and labor requirements and the procedures involved in the takeoff.

Circuit Breakers

Circuit breakers are used in general distribution and in branch circuits to protect the wires and equipment downstream from current overload. Circuit breakers are rated in amperes and are capable of interrupting their rated current at their rated voltage. There are several types of circuit breakers: magnetic trip only, molded case, current-limiting (which includes three coordinated current-limiting fuses), and electronic trip. An important parameter in selecting a breaker is its fault current interrupting capacity. Several different grades of breakers are available in most sizes, for different uses and conditions. The common Ampere Interruption Capacity ratings are 10,000 AIC; 22,000 AIC; 42,000 AIC; and 65,000 AIC. Their application is determined by the amount of energy available at the breaker's line side during a short-circuit fault.

Breakers are available in several voltages from 120 to 600, in one, two, or three poles. Enclosed breakers are available up to 2000 A. Breakers come in frame sizes of 100 A, 225 A, 400 A, 1000 A, 1200 A, and 2000 A. Several different ampere ratings use the same frame size.

Example: 400 A frame size has ratings of 125 A, 150 A, 175 A, 200 A, 225 A, 250 A, 300 A, 350 A, and 400 A, all of which have the same price. When estimating circuit breakers, it is important to use correct NEMA designations pertaining to areas of use.

Units for Measure: Circuit breakers are characterized in terms of each (EA.) breaker.

Material Units: The cost for each circuit breaker generally includes four lead anchor-type wall fasteners.

Labor Units: The following procedures are generally included per unit:
   Unloading and uncrating
   Hauling equipment
   Measuring and marking the circuit breaker location
   Installing the circuit breaker
   Connecting and phase marking wire on primary and secondary
      terminals

These additional procedures are listed and extended:
   Primary or secondary conduit
   Backboards
   Wire

Takeoff Procedure: First, set up the work sheet by circuit breaker type, voltage, number of poles, NEMA classification, and ampere rating. Count the circuit breakers, listing each one under the proper designation on the quantity sheet as you count. In this way, there is no need to hunt for like circuit breakers to count them before proceeding with the next type. Then transfer the total quantities to a cost analysis sheet and extend.

Cost Modifications: If several circuit breakers are installed in a common location by the same electrician or crew, an adjustment can be made. Deduct the following percentages from the labor units:

0-5	− 0%
5-10	− 5%
10-20	−10%
21-30	−15%
Over 30	−18%

Example: Six 30 A 600V circuit breakers are to be installed from common 12″ x 12″ wireway. Adjust the labor-hours in this way:

$$\frac{Quantity}{6} \times \frac{Labor\text{-}Hours}{2.5} \times \frac{Adjustment}{.95} = \frac{Adjusted\ Labor\text{-}Hours}{14.25\ L.H.}$$

Control Stations

(Also see "Control Switches," listed later in this chapter.)

Control stations are enclosures for mounting control switches and pilot lights.

Standard-duty control stations usually come completely assembled as an enclosure with control switches and legends. Standard-duty control stations have a capacity for up to three units and use either push buttons or selector switches. Pilot lights are also available with these stations.

Control stations are assembled in a wide variety of configurations and NEMA classifications. Standard-duty stations with NEMA enclosures have one to three positions (holes), while NEMA 4, 7, and 9 have one or two positions.

Other control stations (without switches) are heavy-duty oiltight NEMA 4 and 13 with up to 30 positions; or watertight, corrosion-resistant NEMA 4, 4X, or B for up to 25 units.

NEMA 1 enclosures come with prepunched knock-outs. However, other NEMA enclosures should be specified for hole sizes and arrangement at the time of purchase.

Oiltight and watertight enclosures may be ordered with controls premounted. This saves considerable labor-hours in the field.

Units for Measure: Each station (enclosure) is counted as a unit (EA.).

Material Units: The following items are generally included per control station:

Enclosure
Switch assembly (for some stations)
Wire marker for each contact
Legend tag for station

These additional items are listed and extended:

Branch wire
Branch conduit
Switches, pilot lights, and legends for each station

Labor Units: The following procedures are generally included per control station:

Installing enclosure
Mounting switches if required
Testing

These additional procedures are listed and extended:

Installing branch wire to enclosure
Terminations of control wires
Marking of control wires
Installing conduit to enclosure
Cutting or punching mounting hole (see "Cutting and Drilling" in
    Chapter 12: Raceways)

Takeoff Procedure: Set up the work sheet by type. Take care to note how many devices are in each enclosure and in each type of enclosure. In most cases, this work can be taken off most conveniently at the same time as motors and motor controls are taken off.

Fuses

Fuses are used to interrupt a circuit in the event of overload. Fuses have a fusible link through which the current must flow. If too much current flows, the resulting heat melts the link. This stops the flow of current. There are many different types of fuses, such as plug, cartridge, and bolt-on. Fuses are designed with fast-acting or time-delay links. Both types will have the ability to react quickly to short-circuit currents.

Some plug fuses have an Edison screw base, which is the same as a medium base lamp. Others have a type "S" base, which requires an adapter screwed into the medium base socket. The purpose of these adapters is to discourage the use of fuses larger than the size appropriate to the existing wiring. Plug fuses are made up to 30 A at 125V. Cartridge fuses are available in many types, including renewable and non-renewable, dual element, time delaying, and current limiting. Most are rated 250V or 600V and ampacities up to 600. Bolt-on (cartridge) fuses are available to 6000 A. Cartridge fuses are categorized by class designations such as Class H, K, RK5, J, RK1, or L. These designations indicate the interrupting rating (i.e., 10,000 A; 100,000 A; or 200,000 A) and the performance characteristics of the fuse.

Units for Measure: Fuses are counted as each (EA.). Categorize fuses by voltage rating, current rating, and class.

Material Units: The fuse itself is generally the only item included.

Labor Units: The following procedures are generally included per unit:
Replacing the fuse if necessary
Installing new fuses
Testing with a continuity tester

Typical Job Conditions: The fuseholder is to be in an easily accessible location in an unlocked enclosure.

Takeoff Procedure: Be careful to identify the particular type of fuse that is to be used. List by ampere, voltage, and type or class. Be sure to count one fuse for each line (or phase) being protected. List on the quantity sheet and mark the drawing.

Load Centers

A load center is a specialized type of panelboard used principally for residential applications. These panels are designed for lighter sustained loads than those used in industrial and commercial applications.

Load centers are available from 100 A to a maximum 200 A rating in several configurations: i.e., 120/240V, 1 phase, 3 wire; 120/208V, 3 phase, 4 wire; 240V, 1 phase, 2 wire; 120/240V, 3 phase, 4 wire; and 240V, 3 phase, 3 wire. Load centers generally use plug-in circuit breakers. The single-pole breakers range from 15 A to 50 A; double-pole breakers from 15 A to 100 A; and three-pole breakers from 15 A to 100 A. Two- and three-wire switched neutral and ground fault interrupting styles are also available.

Lighting and appliance load centers are limited to a maximum of 42 overcurrent devices in each cabinet.

Units for Measure: Load centers are counted as each unit (EA.) by type and size. While standard breakers may be included, care must be taken to ensure that all special service breakers are noted and priced as additional items.

Material Units: The following items are generally included with load centers:

Breakers
Box
Cover
Trim

Labor Units: The following procedures are generally included per load center:

Receiving
Measuring and marking walls
Drilling four lead anchor-type fasteners using a hammer drill
Mounting and leveling panel
Preparation and termination of feeder cable to lugs or main breaker
Testing and load balancing
Marking panel directory

These additional procedures are listed and extended:

Modifications to enclosure (extra breakers)
Structural supports
Additional lugs
Plywood backboards
Painting or lettering

Note: Knockouts are included in the price of terminating conduit runs and need not be added to the load center costs.

Takeoff Procedure: When pricing load centers, list panels by size and type. List breakers in a separate column of the quantity sheet, and define by phase (poles) and ampere rating.

Cost Modifications: If a load center does not include a full panel of single-pole breakers, use the following method to adjust material and labor costs. For example, in an 18-circuit panel, only 16 single-pole breakers are needed.

18 breakers included
16 breakers needed
———————————————
 2 breakers need to be deleted

To adjust for the breakers that are not required, find the unit cost of a 20 A single-pole breaker:

Typical Costs

Single pole breaker = $ 7.75 for material
$19.00 for labor
$26.75 total material and labor

Multiply the material price of the breaker by .50.

$7.75 × .50 = $3.88

Multiply the labor price by .60.

$19.00 × .60 = $11.40

The cost to delete per breaker will be $3.88 for material and $11.40 for labor. Multiply these figures by the number of breakers not required: in this case, two.

$ 3.88 × 2 = $ 7.76 material
$11.40 × 2 = $22.80 labor
$30.56 to be deducted from the cost of the panel

Meter Centers and Sockets

Meter sockets are enclosures designed to receive the plug-in utility watt meters that monitor a customer's power usage. For multiple tenants in commercial or residential buildings, meter centers may be used to monitor and distribute a single service entrance cable to two or more different users. This is accomplished with multiple sockets.

A meter center may have a main breaker, a fusible disconnect, or a remote protection device. If it feeds two or more branch services, a meter center will usually have individual meter breakers. Meter centers are available in a variety of configurations for one to six meters and can be bussed together for larger groupings. Bus capacities normally range from 125 A to 800 A, though meter centers with a capacity to 1200 A may be special ordered.

The two styles of enclosures commonly used are surface-mounted and semiflush; NEMA 1 (general, indoor) and NEMA 3R (outdoor, rainproof) are available with provisions for top or bottom feed of the main service cable.

Meters are owned and installed by the utility company. Therefore, no cost allowance needs to be made for material or labor.

Units for Measure: Meter sockets are counted as units (EA.). A meter center is a unit (EA.) for multiple sockets.

Material Units: The following items are generally included per unit:

    Meter socket or a meter center

    Wall anchor fasteners

These additional items must also be listed and extended:

    Main circuit breaker or fused disconnect

    Tenant (or meter) circuit breakers

    Conduit

    Termination lugs

Labor Units: The following procedures are generally included per meter socket or meter center:

    Receiving

    Handling

    Mounting and alignment

    Legend identifications

These additional procedures must be listed and extended:

    Conduit

    Cables

    Terminations

    Breakers

    Testing

Takeoff Procedure: For meter sockets:

    List all sizes and types of the sockets required.

    Count each meter socket and list it under the appropriate heading.

    Total each column, transfer these figures to a cost analysis sheet, and extend.

For meter centers:

    List each meter center, noting its bus capacity, number of meter sockets, and type of enclosure.

    Take off the size of the main breaker or fusible disconnect switch.

    List the size of each tenant breaker.

    Total each column, transfer these figures to a cost analysis sheet, and extend.

Motor Control Centers

Many commercial buildings and process plants maximize efficiency by grouping electrical controls into centralized locations. Motor control centers (MCC's) serve this need by providing a structure for mounting a variety of motor starters, auxiliary controls, and feeder tap units. A motor control center is a collection of motor control equipment and bus bars assembled in a series of steel-clad enclosures. The enclosure, including the bus, is called a "structure" and will take any combination of starters up to 72" high. Some structures allow for mounting starters on both the front and back sides.

A starter combination MCP, FVNR with control transformer size 1 is 12" high; thus six size 1 starters could fit into one structure. Size 2 is 18" high, so four size 2, or two size 2 with three size 1 would be acceptable. Size 3 is 24", 4 is 30", 5 is 48", and 6 is 72". Assorted combinations of these (and other) controls can be assembled. Also, many structures may be "bussed" together to expand the MCC. The enclosures are commonly available in NEMA classes:

NEMA 1:	General purpose, indoor
NEMA 2:	Dripproof
NEMA 3R:	Rainproof
NEMA 12:	Dusttight and driptight, indoor

There are two class designations for MCC wiring. In Class I, all internal control wiring is done in the field. In Class II, the control circuits are factory-wired to terminal strips. There are also three NEMA-type designations: Type A, B, or C. The type indicates how the control and power cables are terminated (i.e., wired to terminal blocks or direct to the devices).

Internal bus bars are usually aluminum, but copper is often specified. We recommend that you contact manufacturers for complete material prices. Generally, an MCC is ordered as a complete assembly, including starters, breakers, doors, etc. The MCC can, however, be modified with field-installed components.

Units for Measure: Each section is counted as one unit (EA.). All components are listed and totalled.

Material Units: The following items are generally included in the takeoff:
Motor control center, complete as required
Thermal heaters as required
Fuses as required
Wire markers

Labor Units: The following procedures are generally included in the labor-hours:
Receiving
Handling
Setting equipment
Leveling and shimming
Anchoring
Cable and wire terminations (power only, not control cables)
Cable identification (power)

These additional procedures are listed and extended:
Rigging
Equipment pad
Steel channels embedded or grouted in concrete
Conduit and wire
Testing

Takeoff Procedure: When pricing the structure, be careful to check the specs for NEMA class, bus size, copper or aluminum bus, and NEMA type. List each MCC by the engineer's designation, and every section in each MCC. List (per MCC) all components that will be ordered in the MCC. (Do not add labor when components are factory-installed.)

Motor Control Center Components

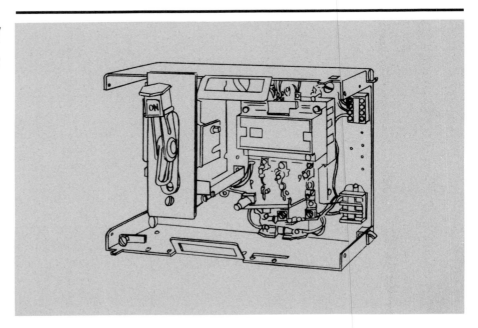

Motor control center (MCC) components are modular devices that plug into an MCC structure's bus. They are generally called out, ordered, and shipped with the MCC as a complete assembly. Occasionally, components are purchased individually to be installed into an existing MCC. When ordering components to fit an existing installation, it is necessary to order the same make and model of components. The products of different manufacturers may not be interchangeable.

Some of the commonly used components are combination starters with either circuit breakers or fused disconnects; reversing and two-speed motor starters; feeder circuit breakers; main circuit breakers; lighting panelboards; and transformers.

The N.E.C. wiring class and type must also be noted. For example, with type A components, all field control wiring must be terminated directly to the device. This unit is less expensive to purchase but more costly to install. A type B component has all intra-wiring brought out to terminal blocks (only the power cable is terminated directly to the starter). This approach simplifies field installation and maintenance repairs. Type C components are similar to type B except that terminal blocks are also provided for the load terminals in starters size 3 and under. Installation labor is about the same for types B and C, but maintenance and service are easier to perform.

While some general material costs are available from reference books, by far the most reliable pricing source will be the specified manufacturer or manufacturer's representative.

Units for Measure: MCC components are listed as each unit (EA.) with careful attention to the use and to specifications.

Material Units: The following items are generally included per MCC component:

    Starter or other components as required
    Thermal heater as required
    Fuses as required
    Wire markers

These additional items are listed and extended:

    Motor control center structure
    Any wire or raceways to the structure

Labor Units: The following procedures are generally included per MCC component:

    Receiving
    Equipment handling
    Installing components in structure
    Connecting power wires to components
    Wire identification
    Installing three thermal heaters where required

These additional procedures are listed and extended:

    Testing
    Control cables

Typical Job Conditions: Productivity (labor) is based on the MCC being in place, ready to receive components.

Takeoff Procedure: List all components on the quantity sheet, being careful to categorize each component by location, size, type, class, and service. Total like items, transfer these figures to a cost analysis sheet, and extend.

Motor Connections

A motor connection is the means by which the power leads are terminated to a motor. From the estimator's perspective, the motor terminations must also account for connecting the flexible conduit and fittings from the rigid conduit to the motor terminal box.

Flexible conduit to motors serves four functions. First, it can absorb the normal motor vibrations that would, over time, fatigue and crack rigid conduit connections. Second, since the vibration does not loosen flexible conduit as it would rigid parts, the ground path continuity is not disrupted. Third, most motor installations require that the motor be movable so that its shaft can be aligned with the shaft of the driven device. Finally, there is a distinct labor savings in mating a flexible conduit to a motor box over field-bending rigid conduit to fit.

Many motors have a winding space heater. That cable is often routed and counted as a separate connection.

Units for Measure: Each cable to a motor is counted as one unit (EA.).

Material Units: This is actually a mini-system. The size of each component is pre-determined by the standard size of cable and raceway used by each horsepower motor. This approach saves the estimator from having to dig through a conduit plan to find the size of cable and conduit servicing the motor.

The following items are generally included for motor connectors:

    Flex connectors
    Flexible metallic conduit
    Wire markers
    Termination for cable conductors

Labor Units: The following procedures are generally included in the labor-hours for motor connectors:

    Cutting flexible metal conduit
    Installing two flex connectors
    Routing wire through flex
    Terminating leads to motor
    Identifying leads

These additional procedures are listed and extended:

Mounting or placing motor (only when done by electricians)
Disconnect switch
Motor starter
Motor controls
Conduit and wire
Checking motor rotation

Takeoff Procedure: When taking off motor connections, it is advisable to list connections on the same work sheet as motors and/or motor starters. Set up columns by the horsepower rating of the motors. Count the number of motors to be connected and transfer the results to the quantity sheet. Be sure to mark all motors that are counted on the print. Transfer quantities from the takeoff sheet to a cost analysis sheet and extend.

Cost Modifications: If several motors are to be connected in a concentrated area by the same electrical crew, the following percentages can be deducted from labor only:

1	to	10	– 0%
11		25	–20%
26		50	–30%

Motors

Motors are machines for converting electrical energy into mechanical energy. They are used in appliances, elevators, and all kinds of machinery. Motors are available in a multitude of sizes, voltages, types, and enclosures. Motor sizes vary from fractional HP, single phase, to as high as 2000 HP, 3 phase. Voltages typically range from 120V to 4160V AC. The most common are fractional 110V to 200 HP 600V. The most common housings are dripproof and totally enclosed.

A range of DC motors operating at voltages from 12V DC to 250V DC are used for some special applications (such as elevators). Their use is, however, quite rare. For estimating purposes, use cost data from the next size larger AC motor.

Motors are not usually placed by the electrician, but rather by the trade furnishing the equipment they power.

Units for Measure: The unit for measure in this case is each motor (EA.).

Material Units: Included in the material units is the motor only. These additional items are listed and extended:

Pulleys

Sheaves

Couplings

Labor Units: The following procedures are generally included per motor:

Receiving

Handling

Setting the motor in place

Bolting or fastening

Preliminary alignment

These additional procedures are listed and extended:

Connecting the motor

Testing for rotation

Final alignment (usually by millwrights)

Heater connections (temporary power) for motors in storage

Takeoff Procedure: Carefully list all sizes of motors by horsepower, number of phases, and voltage. Motors should be listed at the same time as starters, disconnects, controls, and motor connections. Before pricing motors, check to see who furnishes them.

Motor Starters and Controls

Motor starters and across-the-line starters are manufactured in a variety of sizes and types. The most common types of across-the-line starters are the following:

   Motor-starting switch with no overload protection
   Single throw switch with overload protection
   Magnetic switch with thermal overload protection

A *motor-starting switch* is simply a tumbler rotary, lever, or drum switch. It does not provide any protection against overload or inadequate voltage. It is used for nonreversing duty in small-size motors up to 2 HP, and for reversing duty up to 10 HP.

A *single throw, across-the-line switch* can obtain thermal overload protection by means of thermal cutouts, time-lag fuses, or by a thermal overload release device. In switches with a thermal overload release device, the overload trips the holding catch of the switch and allows the switch to open. These starters do not provide protection against inadequate voltage.

Magnetic across-the-line starting switches (motor contactors) are magnetically operated and controlled from a push-button station—either integral or remote. They are manufactured with thermal-relay protection against overload and inadequate voltage. Pressing the start button closes the circuit to the operating coil of the magnetic switch. When the stop button is pressed, the operating coil circuit is opened, allowing the switch to spring open; the motor is stopped. Motor contactors are made in a variety of types, including both non-reversing and reversing duty, and for dual-speed motors. The reversing types consist of two contactors electrically and mechanically interlocked so as to prevent the closing of both switches at the same time.

Variations of magnetic across-the-line starting switches are as follows:

Combination, with motor circuit-breaker protection

Combination, with fused switch

Magnetic (FVR) full voltage reversing with control circuit transformer

Magnetic (FVR) full voltage dual-speed with control circuit transformer

Combination (FVR), fused, with control transformer and push buttons

It is important to identify not only the types of starters, but also the type of enclosure for each starter. Most estimating standards price motor starters with enclosures included to show the costs of the different types. For example, the material cost of a 10 HP size 1 starter with a NEMA 1 enclosure is $180.00. The same starter with a NEMA 7 enclosure is $690.00.

Starter sizes are determined by the voltage and horsepower rating of the motors being controlled. The following chart can be used if the horsepower of the motor is known, but the starter size is not specified.

Starter Sizes

Motor Voltage (60 Hz)	Motor Horsepower (max.)	Starter Size
Single Phase		
115 volt		
	1/3	00
	1	0
	2	1
	3	2
230 volt	1	00
	2	0
	3	1
	5	1
	7-1/2	2
Three Phase	1-1/2	00
200/230 volt	3	0
	7-1/2	1
	10/15	2
	25/30	3
	40/50	4
	75/100	5
	150/200	6
	300	7
	450	8
	800	9
460/575 volt	2	00
	5	0
	10	1
	25	2
	50	3

460/575 volt (cont.)	100	4
	200	5
	400	6
	600	7
	900	8
	1600	9

Units for Measure: Starters and contactors are priced as each (EA.). Starters may or may not designate a mini-system (i.e., with circuit protection and/or controls included).

Overload heaters are priced per line phase (EA.).

Material Units: The following items are generally included in the material cost for each starter:

    Starter and enclosure
    Four lead anchor-type fasteners
    Six wire markers
    Three thermal overload heaters
    Three dual-element cartridge-type fuses (for a combination-type starter)

Note: When pricing motor controls, be sure to consider the control system to be utilized. If the controls are factory-installed and located in the enclosure itself, then two options must be considered in pricing: (1) Is the integral control already included in the price of the starter? (2) If the control is not included, then its price must be added to the cost of the starter.

These additional items are listed and extended:

    Raceway to or from the starter
    Wire
    Control switches (unless included in material price line)
    Control transformer
    Plywood backboard (if required)

Labor Units: These procedures are generally included in the labor-hours for starters:

    Unloading, uncrating, and handling of starters
    Measuring and marking
    Four lead anchor-type fasteners
    Termination of power (line) and load side cables
    Wire identification
    Installing three thermal overload heaters

This additional procedure must be listed and extended:

    Testing

Typical Job Conditions: Productivity is based on new construction and an installation height of 5' above grade.

Takeoff Procedure: Note: Ensure that the starters are not furnished by others. Check the specifications. (Very often the starters are furnished as part of a mechanical or HVAC package.)

List the starters by size, voltage, NEMA enclosure, and type. Count each starter and list it in the proper grouping, rather than searching for all of one type and size before proceeding to another. Most starters are listed on a legend schedule, which will indicate whether integral controls are to be included. If the control is remotely located, the starter can be priced alone.

If it is not, then an integral control system must be added to that starter's price. Transfer quantities to a cost analysis sheet and extend.

Be aware of what is included in the material cost of each starter. If a total material list is required for purchasing, then list each component on the same sheet and extend against the quantity of each size starter. Do not assign a material or labor cost, because these are included in the cost units.

Note: The selection and purchasing of overload heaters for starters must be based on the actual name plate amps of the motors installed. It is not prudent to purchase overload heaters from general charts or tables.

Cost Modifications: When several magnetic starters are installed in a common location by the same electrician or crew, the following percentages can be deducted from the labor units:

0-5	− 0%
5-10	− 5%
11-20	−10%
21-30	−15%
Over 30	−18%

Contactors

A magnetic contactor is basically a relay with heavy-duty contacts. An electromagnetic coil is energized to close the contacts and hold them closed. Magnetic contactors are used to switch heating loads, capacitors, transformers, or electric motors. They do not have overload protection and are available from one to five poles (i.e., separate circuits). Contactors are controlled by a wall switch or push-button station. Magnetic contactors are similar to magnetic motor starters, with the exception that they do not contain overload protection devices.

Lighting contactors are a combination of a magnetic contactor with either fuse clips or a circuit breaker. They are used to control lighting and electric resistance heating loads.

Units for Measure: Count each contactor as one unit (EA.).

Material Units: The following items are generally included per unit:
  Contactor
  Enclosure
  Fasteners

These additional items must be listed and extended:
  Conduit
  Wire
  Control switches
  Tags or labels

Labor Units: The following procedures are generally included per unit:
  Receiving
  Handling
  Mounting

These additional procedures must be listed and extended:
  Control and power terminations
  Control switches

Takeoff Procedure: List the contactors by size, voltage, and amp ratings. Note the enclosure types required. Enter each contactor (as it is encountered) onto the takeoff sheets, rather than trying to search out all the devices of one category before proceeding to the next. Transfer the quantity totals to a cost analysis sheet and extend.

Relays

A relay is a control device that takes one input to a coil and operates a number of isolated circuit contacts in a control scheme. An electromagnetic coil is used to operate an armature, which holds the contacts. The relay's contacts may be set up in the following ways: open at rest (normally open), and closing when energized; or closed at rest (normally closed), and opening when energized. A relay may have from 1 to 12 or more poles.

A wide variety of relay configurations is available. Some common variations are time-delay relays (either delay on or delay off); latching relays (mechanically held needing two coils: one for on, another for off); and AC or DC relays.

Coils for relays can be specified for either AC or DC circuits and for voltages from 6 to 480.

Although relays can be purchased in an enclosure such as a NEMA 1 general-purpose indoor, they are usually bought individually for assembly into a larger enclosure.

Units for Measure: Relays are counted as units (EA.).

Material Units: Generally, only the relay itself is included. These additional items are listed and extended:

Enclosure

Fasteners

Labor Units: The following procedures are generally included per unit:

Installing the relay in an enclosure

Connecting the wires (coil only)

These additional procedures are listed and extended:

Mounting the enclosure

Fastening to the wall

Conduit

Wire

Control terminations

Takeoff Procedure: Relays should be taken off on the same sheet as the item they control. Price this item by carefully checking the catalog number. There are many types of relays, and prices vary considerably.

Carefully note the coil voltage, contact voltage and amp rating, number of poles, and type of operation. List each relay on the quantity takeoff and total. Transfer the totals to a cost analysis sheet and extend.

Panelboards

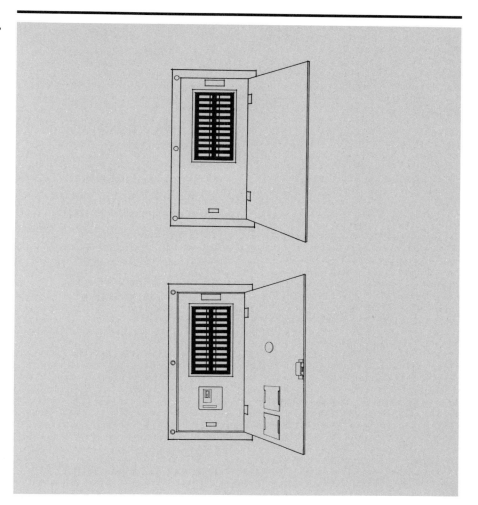

Panelboards are used to group circuit switching and protective devices into one enclosure. Lighting and appliance panelboards for residential applications are referred to as load centers. (See the section on "Load Centers" earlier in this chapter.)

Panelboards consist of an assembly of bus bars and circuit protective devices housed in a metal box enclosure. The box provides space for wiring and includes a trim plate with a cover.

Although panelboards are available as fused models, styles using molded case circuit breakers are far more common. Panelboards are available in a variety of configurations, including AC styles up to 600V and DC styles up to 250V. The AC styles can be single- or three-phase. Models for AC up to 240V, with mains up to 600 A and branch circuits up to 100 A, are commonly available for lighting and power distribution. Panelboards for motor starters and power distribution may have mains up to 1200 A and branch breakers up to 600 A.

Panelboard enclosures are also available to suit a variety of NEMA classifications, including NEMA 1, 3, and 12.

Because of the wide variety of options and configurations available, it is best to consult a vendor or manufacturer's representative for pricing information.

Units for Measure: List by size (ampacity) and type, voltage, and fault current capacity. List each panelboard (EA.). Then record the breakers with each board and price each (EA.). (Note: Some standard board and breaker assemblies are available as pre-assembled units.)

Material Units: The following items are generally included per panelboard:

    Panelboard
    Fasteners

Labor Units: The following procedures are generally included for panelboard installation:

    Receiving
    Measuring and marking
    Drilling four lead anchor-type fasteners using a hammer drill
    Mounting and leveling panel
    Preparation and termination of feeder cable to lugs or main breaker
    Branch circuit identification
    Lacing using tie wraps
    Testing and load balancing
    Marking panel directory
    Cover and trim

These additional procedures are listed and extended:

    Modification to enclosure (additional breakers)
    Structural supports
    Additional lugs
    Plywood backboards
    Painting or lettering
    Adding breakers
    Field assembly
    Terminating branch wiring

Note: Knockouts are included in the price of terminating conduit runs and need not be added to the panelboard costs.

Material and labor prices generally include breakers.

Takeoff Procedure: When pricing panelboards, list the panels by size, type, and voltage. List breakers in a separate column of the quantity sheet, and define by phase (poles) and ampere rating.

Cost Modifications: If you do not plan to include a full panel of single pole breakers, use the method as described in the "Load Centers" section earlier in this chapter.

Panelboard Circuit Breakers

A panelboard circuit breaker is a molded-case plastic breaker (with one, two, or three poles). Two styles are available: plug-on and bolted (to the bus bars). There are models for either DC service up to 250V or for AC service up to 600V. Main circuit breakers come in many sizes ranging from 100 A up to 1200 A and branch circuit breakers from 15 A to 800 A.

A major consideration in selecting and pricing circuit breakers is interrupting capacity (IC). This is a breaker's ability to stop the flow of electricity when a high-current fault exists (which is dependent on the amount of energy available from the source). Breakers are made with IC ratings as low as 5,000 A and range up to 200,000 AIC. A typical lighting and branch power panel might have a 150 A main rated at 65,000 AIC with branch breakers from 15 A to 30 A rated at 10,000 AIC.

Most circuit breakers have two modes of tripping: time (thermal) trip and instant (magnetic) trip. Some breakers also have a third mode — ground fault (shunt coil). The first type of trip occurs in the case of mild overloads and works by heating a thermal trip device. The time required for this function is related to the amount of the overload current. For example, a 200% overload may trip the breaker in 100 seconds, while a 600% overload can trip in two seconds.

Breakers also operate on high-fault overloads via a magnetic trip device. This function is referred to as an "instantaneous" trip. The time required for this function is from 1/2 to 1 cycle or .0083 to .0166 seconds. The magnetic trip function generally operates at between 10 and 20 times (1000 to 2000%) the rated current and above. The wide variety of breakers available includes many that are designed to differ from these characteristic tripping curves.

Ground fault tripping breakers are the third type. Most breakers do not have this kind of trip function. Nevertheless, it is a requirement for specific applications that involve potential personal hazards. In ground fault tripping breakers, a sensitive current coil is used to ensure that the amperage going out of the breaker closely equals the current returning through the neutral wire. When these two currents are unbalanced by as little as 5 mA, the coil activates a shunt-tripping device. This process occurs as quickly as 8 milliseconds.

Units for Measure: List by size, type, AIC rating, and manufacturer, and price per each (EA.) breaker.

Material Units: The following items are generally included for panelboard circuit breakers:

    The breaker itself and the lugs

These additional items must be listed and extended:

    Panelboard
    Wiring
    Tags and markers

Labor Units: The following procedures are generally included:

    Removing the trim from the panelboard
    Installing the circuit breaker
    Connecting the wires to the circuit breaker
    Installing the trim

These additional procedures must be listed and extended:

    Wire and conduit connections to the panelboard
    Stripping jackets from the wires

Takeoff Procedure: List the breakers by amps, number of poles, voltage, and plug-in or bolt-on. Note on the takeoff the brand and model of panelboard in which the breaker is to be installed. Use the catalog number if it is available. (Use a cost book for pricing, but the catalog number when purchasing.)

Note: Some manufacturers' breakers are interchangeable, but many are not.

Safety Switches

Safety switches are intended for use in general distribution and in branch circuits. They provide an assured means of manually disconnecting a load from its source. The salient feature of a safety switch is that its operating handle is capable of being padlocked in the "OFF" position. This feature protects those working on the equipment from the possibility that someone might inadvertently energize the circuit. For some devices, such as fans, not only is a safety switch required by code, but the switch must be installed within sight of the fan.

Safety switches are designated in three different categories. General-duty safety switches are rated from 30 A to 600 A at 240V AC. They are available in two-, three-, and four-pole styles, fusible or non-fusible.

Heavy-duty safety switches are rated from 30 A to 1200 A and 250V AC or DC, or 600V AC. They are available in two-, three-, or four-pole and in either fusible or non-fusible models.

Motor circuit switches rated at 30 A to 200 A are intended specifically for applications where the switch must be within sight of the motor. They are non-fusible and have either three poles or six poles (for dual-speed motors).

The safety switches described above are furnished in a number of different NEMA class enclosures. It is important to the estimate that the appropriate enclosure be priced. For example, a heavy-duty switch in a NEMA 1 enclosure may cost around $310, while the same switch in a NEMA 4 enclosure could cost about $1750.

Units for Measure: Safety switches are priced each (EA.) by size, type, poles, voltage, and enclosure ratings.

Material Units: The following items are generally included per unit:

> One safety switch
> Four lead anchor-type fasteners
> Fuses (if fused type)

These additional items must be listed and extended:

> Cable and conduit terminations
> Tags and labels
> Brackets or supports (if needed)

Labor Units: The labor-hours for each safety switch generally include these items:

> Receiving
> Material handling
> Measuring and marking the switch location
> Installing the switch on a masonry wall
> Connecting and phase marking wire on primary and secondary
>   terminals

These additional procedures are listed and extended:

> Primary or secondary conduit
> Backboards, brackets, or supports for enclosure
> Wire

Takeoff Procedure: Set up the work sheet by duty type, voltage, number of poles, NEMA classification, and ampere rating. Count the switches, transferring each into its proper designation on the quantity sheet as you count. In this way, you can avoid hunting for like switches before proceeding to the next type. Finally, transfer the quantities to a cost analysis sheet and extend.

Cost Modifications: If several disconnects are being installed in a common location by the same electrician or crew, the following percentages can be deducted from the labor units:

0	to	5	− 0%
5		10	− 5%
Over 10			−10%

Switchboards

Switchboards are used in buildings that have larger load requirements than can be serviced by a single load center panelboard and its disconnect device. A switchboard is a modular assembly of functional sections or compartments. These include the service section, auxiliary section, metering compartment, and distribution sections.

The service section contains the main (incoming) breaker, which may be rated from 200 A to 4,000 A. An auxiliary section is a blank compartment that may be used to facilitate cable pulling. A transition section is provided where needed to interface with transformers, special distribution sections, or an MCC. A metering compartment may contain current transformers (CT's), potential transformers (PT's), and relays, as well as meters for amps, volts, and watts. The distribution sections may contain any combination of fused disconnect switches, branch circuit breakers, or motor starters. The branch circuit breakers may be rated from 30 A to 1200 A.

Bus bars are available in ratings ranging from 200 A through 4,000 A at 250V DC or 600V AC. Bus bars are generally braced to withstand 50,000 A fault currents, but optional bracing is available to increase that rating up to as much as 200,000 A. Bus bars are aluminum, but copper bars are an available option.

Three options are available for wiring: Type A—without terminal blocks; Type B—with terminal blocks for control wiring at the side of each unit; and Type C—with master terminal blocks at the top or bottom of each switchboard section.

Units for Measure: Switchboards must be itemized per section (EA.); the subcomponents of each distribution section must be listed and detailed per unit (EA.). Note any modifications or extras (such as the copper bus option) and quantify accordingly (per section, for example).

The material and labor units for each section type generally assume that the entire unit is specified in detail during the procurement phase and that the equipment will be factory assembled with all requisite components in place. Some sections may be shipped separately and bolted together in the field.

Material Units: The material cost units for switchboards include:
> The equipment as shipped from the manufacturer
> Bolts, bus ties, and insulators to connect shipping segments
> Anchor bolts and fasteners
> Minor components (such as relays), which may be shipped for field insertion—does not include wiring or connections to such devices by field personnel

These additional items are listed and extended:
> Equipment pads
> Steel channels
> Special knockouts
> External controls
> Conduit
> Wire and cables

Labor Units: The following procedures are generally included for the installation of switchboard components:
> Receiving
> Equipment handling to location
> Assembly of shipping sections
> Anchors and bolting in place
> Leveling, shimming, and alignment
> Interconnection of bus bars and wiring
> Marking panel legend

The following activities are listed and extended as additional labor items:
> Conduit
> Wiring and terminations
> Wire tagging and identifications
> Testing
> Adding breakers, switches, and meters to existing switchboards

Takeoff Procedure: Switchboards and their associated components should be quoted from equipment manufacturers as a factory-assembled unit. The following items should be included:
> Switchboards
> Feeder sections
> Instruments
> Distribution sections and subcomponents
> Options and modifications

The takeoff procedure must identify the equipment by section and by the subcomponents within each section. Parameters such as amperage, voltage, type, bus material, and breaker sizes, should be detailed. List the sections by amps, volts, and type. Identify the section's components by type and size. List any options or modifications per section and extend.

Substations

A substation, or secondary unit substation, is an assembly comprised of a high-voltage incoming line section; a step down, three-phase power transformer; and a secondary low-voltage distribution section. Substations have two principle applications, both of which are industrial. The first is as an incoming service center; the second is as a power center with dense, high-power requirements.

There are many advantages in locating the power transformer and its distribution section close to the load. First, the cable and/or bus lengths can be reduced. There is also better voltage control, reduced power loss, and a minimum installed cost.

Typical transformer ratings are from 112 kVA through 2500 kVA. The most common primary voltages are 4.16 kV and 13.8 kV, but the available range is from 2.4 kV through 34.5 kV. The most common secondary voltage is 480/277V, but 208V, 240V, and 600V are also used.

Depending on the application, the high-voltage line section may be a terminal compartment for cables to connect to the transformer, or it may contain a disconnect switch (fused or non-fused).

The distribution section is an attached switchboard that usually uses draw-out circuit breakers for power distribution. The bus ratings typically run from 800 A to 4,000 A. The draw-out breakers can be operated manually or electrically. Distribution sections with molded case breakers are also available. In most cases, one compartment of the distribution section is devoted to meters, instruments, and trip relays.

Units for Measure: Each substation must be taken off individually and listed in terms of its component sections and their subcomponents (EA.).

As is the case with most major electrical assemblies, substations are normally specified for purchase as a factory-assembled unit. The various sections, however, are usually split for shipping and are then set and bolted together in place at the site. Draw-out breakers are shipped individually to be slid in after the equipment is set.

Material Units: The following items are generally included in the material cost unit:

> The transformers
> Incoming line section and switch
> Distribution section with breakers
> Anchor bolts
> Bus bars and bolts for interconnections

These additional items are taken off and listed:

> Equipment pads and rails
> Rigging
> Conduit
> Cable
> Terminations

Labor Units: The following procedures are generally included per unit:

> Receiving
> Equipment handling
> Setting, shimming, and leveling
> Anchoring in place

These additional procedures must be listed and extended:

> Cables and terminations
> Potheads
> Testing

Takeoff Procedure: List each substation individually by size, voltage, and type of transformer. Then list each component section with its subcomponents. Transfer to a cost analysis sheet and extend.

Control Switches

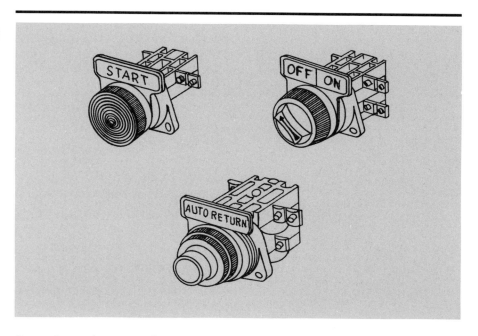

Control switches provide manual input to the control circuits of relays or magnetic starters. Control switches are used for equipment such as valves, fans, pumps, conveyors, and air conditioners. Control switches are assembled or "built-up" using the following three types of components:

the legend plate, the operator mechanism, and the contact blocks. Each component is available in a multitude of styles and types that can be combined in nearly endless variations to suit the particular application.

Legend plates are used to describe the functions controlled by a particular control switch. They are ordered either by stock descriptions (stop, start, jog, up, down, etc.) or with unique inscriptions. The legend plate is usually included in the material and labor pricing of the operator.

Operators are the mechanical devices that position the contacts. A whole range of operators is available. Some common types are listed below:

Selector switch—maintained position
Selector switch—spring return
Push button—spring return
Push button—with illuminated button

Also available is a variety of indicating lights, styled to match the operator. These lights indicate the operating status of the equipment.

Contact blocks provide control and are mounted behind the operator in modular (stackable) fashion. Contacts are described at their "rest" position as either "normally open (N.O.)" or "normally closed (N.C.)". A third contact arrangement is a block that has one N.O. pole and one N.C. pole. The majority of switches use some combination of these three basic contact blocks. An operator can move the contact to the "held" position to effect control.

Common operator and contact arrangements are assembled and "in stock," while others must be ordered as components and field assembled. Attention must be paid to the voltage and amp ratings of the contacts when ordering.

Control switches may be installed into distribution equipment such as motor control centers for local control. Control switches may also be installed into control station boxes for remote control functions.

Units for Measure: Control switches are counted individually (EA.) and listed according to type, contact arrangement, and legend function. Each pilot light is counted and listed according to color and voltage.

Material Units: The following items are generally included in the material cost of each control switch:

Legend plate
Retaining rings
Operator
Contact block
Wire marker for each contact

These additional items are listed and extended:

Enclosure
Wire
Branch conduit

Labor Units: The following procedures are generally included in the labor-hours for control switches:

Installing control switches in a pre-punched enclosure
Marking control wires
Testing switch

These additional procedures are listed and extended:

Installing wire to control switch

Termination of control wires

Cutting or punching mounting hole

Installing enclosure

Branch conduit to enclosure

Takeoff Procedure: The biggest misconception on pricing control switches is that the estimator needs to understand all the functions being controlled by the switches. Most control prints contain a detailed legend of control components, including types and catalog numbers. Thus the estimator need not be involved with the operation of the equipment.

Set up the work sheet by the type of control switch. Quantities are best taken off from a schematic control drawing. Be sure to identify those installations that involve manually punching or cutting mounting holes. Transfer the quantities to the work sheet and extend.

Cost Modifications: Most control station enclosures are prepunched. However, if control switches are to be installed in a custom-made enclosure where the holes must be field determined and punched, the labor cost must be increased. Refer to "Cutting and Drilling" in Chapter 12: Raceways, or to other standards being used; then choose the hole size required.

For a large concentration of control switches in the same enclosure, the following percentages can be deducted from labor-hours:

1	to	10	− 0%
11		25	−20%
26		50	−25%
51		100	−30%
Over 100			−35%

Chapter 16

Transformers and Bus Duct

Transformers are devices with two or more coupled windings, with or without a magnetic core. They introduce mutual coupling between circuits and are used to convert a power supply from one voltage to another. Bus duct, or "busway," is a prefabricated unit that contains and protects one or more busses. In this chapter, there are five sections on: transformers, isolating panels, two types of bus duct, and Uninterruptible Power Supply (UPS) systems. Units for measure, material and labor requirements, and a procedure for takeoff follow each description.

Transformers

Transformers are used in Alternating Current (AC) systems to convert from one voltage to another. They cannot be used in Direct Current (DC) systems. The total energy entering a transformer is equal (except for minor losses) to the energy leaving the transformer. Thus when the voltage is changed (stepped down, for instance), the current changes in inverse proportion (in this case, it increases). A transformer's capacity can,

167

therefore, be designated in terms of the product of the voltage (V) and the amperage (A), i.e., as volt-amps (VA) at either side. Larger transformers are often designated in thousand volt-amps (KVA).

Transformers are used for four basic applications: 1) instrument transformers; 2) control transformers; 3) isolating transformers; and 4) power transformers. Their capacities range from fractional VA to thousands of KVA. The first two are single-phase types only, but the second two may be single- or three-phase designs.

Power transformers may be either dry-type air-cooled or liquid-cooled. Both can be furnished for indoor or outdoor use (dry-type in a NEMA 3R enclosure). Voltage ratings are always described from the primary (incoming) to the secondary (output).

Units for Measure: Each transformer is counted as a unit (EA.).

Material Units: The following items are generally included in the material unit price:

Transformer
Anchor bolts or screws
Identification tag

These additional items must be listed and extended:

Transformer pad
Grounding
Conduit wire and cables
Termination plugs

Labor Units: The following procedures are generally included in the labor-hours for transformers:

Receiving
Handling
Crane (if needed)
Setting or hanging in place
Anchor bolts

These additional procedures must be listed and extended:

Supports, brackets, etc.
Conduit and connections
Cables and terminations
Grounding
Testing

Typical Job Conditions: The labor units assume reasonable access and distance from the loading dock at about 100 feet. Adjustment factors will need to be applied for work in congested areas or for material handling that involves especially long distances.

Takeoff Procedure: List the transformers by VA rating and service voltages on the material takeoff sheet, and total. Transfer the totals to a cost analysis sheet. Price and extend.

Isolating Panels

Isolating panels are used in hospitals, where they serve as added protection—to patients and sensitive monitoring equipment—from the effects of ground potentials. This kind of protection is particularly important in a hospital environment because of the numerous electrical instruments and appliances with wet systems. An operating room panel typically consists of a back box with stainless steel trim. It contains an isolating transformer, a primary circuit breaker, eight 20 A two-pole secondary circuit breakers, and a line isolation monitor.

The critical care area panels are the same as operating room panels, with the addition of eight power receptacles and six grounding jacks.

The X-ray panels are also similar to operating room panels, but they have one 60 A, two-pole breaker instead of eight 20 A, two-pole breakers. Up to eight outlets can be controlled from this panel.

Units for Measure: Each panel is a unit (EA.) including breakers, transformers, etc.

Material Units: A complete panel with anchors is generally included in the material unit price.

Labor Units: The following procedures should be included in the labor-hours per unit:

    Receiving
    Handling
    Setting in place with wall-mounting hardware

These additional procedures are listed and extended:

    Making the connections to primary and secondary
    Testing
    Structural support

Takeoff Procedure: List the panels individually on the price sheet.

Bus Duct

Bus duct provides a flexible distribution system for power in industrial and commercial buildings. The busway itself consists of copper or aluminum bars mounted in a sheet metal enclosure. There are several types available. The most common are feeder-type (indoor), plug-in type (indoor), and weatherproof feeder-type.

In some styles of bus ducts, branch taps can be readily changed to conform to new locations of motors and equipment. This system is widely used in industrial plants where equipment is continually changed to meet new manufacturing conditions.

Feeder-type bus duct is used primarily in industrial buildings to connect the service entrance to the main switchboard, or for high-capacity feeders to distribution centers, including feeder risers. Feeder types have no access (or taps) between the service starting point, or main, and the point of use.

Plug-in bus duct is used for indoor systems where flexibility is needed for power over a wide area. It is available in ratings from 225 A to 3000 A in a three-pole, four-wire arrangement. Sections are available in 1' through 5', and 10' lengths. Provisions for plug-in taps are made through outlets located on both sides of the duct.

Weatherproof feeder-type bus duct performs the same function as feeder type busway, but it is enclosed in a weatherproof casing for use outdoors or in damp, indoor areas.

Plug-in Units

After the bus or feeder duct has been installed, plug-in modular units are used to tap or branch off from the main bars of the bus duct. There are various types of modules designed for specific branch circuit needs. Some of the most common are listed below:

Fusible 30 A to 400 A capacity
Fusible with contactor 30 A to 200 A capacity
Circuit breaker type 30 A to 1600 A capacity
Circuit breaker with contactor 30 A to 225 A capacity

Bus Duct Fittings

Standard components are available to provide elbows, offsets, "T" connections, and crossovers. Other fittings include reducers for changing the size of the busway, end closers, and expansion fittings. Cable tap boxes are available to provide cable or conduit tap-offs or feeders. They are made in two types:

> End cable tap boxes for attachment at the ends of a plug-in busway run
>
> Center cable tap boxes for installation at any point in a busway run

Units for Measure: Straight sections of bus duct are measured in linear feet (L.F.) and any part sections (less than 10′) as each unit (EA.). Fittings are counted and listed as units (EA.).

Material Units: The following items are generally included in the L.F. cost of bus duct straight sections:

> Bus duct (based on 10′ length)
> Hanger every 5 L.F.
> 2′ of threaded rod per hanger
> One beam type clamp per hanger

These additional items must be listed and extended:

> Bus duct fittings
> Support brackets
> Auxiliary steel
> Wall penetrations
> Scaffold rentals

Labor Units: The following procedures are generally included in the labor-hours for straight sections of bus duct:

> Receiving
> Handling
> Measuring and marking
> Set up of rolling staging
> Installing hangers (beam clamp type)
> Hanging and bolting sections
> Aligning and leveling

These additional procedures are listed and extended:

> Bus duct fittings
> Modifications to structure for hanger supports (auxiliary steel)
> Threaded rod in excess of 2′ per hanger
> Welding (if required)
> Penetration through walls
> Installing fittings, 90's, T's, crosses, etc.
> Testing

Takeoff Procedure: Set up the quantity sheet by type, ampere rating, and voltage. Measure from the source and work out to the point of use or end, depending on the type of bus duct.

Caution: When pricing the material, do not assume that all bus duct sections are 10-foot lengths.

While most estimating standards base their linear foot (L.F.) price on the cost of 10′ sections, those that are less than 10′ are much more expensive per linear foot. Care should be taken to identify variable lengths. Keep these odd lengths separate from the linear foot totals and price them using manufacturers' quotations.

Go back over the print; count the fittings; and identify them by type, ampere rating, and configuration. Count accessories, such as wall flanges, weather stops, enclosures, switchboard stubs, and spring-type hangers. Transfer the quantities' totals to a cost analysis sheet and extend.

Cost Modifications: A large quantity of bus duct might be installed at varying heights. The estimate can be adjusted for these conditions.

Labor-hours are generally based on elevations up to 15′. Add the following percentages for higher runs:

16′	to	20′ high	+ 10%
21′		25′	+ 20%
26′		30′	+ 30%
31′		35′	+ 40%
36′		40′	+ 50%
Over 40′			+ 60%

Add these percentages to the labor-hours only for the installation of those quantities that exceed the specified height levels.

Bus Duct/Busway— 100 A and Less

100 A plug-in busway is similar to larger busway (as described previously in this chapter). It differs in that it has plated round aluminum or copper bars instead of flat bars. 100 A bus duct is typically used for branch power feeders to panel boards or motors, or for small, distributed loads.

30 A and 60 A plug-in busway has an open bottom into which the terminal plug is inserted. It is available in 4′ or 10′ lengths and in two- and three-wire configurations. The bus can be cut with a hacksaw to length, but it must then be capped. A strength beam is available to aid in mounting and to add rigidity. This kind of busway is designed to distribute power for all types of lighting, but it can also be used for light-duty power.

Like 30 A and 60 A busway, 20-amp plug-in busway has an open bottom and has similar applications. It is also used for small portable tools and for drop light cords and receptacles.

Units for Measure: Take off the linear feet (L.F.) of straight sections and the required fittings (EA.).

Material Units: The following items are generally included with bus duct for 100 A and less:

    Straight sections of bus
    Connectors and bolts
    One hanger every 5′
    Beam clamp and 2′ threaded rod for each hanger

These additional items must be listed and extended:
Fittings
Scaffolding
Brackets
Auxiliary steel

Labor Units: The following procedures are generally included:
Receiving
Handling
Installing hangers
Installing bus duct
Leveling and alignment
Rolling scaffold

These additional procedures must be listed and extended:
Wall penetrations
Supports and auxiliary steel
Welding (if needed)
Fittings

Takeoff Procedure: See the "Bus Duct" section earlier in this chapter for takeoff methods, labor assumptions, and cost modifications.

Uninterruptible Power Supply Systems

Uninterruptible power supply (UPS) systems are used to provide power for legally required standby systems. They are also designed to protect computers and provide optional additional coverage for any or all loads in a facility. For a typical configuration for a UPS system with a generator set, see the reference section in *Means Electrical Cost Data* under reference number R164-335. Detailed information relating to generator sets will be discussed in Chapter 17: Power Systems and Capacitors. This section will address the UPS double-conversion technique. A rectifier/charger converts AC to DC, and a continuously running inverter converts DC back to AC. If the primary incoming AC power has problems, the inverter will draw power from the batteries.

Units for Measure: UPS systems are counted as each unit (EA.).

Material Units: The following items are generally included per unit:

Self-diagnostic monitoring and control package battery

These additional items must be listed and extended:

Extended runtime batteries
Warranty enhancement plans

Other accessories include battery cabinets, battery racks, and remote control panels.

Labor Units: The following procedures are generally included:

Receiving
Handling
Measuring and marking the location
Setting

These additional procedures must be listed and extended:

Wire and conduit
Testing

Takeoff Procedure: Check the UPS specification and obtain the material costs from the manufacturer as a package. Installation costs should be obtained from a vendor or contractor. Note all the pertinent options and accessories.

Larger systems can be configured by parelleling two or more standard small-size single modules. Extend the information in the cost analysis sheet.

Chapter 17

Power Systems and Capacitors

Power systems are stand-by or emergency generator sets for providing power to essential services during a loss of normal power. Capacitors are used for power factor correction to increase efficiency, thus reducing electrical utility bills. Definitions are provided for each of the components in this chapter. Units for measure, material and labor requirements, and a takeoff procedure are also provided.

Capacitors

Power factor is a measurement of the ratio between true power and apparent power, i.e., P.F. = W / VA. The ideal P.F. is 1.0. In industrial and commercial buildings, reactive loads, such as motors, can cause phase shifts between the voltage (V) and the current (A) which, in turn, create undesirable power factors (0.51 − 0.80). By installing a capacitive load in the system, the P.F. can be adjusted toward 1.0.

Industrial capacitors are metal-clad units that include one (single-phase) or three (three-phase) capacitors and discharge resistors. Industrial capacitors may be connected to the loads of each individual motor or to the main incoming lines. Capacitors are sized in terms of kVAR at a specific voltage and according to the number of phases.

Units for Measure: Capacitors are counted as each unit (EA.).

Material Units: The following items are generally included per unit:
Capacitor
Fasteners

These additional items must be listed and extended:
Cable
Terminations

Labor Units: The following procedures are generally included per unit:
Receiving
Handling
Measuring and marking the capacitor location
Mounting

These additional procedures must be listed and extended:
Wire
Connecting and marking wire terminals
Conduit
Testing

Takeoff Procedure: Take off capacitors at the same time as motors and controls. Check to see if they are included in the price of switchgear. Be sure to specify voltage, phase(s), and kVAR size. List each capacitor according to its size and type; add the total quantities. Transfer the quantities to a cost analysis sheet and extend.

Generator Set

Generator sets are used as an emergency or stand-by power source in the event of the loss of normal power. They are rated in terms of their capacity in kilowatts (kW). Generators are available in single-phase or three-phase and may be specified at 120V through 6600V. (Typical units are used at 120V single-phase or 480V three-phase.)

The motors may be fueled by gasoline, propane (or natural) gas, and diesel fuel. Gasoline engines have a low initial cost and start well in cold weather. Gaseous fuels require less engine maintenance and are generally more convenient to supply. Diesel units consume far less fuel than gasoline and gaseous units, are generally available in larger capacities, and the motors require less maintenance. Diesel fuel also has a higher flash point than gasoline or gaseous fuels and thus is safer to handle.

In general, gas generator sets are available from 10 to 170 kW and diesel-powered sets range from 15 to 1000 kW. (Even larger diesel units are available as custom-ordered units.) Although some small models may be started with a recoil rope starter, most units are fitted with electric starters and batteries. Control options include local or remote start/stop functions, engine heaters, exhaust mufflers (larger units), and annunciators.

Units for Measure: Generators are counted as units (EA.).

Material Units: The following items are generally included per unit:
    Engine generator with a control panel
    Battery
    Charger
    Muffler (small units)
    Day tank for fuel (small units)

These additional items must be listed and extended:
    Control and accessory items
    Conduit
    Cables
    Transfer switch
    Weather-tight enclosure

Labor Units: The following procedures are generally included per unit:
    Receiving
    Equipment handling
    Setting, leveling, and shimming
    Anchoring

These additional items are listed and extended:
    A muffler and exhaust piping (large units)
    Fuel and fuel piping
    Large fuel tank
    Concrete pad
    Steel channels other than normally supplied by the manufacturer
    Rigging
    Connecting of wire and cable
    Testing

Takeoff Procedure: Check the generator specs and get quotes from manufacturers. The generator is usually priced as a lump sum for all parts listed under "Materials." Check to see who furnishes the materials listed above as "These additional items. . ." It might be necessary to get the prices for these items from other trades (such as for cooling water). List each generator on a cost analysis sheet and extend. Note all pertinent options and accessories. Also note any special cranes or equipment needed for handling. Determine if any accessories will need to be field assembled.

Note: Some manufacturers will require that their service representative be present for initial start-up to validate the warranty. This will usually be an extra-cost item, but it can be a very sound investment.

Automatic and Manual Transfer Switches

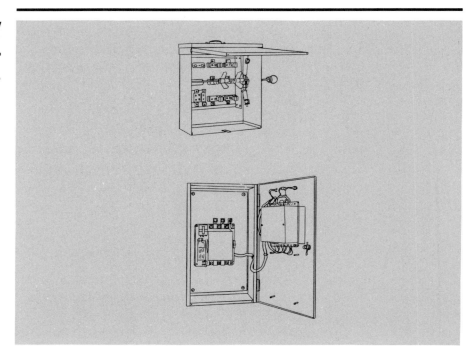

Transfer switches are used to change from the normal source of power to an alternate source, such as a generator set or a battery-powered inverter. There are two basic types of transfer switches: manual or automatic.

A manual transfer switch is a lever- or handle-operated double-throw device with a pole for each line wire. This type of switch is available from 30 to 600 A.

Automatic transfer switches are designed to monitor the normal line source and to switch the load electrically to the backup source should the normal source fail. Automatic transfer switches are rated from 30 to 2000 A.

A number of extra-cost options and accessories are available for automatic transfer switches. A few of the options are: auto-start relays to signal a generator when normal power fails; sensing relays to prevent transfer until the backup source is at full voltage; status-indicating lights; timed relay transfer to restore the load to normal power after it has been energized for several minutes; time-delay engine-stop relay to keep the generator running unloaded for a few minutes to cool the windings; and test and exercise control switches to permit the generator set to be started periodically and run.

Units for Measure: Switches are counted as units (EA.).

Material Units: The following items are generally included per unit:
    Transfer switch, complete in enclosure
    Fasteners

These additional items are listed and extended:
    Optional control functions
    Conduit

Cable
Terminations

Labor Units: The following procedures are generally included per unit:
Receiving
Material handling
Measuring and marking
Drilling four lead-type anchors, using a hammer drill
Mounting and leveling

These additional procedures are listed and extended:
Modifications in the enclosure
Structural supports
Preparation and terminating the cable to the lugs
Circuit identification
Testing
Plywood backboard
Painting or lettering
Conduit

Takeoff Procedure: When taking off transfer switches, identify by type (auto or manual), voltage, amperage, and number of poles. List each on a cost analysis sheet, along with any required options or accessories, and extend.

Note: It is best to get a vendor's quote for pricing, particularly if control options are specified. Also, check the generator package, as the switches can often be purchased from the same manufacturer. If not, the control interface may not be compatible.

Lighting

By far the most elemental portion of electrical construction is lighting. The first commercial use of electricity was for lighting. Today, virtually every building, industrial plant, house, bridge, and roadway sign makes extensive use of lighting fixtures. In building construction, lighting is still the largest single electrical cost center. This fact is evidenced in the sample estimate in Part III of this book. Lighting accounts for 30% to 40% of the electrical operating costs in commercial buildings. Therefore, taking into consideration the initial cost of the lighting system, the life cycle costs, and the responsibility of meeting energy conservation requirements, lighting systems play an important role.

This chapter contains descriptions of seven different types of electrical lighting, fixtures, and fixture whips. In addition to the description, each component section includes guidelines on units for measure, material and labor requirements, and a step-by-step takeoff procedure. Where applicable, cost modification factors—for economy of scale or difficult working conditions—are provided. *Means Electrical Cost Data* covers energy-saving lighting devices—occupancy sensors, automatic wall switches, and photoelectric controls—in Section 166-170.

Interior Lighting Fixtures

Fixture styles for interior building lighting can be either surface-mounted or recessed in a wall or ceiling. Other options are pendant or hanging fixtures. There are, of course, numerous variations of all of these styles.

Not only is lighting a major cost center for installation, but it is also a significant factor in the operating costs of a facility. In the past 15 years, much attention has been given to the development of more efficient lamps. Efficiency in fixtures is measured in the number of lumens per watt. The color spectrum of light from various lamps is also a prime factor in judging efficiency. If a bulb could be made that was, for example, 80% efficient at converting watts to lumens, but the light energy was entirely in the ultraviolet region (invisible to human eyes), its useful output would be zero.

Lamps for interior lighting fixtures can be incandescent, fluorescent, or high-intensity discharge (HID). HID lamps include mercury vapor, metal halide, or high-pressure sodium. (Low-pressure sodium lamps are used principally for outdoor applications because of their strong yellow color.)

Incandescent bulbs are the least efficient of the above, but their low initial cost keeps them attractive. Also, their "warm" (high red content) color spectrum is pleasing for many applications. One significant advantage of incandescent bulbs is that they light up instantly.

Fluorescent bulbs require the use of ballast coils or electronic and dimmer-type ballasts, which makes initial fixture costs somewhat higher than the cost of incandescent fixtures. Fluorescent bulbs are, however, more efficient; for example, for twin compact and 4' T8, 32 watt energy-saver lamps. In addition, their color spectrum far more closely imitates natural daylight; for instance, full spectrum lamps for ADA (Americans with Disabilities Act) requirements have excellent color rendering. A few different fluorescent lamp constructions are available that offer trade-offs among efficiency, color spectrum, and bulb cost.

Fluorescents find their widest application in office buildings where people spend long periods of time reading and/or working with documents. The output for 48" fluorescents is approximately 60 lumens per watt. Fluorescent fixtures are available with a rapid-start requiring only a couple of seconds.

HID lamps generally are more efficient than fluorescent but do not generate the same broad light spectrums. HID lamps require special ballasts and require several minutes to warm up before full output is reached.

Mercury vapor lamps put out about 65 lumens/watt and have a green-blue color. Because they have little or no red component in their spectrum, they distort the actual color of objects. They require three to seven minutes after starting to reach their full brilliance. Since the bulb must cool before it can restrike, it takes about the same amount of time to light up again after a power disruption.

Metal halide lamps are 1.5 to 2 times more efficient than mercury vapor lamps. Their color is blue-white, and they render color slightly better than mercury vapor lamps. They take longer to warm up or restart—about 15 minutes.

High-pressure sodium lamps have an efficiency of about 110 lumens/watt. They have a golden-white color and distort colors considerably. About 15 minutes are required for a high-pressure sodium light to reach full luminance, but it can restart quickly after momentary interruption — in only 1-1/2 to 2 minutes.

Units for Measure: Lighting fixtures are counted on a unit basis (EA.). The number of lamps (for purchasing purposes) is determined per fixture and listed as each lamp (EA.).

Material Units: The items included in the material unit for fixtures depend somewhat on the style of fixture. In general, the unit will include the following:

    Fixture
    Lamps
    Wire nuts
    Fasteners or hangers as required (chain, S-hooks, bolts, screws, etc.)
    Canopies as required by the type of fixture

These additional items must be listed and extended:

    Boxes
    Plaster rings
    Conduit or raceways
    Wire
    Fixture whips
    Switches

Labor Units: The following procedures are generally included in the labor units for fixtures:

    Receiving
    Fixture handling
    Layout
    Installing (hanging or mounting) the fixture
    Terminating wires at the fixture
    Installing lamps and assembling the fixture
    Testing

These additional procedures must be listed and extended:

    Conduit
    Wire
    Fixture whips
    Special support brackets or channels
    Switches

Takeoff Procedure: When taking off interior lighting fixtures, it is advisable to set up the quantity work sheet to conform to the lighting schedule as it appears on the print. Include both the alphanumeric code and the symbol on your work sheet.

Take off one particular section or floor of the building at a time, counting the number of each type of fixture before going on to the next type. It is also advantageous to include on the same work sheet the conduit, wire, and fittings associated with a particular lighting system. This method makes material purchases more specific, helping to define when and how much to order.

After totalling all quantities, add 5% to the conduit takeoff and 10% to wire for waste. Transfer the quantities to a cost analysis sheet and extend.

Cost Modifications: Productivity is based on new construction in an unobstructed floor location, using rolling staging to 15' high. Add the following percentages to labor only for elevated installations:

15'	to	20' high	+10%
21'		25'	+20%
26'		30'	+30%
31'		35'	+40%
36'		40'	+50%
41' and over			+60%

For large concentrations of lighting fixtures in the same area, deduct the following percentages from the labor units:

25	to	50 fixtures	−15%
51		75	−20%
76		100	−25%
101 and over			−30%

Exit and Emergency Lighting

Exit lights are available with mounting arrangements for walls or ceilings and with or without an arrow. Explosion-proof enclosures can be obtained for these lights. Exit signs have either incandescent or fluorescent lamps. Six-inch "EXIT" letters are standard.

Battery-operated emergency lights are available with either battery-mounted or remote heads. Several different types of batteries and voltages are available. Emergency lights are usually surface-mounted. (A special lamp pack is available for use in fluorescent fixtures; it mounts either in the ballast channel or on top of the fixture.)

Units for Measure: Exit light fixtures are counted individually (EA.).

Emergency lights are counted as each unit (EA.). If the battery is used with remote heads, count each head (EA.) and battery unit (EA.).

Material Units: Exit lights generally include the Exit sign with lamps, and anchors and wire nuts as required.

Emergency lights generally include the battery unit and remote head complete with lamps and mounting brackets, anchors, and plug and cord or wire nuts.

Labor Units: The following procedures are generally included per unit:

Exit Lights:
   Receiving
   Material handling

Layout
Installing the fixture and lamps
Testing

Additional items to be listed and extended:
Conduit
Wire
Boxes
Connectors

Emergency Lights:
Receiving
Handling
Layout and installing mounting bracket
Connection in outlet box
Battery connection and testing

Additional items to be listed and extended:
Receptacle or boxes
Wire
Conduit

Takeoff Procedure: Generally, emergency lighting fixtures are taken off with interior lighting. (Refer to the "Interior Lighting Fixtures" section earlier in this chapter for guidelines.)

Note: Take care to list and count battery packs and/or remote heads if they are used.

Exterior Fixtures

Exterior lighting serves both utilitarian and decorative purposes. The same assortment of lamps used for interiors (discussed previously in this chapter) is also available for exterior use. Low-pressure sodium (LPS) is an additional option for exterior fixtures.

Low-pressure sodium lamps generate an almost monochromatic, yellow light. They are, however, highly efficient, putting out over 170 lumens per watt. They require 7 to 15 minutes to reach full light output but will restart immediately after interruption of the power source.

Fluorescent lamps have special concerns when used outdoors. They are sensitive to low temperatures and require more starting energy in cold weather.

Ballasts are available for each of the following temperature ranges: above 50°F for indoor applications, above 0°F for outdoor temperature applications, and above -20°F for outdoor applications. Also, the surface temperature of fluorescent lamps has a direct impact on light output (it drops by 35% at 0°F). Again, there are fluorescent lamps specially designed to compensate for this factor.

Most exterior fixtures are either wall- or pole-mounted.

Units of Measure: Each fixture is counted as a unit (EA.).

Material Units: The following items are generally included per unit:

> Fixture
> Lamp
> Wire nuts
> Fasteners or brackets as required

These additional items must be listed and extended:

> Conduit
> Wire
> Pole
> Pole arms
> Photocell control

Labor Units: The following procedures are generally included per unit:

> Receiving
> Fixture handling
> Layout
> Mounting or installing (up to 15′ high)
> Lamp and fixture assembling
> Wire connections
> Testing and aiming

These additional procedures must be listed and extended:

> Conduit
> Boxes and fittings
> Wire
> Pole and arm installation (pole base)
> Lightning protection
> Photocell control

Takeoff Procedure: When taking off exterior lighting fixtures, it is advisable to set up the quantity work sheet to conform to the lighting schedule as it appears on the print. Include both the alphanumeric code and the symbol on your work sheet.

Take off one particular section or area of the building at a time, counting the number of each type of fixture before going on to the next type. It is also advantageous to include on the same work sheet the conduit, wire, and fittings associated with a particular lighting system. This method makes material purchases more specific, helping to define when and how much to order.

After totalling all quantities, add 5% to conduit takeoff and 10% to wire for waste. Transfer the quantities to a cost analysis sheet and extend.

Lamps

Refer to the sections on "Interior Lighting Fixtures" and "Exterior Lighting Fixtures" (earlier in this chapter) for a detailed discussion of the various lamps that are used in most fixtures. Since fixture costs are normally calculated to include lamps, this category is most useful for listing lamps to be replaced.

Units for Measure: Lamps are counted individually (EA.).

Material Units: The material cost generally includes only the cost of the lamp.

Labor Units: The following procedures are generally included per unit:

Receiving
Material handling
Use of rolling staging
Opening of the fixture
Removal of the old lamp
Installation of the new lamp and testing
Hauling the old lamp for disposal

Note: The labor units should presume installing new lamps for entire areas — not just one or two at a time.

Takeoff Procedure: List the number of each type of fixture. Then multiply this figure by the number of lamps in each fixture. List the lamps by type and wattage. Total the quantities, transfer these figures to a cost analysis sheet, and extend.

Track Lighting

Track lighting is a versatile system designed to adapt easily as requirements change. Track lights can be swivelled and rotated to aim in any direction. This kind of flexibility is in highest demand and most often used in offices, homes, and galleries.

The basic component of a track light system is the track, which serves as both a raceway and a source of power for the lights. Tracks may be mounted on walls or ceilings, and come in standard lengths of 4', 8', and 12'. They may contain one, two, or three circuits. To connect sections of track, a joiner coupling is required; this coupling must also be one, two, or three circuits. Joiners are available in the following configurations: straight, "L"s, "T"s, and cross connectors. A feed kit is required to connect branch power sources to the track.

Track lighting fixtures are manufactured in a wide range of styles and finishes. Wattages range from 50 to 300. Fixtures can be mounted anywhere along the track simply by twisting the base of the fixture 180 degrees into the track and depressing a locking tab on the fixture itself.

Caution: Although most estimating standards give a typical price for an average fixture, prices for track lighting fixtures range from $25.00 to $320.00 per unit. Consult the specifications for the exact type of fixture before pricing. If the type of fixture is not specified, use the standard, but note that it is an allowance. Then, if a more expensive fixture is specified later, the estimator can submit a change order for the balance.

Units for Measure: Count the track in standard length segments (EA.). Count the fixtures as separate units (EA.).

Material Units: The following items are generally priced separately:
    Track (including mounting screws)
    Light fixtures

These additional items must be listed and extended:
    Feed kits
    Joiner couplings
    Switches

Labor Units: The following procedures are generally included in the labor-hours for track lighting:

    Receiving
    Handling
    Measuring and marking
    Installing each component
    Aiming and testing

These additional procedures are listed and extended:

    Branch conduit
    Wiring to the track system
    Remote switching or dimmers

Takeoff Procedure: Organize your work sheet by:

    Track — according to size and number of circuits
    Feed kits by number of circuits
    Fixtures — by type, catalog number, and wattage

Measure the track lengths, noting the different lengths of sections, and transfer this information to the takeoff sheets. Count all feed and end kits and transfer these figures to the takeoff sheet. Then count and list all fixtures. Transfer the quantity totals from the takeoff sheet to a cost analysis sheet and extend.

Cost Modifications: Add the following percentages to labor only for elevated installations:

15′	to	20′ high	+10%
21′		25′	+20%
26′		30′	+30%
31′		35′	+40%
36′		40′	+50%
41′ and over			+60%

Fixture Whips

A fixture whip is a flexible connection consisting of wire in flexible metallic conduit. A fixture whip is used to connect the fixture, such as a troffer fixture for a suspended ceiling, to an outlet box when the fixture is not mounted directly to the box. Fixture whips are usually 4′ to 6′ long.

Units for Measure: Fixture whips are counted as units (EA.).

Material Units: The following items are generally included per unit:

    Fixture whip complete with two greenfield connectors and the
        ends of the wire already stripped
    Wire nuts for one end

Labor Units: The following procedures are generally included per unit:
  Receiving
  Material handling
  Connecting to fixture and outlet box
  Use of rolling stage in unobstructed area up to 15' high

Takeoff Procedure: Check the fixture schedule for suspended fixtures. Allow one whip per fixture (or one whip per row of fixtures) as shown on the drawings. For detailed takeoff guidelines, see "Interior Lighting Fixtures" at the beginning of this chapter.

Cost Modifications: Productivity is based on new construction in an unobstructed floor location, using rolling staging to 15' high. Add the following percentages to labor only for elevated installations:

15'	to	20' high	+10%
21'		25'	+20%
26'		30'	+30%
31'		35'	+40%
36'		40'	+50%
41' and over			+60%

For large concentrations of lighting fixtures in the same area, deduct the following percentages from the labor units:

25	to	50 fixtures	−15%
51		75	−20%
76		100	−25%
101 and over			−30%

Chapter 19

Electrical Utilities

Electrical utilities include the site work required for the installation of electrical or telephone wires and the actual underground installation of those wires or cables. This chapter addresses electrical and telephone site work and underground duct banks. Each of these components is described in terms of what is included and required—for both materials and labor. A takeoff procedure is also provided.

Electric and Telephone Site Work

This category covers the distribution methods used to route power, control, and communications cables onto a facility's property and between its buildings and structures. There are three basic options: direct burial cables, underground in duct banks, and overhead on poles.

Direct burial cables are the least versatile; they are generally used for residential applications where aesthetics are a more important factor than flexibility or an allowance for future changes. Occasionally, direct burial is used in commercial and industrial facilities to route a branch feeder to unique equipment, such as a well pump or roadway lighting. Two techniques are used to place direct buried cables. A trenching machine may dig a narrow slot two to four feet deep for a single cable or a trench one to two feet wide for multiple cables. The trench is usually backfilled with a few inches of sand—below and again above the cables—for protection. About 12 inches above the cable, concrete planks or plastic marker tape may be placed as a warning to future excavation and digging. Finally, on the finished grade, concrete, monuments, or markers may be placed every 100′ to indicate the path of the buried cable and to denote changes in direction.

Duct banks are a group of two or more underground raceways (conduits) usually encased in concrete. Although more costly than direct burial systems, duct banks offer three advantages. First, the cables are far better protected from hazards and the elements. Second, groups of several cables can be pulled through each conduit (and many conduits may be installed in each duct bank). Finally, new cables may be pulled (or failed cables replaced) quickly and economically to meet future needs.

For duct banks that cover long distances, access must be provided to the run for pulling cables. When only a few conduits are installed, a hand-hole meets this requirement. For multiple conduit banks and for large conduits, a manhole is installed. Hand-holes and manholes may also serve to change the direction of a run or to split up a run. Both are usually made of precast concrete, and manholes are sized large enough for both men and pulling equipment. Pulling eyes (steel inserts) are normally cast into manholes opposite the cable entry points. This is done to facilitate the rigging process for cable pulling. Hangers may also be cast into the boxes to carry or support the installed cables.

Duct banks are generally buried, allowing two to four feet from grade to the top row of conduits; the conduits are separated by plastic spacers and held fast with tie-wires. When the conduit is encased in concrete, it is important to prevent the conduit from "floating" in the pour. A minimum of two inches of concrete is required on all sides.

The most common duct bank conduit material was formerly asbestos cement. In recent years, however, asbestos has been discontinued entirely in favor of plastic (PVC) and fiber duct. Galvanized steel may also be used, especially when power cables and instrumentation will be pulled into separate conduits in close proximity to each other. Plastic conduit comes in 20′ lengths and is bent in the field with a heater. Couplings and fittings are glued on. Unless the run is very short (under 100′), the installation of duct conduits of less than 2″ in diameter is very rare.

Poles and overhead routing represent the most conventional method of distributing power and communication cables. Many cables are built and rated for aerial service. Some cables include "strength members" to carry the tensions of the stretched cables. Still other types of cable, such as service drops and telephone lines, will be supported by a steel messenger wire. Note: Code requirements may dictate certain minimum heights for suspended cable. Be sure that these codes are understood before pricing aerial installations.

The hole for a line pole is usually made with an auger machine. After the pole is set, crushed limestone or similar fill is placed and compacted around the pole. In some areas, poles will need lightning rods and grounding. Don't forget to look for these requirements on the drawings.

Units for Measure: Several quantity designations may apply to electrical and telephone site work.

> For direct burial trenching, the work is measured per linear foot (L.F.).
> For duct bank conduits, the work is measured per linear foot (L.F.).
> For sand backfill or concrete encasement, measurements are made in cubic yards (C.Y.).
> Manholes and hand-holes are counted as each (EA.).
> Fittings, spacers, and elbows are also counted individually (EA.).
> Poles and crossbars are counted as each (EA.).
> Cable is measured in units of 100 linear feet (C.L.F.).

Material Units: The following summaries list the material items usually included in the material unit for each component:

Trenching:

> Includes no materials.

Additional items to be listed and extended are sand or concrete as required.

Underground conduits:

> Conduit
> Spacers
> End fittings
> Tie-wire

Additional items to be listed and extended are elbows and special adaptors.

Manholes and hand-holes:

> Precast unit with cover and inserts (if required)

Poles:

> Hole
> Compacted steel fill

Additional items to be listed and extended are cross arms, guy wire and anchors, and lightning protection.

Cable:

> Cable only

Additional items to be listed and extended are messenger wire (if not "built in"), terminations, and testing.

Labor Units: The following is a summary of the activities usually included in the labor unit for each component:

Trenching:

> Trench excavation
> Borrowing material for backfill
> Compacting

Underground conduits:

Placing and fitting conduits, spacers, and wire ties. (Note: Spacers and fittings are counted for ordering only, not for pricing.)

Additional procedures to be listed and extended are special fittings and elbows.

Manholes and hand-holes:

Hole excavation
Setting the precast unit in place
Backfill and grading
Placing covers

Poles:

Auger excavation
Placing the pole
Backfill with limestone or suitable material
Compacting the fill
Rough grading

Additional procedures to be listed and extended are cross arms, guy wire and anchor, and lightning protection.

Cable:

Cable only

Additional procedures to be listed and extended are messenger wire, terminations, and testing.

Takeoff Procedure: First, list all components on the takeoff sheets. Measure or determine linear distances between points and note these on the drawings. Next, determine the amount of earth work—i.e., trenching or hole excavation—as well as backfill, materials, etc. Count the number of underground conduits in each run by size, and list the total lengths. Count each manhole or post. Then determine the pulling length required for each cable run, including the indoor portions, to their destinations. List each run for each cable type separately. This information may be useful later when ordering precut cables. For more information, see the section on shielded cable in Chapter 13: Conductors and Grounding. Total the above; add 5% to the conduit lengths and 10% to the cable lengths for waste. Finally, transfer the total quantities to a cost analysis sheet and extend.

Special Systems

Special systems include unique control or monitoring equipment used for specialized applications in residential, commercial, and industrial construction. Included in this chapter are sections ranging from electric heating and residential wiring, to television, public address, and sound systems. Doorbell and hospital paging systems are also covered. Each of these items is first described, then given appropriate units for measure, along with material and labor requirements and instructions for the takeoff procedure.

Clock Systems

A variety of clock systems are available. The most common types have a master clock, a tone generator and control, an antenna, a lightning arrester, and slave clocks. The system picks up radio signals every hour from the National Bureau of Standards to keep the master clock set at the correct time. In turn, high-frequency tone signals are sent out over the regular receptacle wiring to keep the system's clocks on time. In this type of system, the clocks are plugged into the regular receptacle.

Other systems use different methods of resetting clocks. Some have two-motor clocks, with a control that speeds up the clock with the second motor. These systems require separate conduit and an independent wire system. Program signaling is also controlled through the master clock and controller.

Another option, a combination clock and speaker, consists of a back box, trim, and grille for the speaker and clock. The clock is included in the price of the box; the speaker is not.

Units for Measure: Each component is listed (EA.). For convenience, some estimating standards list a complete system cost based upon the number of rooms. In that case, each system is listed (EA.).

Material Units: A complete component with fasteners, box, and connections (wire nuts) is generally included in the material price.

These additional items must be listed and extended:

> Cable and wire
> Conduit

Labor Units: The following procedures are generally included per unit:

> Receiving
> Material handling
> Mounting as required
> Terminations
> Testing

These additional items are listed and extended:

> Conduit
> Wire

Takeoff Procedure: List the items on the takeoff sheet. Transfer this information to a cost analysis sheet and extend.

Note: Because of the variety of systems and manufacturers, it is recommended that a vendor price quote be obtained for material pricing.

Detection Systems

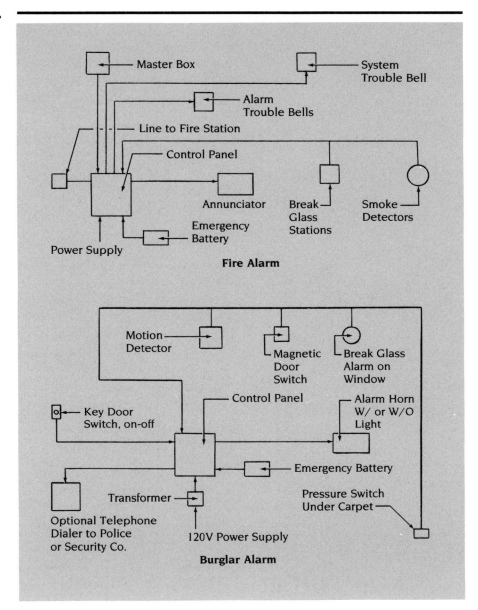

Fire Alarm

Master Box — System Trouble Bell — Alarm Trouble Bells — Line to Fire Station — Control Panel — Annunciator — Break Glass Stations — Smoke Detectors — Emergency Battery — Power Supply

Burglar Alarm

Motion Detector — Magnetic Door Switch — Break Glass Alarm on Window — Key Door Switch, on-off — Control Panel — Alarm Horn W/ or W/O Light — Emergency Battery — Pressure Switch Under Carpet — Optional Telephone Dialer to Police or Security Co. — Transformer — 120V Power Supply

Fire alarm systems and burglar alarm (intrusion detection) systems are similar in both their principles of operation and their installation techniques. Nevertheless, they are two separate and distinct installation components. Rarely do they share any hardware or wiring.

Burglar alarm systems consist of control panels, indicator panels, various types of alarm devices, and switches. The control panel is usually line powered with a battery backup supply. Some systems have a direct connection to the police or protection company, while others have auto-dial telephone capabilities. Most, however, simply have local control monitors and an annunciator. The sensing devices are various pressure switches, magnetic door switches, glass break sensors, infrared beams, infrared sensors, microwave detectors, and ultrasonic motion detectors. The alarms are sirens, horns, and/or flashing lights.

Fire alarm systems consist of control panels, annunciator panels, battery with rack and charger, various sensing devices such as smoke and heat detectors, and alarm horn and light signals. Some fire alarm systems are very sophisticated and include speakers, telephone lines, door closer controls, and other components. Some fire alarm systems are connected directly to the fire station. Requirements for fire alarm systems are generally more closely regulated by codes and by local authorities than are intrusion alarm systems.

Units for Measure: The components of a system are listed and counted as each (EA.).

Material Units: For all of the above listed components, the component itself and its mounting hardware are generally included in the material price.

These additional items must be listed and extended:

Wire connections
Wire
Conduits

Labor Units: The following items are generally included in the labor-hours per unit:

Receiving
Material handling
Installation and testing

These additional items are listed and extended:

Conduit
Wire or boxes, unless the box is part of the component
Terminations

Takeoff Procedure: First, list each component on the takeoff sheet. Then count each type of component, listing all of one type before continuing to the next. Measure conduit lengths with a rotometer; mark the lengths on the drawing and on the takeoff sheets. Using the conduit lengths, figure the lengths of each cable type and list this information on the takeoff sheets. Next, total all components and add 5% to conduit and 10% to cable for waste. Transfer the total quantities to a cost analysis sheet and extend.

Doctors' In-Out Register

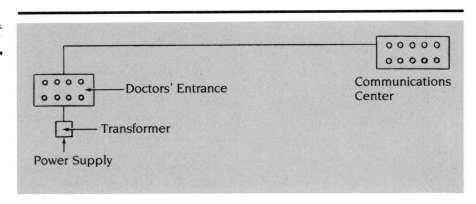

The doctors' in-out register is a system used in hospitals to facilitate communication between staff members. A recording register is located at the entrance. The doctors push their buttons, sending a signal to a register at the hospital control center. The attendant is then able to page or signal the doctor. Pocket paging devices are a material cost only.

Units for Measure: Each system is counted as one unit (EA.). Pocket paging devices, if needed, are counted as each (EA.).

Material Units: The following items are generally included in the material unit price:

  Push button board
  Console monitor
  Fasteners and brackets

These additional items must be listed and extended:

  Wire
  Conduit
  Terminations
  Pocket paging devices

Labor Units: Labor-hours for a doctors' in-out register generally include the following procedures:

  Receiving
  Material handling
  Mounting
  Testing

These additional procedures must be listed and extended:

  Wire
  Conduit
  Terminations

Takeoff Procedure: List the components on the takeoff sheet. Total and add 5% to conduit and 10% to wire quantities for waste. Transfer these figures to the cost analysis sheets and extend.

Note: Whenever practical, obtain material cost quotes from manufacturers' representatives or vendors. This is also a good source of information regarding special installation requirements or instructions.

Doorbell Systems

This system includes a low-voltage transformer (120V/24V), push button(s), and a signal device. The signal device can be a bell, buzzer, or chimes. Because the wiring is low-voltage, conduit is rarely used.

Units for Measure: Each component is listed as a unit (EA.).

Material Units: The following items are generally included in the material cost per unit:

  Doorbell
  Buttons

Transformer
Wire terminations

These additional items must be listed and extended:
Wire
Box for transformer

Labor Units: Labor-hours generally include the following procedures:
Installation
Terminations
Testing

These additional procedures are listed and extended:
Wire
Outlet boxes

Takeoff Procedure: List the components on the takeoff sheet (usually taken off with branch wiring). Total and add 10% to wire. Transfer the total quantities to the cost analysis sheets and extend.

Note: The cost of the chime units can vary widely. Be sure to understand the specified requirements when pricing this item.

Electric Heating

Electric heating is an item that covers a wide range of equipment and applications. A few subcategories are baseboard or wall unit heaters for residential or commercial buildings; heat trace systems for freeze protection of water lines or for maintaining liquid temperature in chemical and oil pipes; radiant ceiling heat panels; and unit space heaters. Clearly, a number of different estimating problems are posed by an electrical component that covers such a broad range. Nevertheless, two specific applications can serve to guide the estimator through the majority of cases. These are space heaters and piping trace cables.

Early in the estimating process, N.E.C. and local building code regulations must be considered as a factor in electric heating. For example, receptacles cannot be located above electric baseboard heaters because of danger to hanging cords. Minimum wall insulation values must also be met when electric heating is installed in residences. It is important to become familiar with these and other requirements before estimating various forms of electric heat.

Electric space heat may be provided with a baseboard arrangement, wall-mounted units, or ceiling-hung heaters. The baseboard units are usually convection types. They are classed in terms of watts per foot, i.e., watt density. Low watt density models produce approximately 175 W/L.F., while high watt density units run 257 W/L.F. (This number suggests the operating temperature of the element.) Baseboard heaters are available in sizes that increase in 2' increments—from 2' to 12' long. They may be rated for operation on 120V, 240V, or 277V.

Unit space heaters generally operate with forced air (fans) blowing across an electric coil. These units are rated in terms of their heat output in kilowatts (kW). Sizes run from 10 kW to 50 kW. Although 208V to 240V single-phase units are used, 240V and 480V three-phase units are far more common.

There are two types of thermostat controls for heater circuits. The first is full (line) voltage thermostat switches. The second is low-voltage, relay-equipped thermostats. Line thermostats are not suited for more than 240V, nor are they used for large heaters at lower voltages.

If no other information is given about heating capacity requirements, there is a general rule of thumb that provides 10 watts per square foot of floor area.

Heat trace is a parallel-resistance heating cable. The purpose of heat trace is to protect a pipe from freezing. This is done by laying a continuous heater wire against a pipe and wrapping both with insulation. Thermostats (with sensing elements against the opposite side of the pipe or at least 90 degrees away) are set to maintain about 40°F. Some liquids, such as heavy fuel oils, require higher temperatures to remain in a fluid state. The heat tracing used on these systems is designed for these higher temperatures. Heat trace systems typically operate from 100° to 300°F. Mineral insulated heat trace cable is commonly used in high-temperature systems.

Heat trace cable is rated in watts per foot. If extra heat is needed, the cable can be wrapped in a spiral around the pipe, thereby increasing the number of watts per linear foot of pipe. The number of turns or wraps per foot is called the "pitch." Tables are available that relate pitch and pipe diameter to total cable footage. Valves, flanges, and other fittings receive extra wrapping to compensate for added heat losses. Special low-temperature heat cable can be used for plastic PVC pipes.

When estimating for heat trace systems, it is important to understand the intended use of the cable. Freeze-protection cable is simply attached to the pipe with a polyester tape band every 12". Another method is to attach the cable to the pipe with a continuous coverage of 2"-wide aluminum tape. This increases heat transfer and temperature distribution around the pipe, allowing higher watt densities without spiral wrapping. Polyester tape bands must still be used every 12". Cable covered with a factory-extruded heat transfer cement maximizes heat transfer. This covering allows temperature maintenance up to 300°F.

Units for Measure: Heaters are counted as units (EA.). Heat trace cables are measured in linear feet (L.F.).

Material Units: The following items are included for heat component units:

Baseboard heaters:

   The heater
   Mounting screws

Additional items to be listed and extended are terminations, wire, and thermostats.

Unit heaters:

   The heater (with thermostat)
   Brackets or hangers
   Wall or ceiling fasteners as required (up to 15′ high)

Additional items to be listed and extended are terminations, wire, conduit, and thermostats (some models).

Heat trace:

   Heat cable
   Attaching tape

Additional items to be listed and extended are a heat cable connection kit, end kit, thermostat, branch circuit wire, and conduit.

Labor Units: The following procedures are generally included in the labor-hours for heating units:

Heaters:

   Receiving
   Material handling
   Installation or mounting of heaters in place

Additional items to be listed and extended are branch wiring, conduit, terminations, and installation of thermostats (if not integral to the unit).

Heat trace:

   Receiving
   Material handling
   Installing heat cable by wrapping with tape (up to 15′ high)

Additional items to be listed and extended are installing end termination kits, terminal kits, thermostats, branch wiring, conduit, and terminations.

Takeoff Procedure: Set up the work sheet by individual components (with heat trace cable, subdivide into volts and watts per linear foot). Add accessories, such as metallic raceway and support clips. Transfer all quantities to the cost analysis sheet and extend.

Notes:

1. If the installation uses transfer cement, keep in mind that one gallon applies approximately 60 linear feet of raceway.
2. If the pipe system contains valves, be sure to add enough cable to wrap them. This procedure is described below, in the "Cost Modifications" section.

Cost Modifications for Heat Trace: For each type of valve, add the following quantities to the linear foot totals of heat trace cable:

Butterfly			Flange			Screwed or Welded		
1/2"	=	0'	1/2"	=	1'	1/2"	=	.5'
3/4	=	0	3/4	=	1.5	3/4	=	.75
1	=	1	1	=	2	1	=	1
1.5	=	1.5	1.5	=	2.5	1.5	=	1.5
2	=	2	2	=	2.5	2	=	2
2.5	=	2.5	2.5	=	3	2.5	=	2.5
3	=	2.5	3	=	3.5	3	=	3
4	=	3	4	=	4	4	=	4
6	=	3.5	6	=	8	6	=	7
8	=	4	8	=	11	8	=	9.5
10	=	4	10	=	14	10	=	12.5
12	=	5	12	=	16.5	12	=	15
14	=	5.5	14	=	19.5	14	=	18
16	=	6	16	=	23	16	=	21
18	=	6.5	18	=	27	18	=	25.5
20	=	7	20	=	30	20	=	28.5
24	=	8	24	=	36	24	=	34
30	=	10	30	=	42	30	=	40

Caution: Pipe insulation is installed after the heat tracing is in place. This is usually performed by the mechanical contractor, but it can sometimes be specified as the responsibility of the electrical contractor.

Lightning Protection

Lightning protection for the rooftops of buildings is achieved by a series of lightning rods or air terminals joined together by either copper or aluminum cable. The cable size is determined by the height of the building. The lightning cable system is connected through a downlead to a ground rod that is a minimum of 2' below grade and 1-1/2' to 3' out from the foundation wall. To effectively estimate lightning grounding systems, we need to incorporate many of the components described in the grounding section of this book. By code, all metal bodies on the roof that are located within six feet of a lightning conductor must be bonded to the lightning protection system. As a result, the lightning protection system is listed with the equipment grounding in our estimating procedure.

One of the basic components of a lightning grounding system is the air terminal. These are manufactured in either copper or aluminum. The most common sizes used are 3/8″ diameter copper at 10″ high for roofs under 75′ high. For roofs over 75′, a 1/2″ diameter by 12″ high terminal is most common. For aluminum air terminals, a 1/2″ diameter by 12″ high is used for roofs under 75′, and a 5/8″ diameter by 12″ high is used for heights over 75′. Air terminals are usually mounted in the perimeter parapet wall and include a masonry cable anchor base. A wide range of configurations is available from manufacturers for mounting air terminals to different roof surfaces. Most do not vary significantly in price.

Cable for main conductor use is calculated in pounds per 1,000′; it is available on 500′ spools. Conductors are manufactured in copper and aluminum. The industry standard Class I minimum weight for copper is 187 lbs. per 1000′ when used on a roof of less than 75′ high, and Class II minimum weight for copper is 375 lbs. per 1000′ for structures over 75′ high. The main conductor for Class I aluminum cable is 95 lbs. per 1000′ for structures under 75′ high, and for Class II, 190 lbs. per 1000′ for structures over 75′ high. Connections to main grounding conductor cable are accomplished in one of three ways: clamping, heat or exothermic welding, or brazing.

Units for Measure: Air terminals are counted as units (EA.). Cable is taken off by the linear foot (L.F.). Terminations are counted as units (EA.).

Material Units: The following items are generally included in the material price of:

Air terminals:
The terminal or rod
One mounting base
Four mounting lead-type anchors and screws

Cable:
Base copper or aluminum cable
One cable clamp for every three linear feet of cable
One lead-type anchor and screw every three linear feet of cable

Included in the material cost of ground connections is only the connector itself.

Labor Units: Labor-hours generally include the following procedures:

Air Terminals:
Mounting on concrete surface
Installing four anchor-type fasteners

Cable:
Receiving main conductor cable on 500′ reels
Hauling to central roof location
Setting up cable reel
Drawing cable
Fastening cable every 3 linear feet using a lead-type anchor

Connections:
Setting up joint configurations using hardware or molds
Attaching and terminating the connection

Takeoff Procedure: Set up the quantity takeoff sheet listing air terminals by size, type, and configuration. List the wire size in pounds per 1000 L.F. and by type of material. List the connections by type, wire-to-wire size, and configuration. Start at one corner of the building and work clockwise around the perimeter of the building, counting the air terminals. Check each terminal with a marker as you count, and avoid jumping from the perimeter to air terminals located in other sections of the roof. After the perimeter count, take off all the other air terminals.

Transfer the count of all quantities to the takeoff sheet. Measure the main ground cable, again following the perimeter route. (Do not, at this point, attempt to incorporate equipment ground cables.) Transfer the quantities (in linear feet) to the work sheet. Then, count the number of drops to the grounding electrode, and multiply this figure by the distance between the connection and the ground rod. Measure the equipment cable runs and terminations to the equipment casing and the main grounding conductor. Transfer the quantities to a cost analysis sheet and extend.

Cost Modifications: Labor-hours are based on the installation of up to 10 air terminals on a common roof. Deduct the following percentages from both air terminals and connections for quantities of:

1	to	10	− 0%
11		25	−20%
Over 25			−25%

Nurses' Call Systems

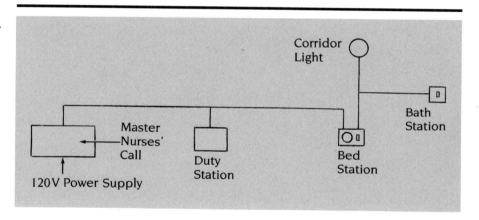

These systems, used in hospitals and nursing homes, enable the patient to signal the nurses' station, and may also turn on a door light in the corridor outside the room. The central component is a master control station, which includes an amplifier, microphone, and speaker. In some systems, patients can speak to the nurses through a bedside call station or a pillow speaker. It is best to call the manufacturer for a price on the complete system.

Units for Measure: The master control unit, bedside station, and corridor light are all counted as units (EA.).

Material Units: The following items are generally included per unit:
    Master control unit
    Bedside stations
    Corridor light for each room

Labor Units: Generally included in the labor-hours are the following procedures:
    Receiving
    Material handling
    Installation
    Testing of devices and master control station

These additional items are listed and extended:
- Conduit
- Wire
- Outlet boxes (unless the box is part of the component)
- Terminations

Takeoff Procedure: List the components on the takeoff sheet (usually taken off with branch wiring). Total and add 10% to wire. Transfer the total quantities to a cost analysis sheet and extend.

Television Systems

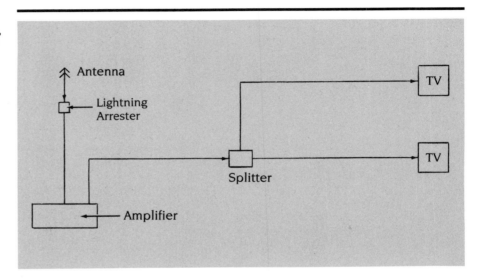

Master T.V. antenna systems are used in schools, dormitories, and apartment buildings. Each system consists of the antenna, lightning arrester, amplifier, splitters, and outlets. The signal is received by the antenna and increased by the amplifier. It then goes through the main cable to the splitter. Here, the signal is split among several branch circuit cables.

A closed-circuit surveillance system consists of a T.V. camera and monitor. These systems are used indoors or outdoors for security surveillance. Some applications require pan, tilt, and zoom (PTZ) mechanisms for remote control of the camera.

Educational T.V. studio equipment is comprised of three cameras and a monitor.

Notes: When estimating material costs for T.V. camera systems and monitors, it is always prudent to obtain manufacturers' quotes for equipment prices. Also, some installations will require special accessories. Often, the sales engineers are a good source of information on these requirements.

Some general precautions are listed below:

- Various models of cameras are sold with a wide choice of lens options. Many are priced above "standard" lens costs. It is common to have one type and model camera specified for a site, with each camera having a different lens. As a result, each camera could have a different price.
- Camera models may have several different video tube options. Those designed for "low light" (used outdoors at night) are more expensive than "standard" tubes.

- For long video cable runs, or runs near power cables and equipment, signal accessories may need to be added to the system. These accessories may include: hum clampers to remove 60 Hz, AC noise; equalizers to balance the signal's frequency spectrum after a long cable run; and line amplifiers to boost signal strength at the midpoint of the run.
- As the camera-to-monitor distance increases, the type of coaxial cable used becomes critical. High-efficiency cables (low signal loss) are, naturally, more expensive to buy and to install.
- Monitors are generally specified in terms of resolution in lines. A high-resolution monitor, say 750 lines, will be more expensive than one rated at 550 lines.
- Specifications may require the use of expensive test equipment during check-out and start-up. The rental cost or purchase price must be included.
- The presence of the manufacturer's service representative or engineer is often required during testing. This expense will not be included in the material cost and must be added to the estimate.

Units for Measure: Each component is listed (EA.).

Material Units: The following items are generally included per unit:

    Components, complete with fasteners and brackets
    Antenna, complete with mounting straps or guys

These additional items must be listed and extended:

    Cable (both 120V power and coaxial signal)
    Conduit
    Terminations

Labor Units: The following procedures are generally included per unit:

    Receiving
    Material handling
    Installation and testing of components

These additional procedures must be listed and extended:

    Conduit
    Wire or cable
    Outlet boxes

Takeoff Procedure: First, list each type of component on the takeoff sheet. Count the like components and enter each on the takeoff sheet. Then measure each type of wire and enter on the takeoff sheet. Next, count coaxial cable connections carefully (watch for long runs that may require splices). Total the items and add 5% to conduit and 10% to cable for waste. Finally, transfer the total quantities to a cost analysis sheet and extend.

Residential Wiring

For estimating purposes we will organize residential wiring into certain defined systems. These systems, when combined, comprise all the electrical components needed for a complete residential electrical installation. Because of the relatively low cost of residential electrical wiring, and the competitive nature of the residential business, most estimating standards combine the expense of assorted materials and list the cost per outlet or per switch. This approach involves little risk, provided the estimator knows in advance what is included in each of these mini-systems. Why use a mini-system approach? If an estimator spends the time to measure every L.F. of #14-2 Romex at a bare material cost of $.16 per L.F., he would still arrive at a cost very close to that derived from a mini-system. Furthermore, he may have spent six times as long to prepare an estimate that might not be any more accurate. The residential industry does not afford that degree of precision, and most residential prints do not include wiring details.

Residential wiring can be broken down into the following categories:

Service
Branch circuit wiring
Appliances
Heating and A/C
Intercom and/or doorbell systems
Light fixtures
Special needs

For purposes of residential estimating, we will define branch circuits as circuits containing any combination of receptacles, switches, and lighting outlets. Using a mini-system approach, the estimator needs only count the number of these items.

Appliance circuits are defined as specific needs, or direct-connected outlets. Examples are range circuits, water heater circuits, exhaust fans, disposal wiring, and dryer circuits. These circuits are run to, but do not include, the appliance itself. There is little variation in the voltage and amperage requirements of appliances. Thus many estimating standards apply the same mini-system approach to both appliance circuits and branch circuit devices or outlets. The wire for appliance circuits must be measured and priced individually.

Residential intercom systems consist of a master station (most commonly located in the kitchen area), up to eight remote speakers, and associated low-voltage wiring. The transformer steps voltage down from 110V to 24V. Remote speakers are interconnected with #18 gauge nonmetallic sheathed cable.

Heating and air conditioning circuits are direct, or "home runs." Most estimating standards do not include the equipment, which is instead supplied and installed by the mechanical contractor; the circuit and tie-in are done by the electrical contractor.

The raceways used in residential wiring vary according to specifications as well as state, local, and national electrical codes. Because of the wide variations in cost, it is important to note the type of raceway material being used. Some of the more common types are listed below:

Nonmetallic sheathed cable (Romex)
BX cable
EMT conduit

Aluminum or steel conduit may also be used.

Units for Measure: Residential wiring devices and outlets are counted on a "mini-system" basis (EA.).

Material Units:

Service:
The following items are generally included in the material price for a 100-amp service using nonmetallic cable:

24' of SE type cable
One service head
One weatherproof SE connector
Two standard SE non-watertight connectors
Four SE two-hole clips
One 8' x 3/8" ground rod
One ground clamp
5' bare CU ground wire
One residential 100 A 20-circuit panel with main breaker
20 single-pole 15 A or 20 A breakers

Note: For a 200 A service, the same quantities apply, but they are sized for the larger installations.

Branch circuits:
Branch circuit wiring is based on an average of 20' between devices, including an allowance for the home run. The following items are generally included in the material unit price:

20' of 14-2 Romex
One device (residential grade)
One single gang plastic box
One plastic device cover
Four staples or clips, and nails

Note: Although the above listing is for a Romex installation, the quantities and component logic also apply to BX, EMT, and conduit installations. Lighting circuits do not contain a fixture.

Appliance circuits:
The following items are generally included per unit for appliance circuits:

20' of cable or raceway (the size depends on the appliance; for example, an exhaust fan requires only #14-2 cable, while a range requires #6-3 cable)
Two connectors—one at the panel, one at the appliance
Four staples of conduit clip

Note: For range and dryer circuits, a surface-mounted receptacle is included.

Residential intercom systems:

The following items are generally included per unit for residential intercom systems:

    Master control unit
    Seven remote speakers
    Seven mounting rings
    300' #18-4 nonmetallic sheathed cable
    One low-voltage transformer

Labor Units:

Service:

Labor-hours for residential service generally include the following procedures:

    Ordering
    Measuring and marking
    Installing service
    Tying in branch wiring to circuit breakers
    Wire identification and marking panel schedule

Branch circuits:

Labor-hours for each branch outlet or switch generally include:

    Ordering, receiving and storing
    Marking box locations
    Mounting boxes
    Drilling wood studs
    Pulling cable or installing raceway
    Making up the gang box
    Installing the device (switch, receptacle)
    Installing the finish cover for the device
    Testing for power

Appliance circuits:

Measuring and marking

    Drilling wood studs
    Running cable or conduit
    Connecting the appliance

Additional procedures to be listed and extended for appliance circuits include:

    Thermostat or controls
    Home run conduit or wiring (over 20')

Residential intercom systems:

    Measuring and marking
    Mounting retaining rings
    Drilling wood studs
    Running low-voltage wire
    Tie-in of speakers and low-voltage transformer
    110V feed to transformer

Takeoff Procedure: Set up the work sheet and define the units by type and print graphic.

For example: 115V Receptacle
               S.P. Switch

Count all units of one type before proceeding to the next. Mark all components with a colored pencil. As mentioned in the appliance section, home runs should be measured back to the panel. Transfer all quantities to a cost analysis sheet and extend.

The fixtures should be counted last. Manufacturers' prices should be used, since fixtures are the single most expensive component and their cost has a significant impact on the estimate. Because of this effect, many contractors issue a fixture allowance for each house or customer, with the electrical contractor responsible for installation.

Check the size and type of the service to be used. Transfer the lighting and service quantities to a cost analysis sheet and extend.

Note: If using the mini-system approach, the subcomponents of each system can be identified and listed separately, then extended against the unit count. This gives the estimator a quantity count of all subcomponents that need to be purchased.

Power Transmission and Distribution

Power transmission and distribution involves the construction of line poles and fixtures; line steel towers and fixtures; overhead line conductors and devices; transmission line right of way; and substation equipment. The purpose of this process is to provide electrical energy for residential, commercial, and industrial loads. Among the factors that influence the cost and performance of power transmission and distribution are: environmental considerations, codes and jurisdiction requirements, established operating practices, and material availability. This chapter provides a general guide to procedures for using Figure 21.1, Average Transmission Line Material Requirements, and for creating budget cost estimates.

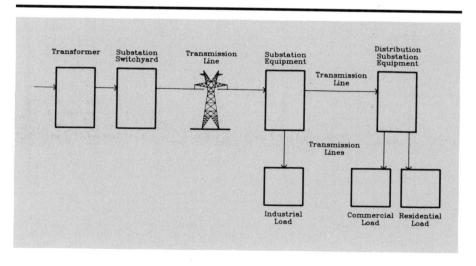

Getting Started

Refer again to Figure 21.1. The terrain has been categorized as flat, rolling, or mountainous. The operating voltages are 69 kV, 161 kV, or 500 kV. Wood and steel are popular choices for use in utility poles or structures. Concrete poles are a good alternative if manufacturers are close to the erection site, with enough stock in sizes and configurations to meet the specifications.

Using Figure 21.1, start the budget estimate using flat terrain, 69 kV, wood pole, and 397,500 circular mil, ACSR (aluminum-conductor steel-reinforced)

R169-115 Average Transmission Line Material Requirements (Per Mile)

Conductor: 397,500 – Cir. Mil., 26/7 – ACSR

Item	Unit	Flat 69KV Wood	Flat 161KV Wood	Flat 161KV Steel	Flat 500KV Steel	Rolling 69KV Wood	Rolling 161KV Wood	Rolling 161KV Steel	Rolling 500KV Steel	Mountain 69KV Wood	Mountain 161KV Wood	Mountain 161KV Steel	Mountain 500KV Steel
Structures	Ea.	12^1				9^2				7^2			
Poles	Ea.	12				18				14			
Crossarms	Ea.	24^3				9^4				7^4			
Conductor	Ft.	15,990				15,990				15,990			
Insulators[5]	Ea.	180				135				105			
Ground Wire	Ft.	5,330				10,660				10,660			

Conductor: 636,000 – Cir. Mil., 26/7 – ACSR

Item	Unit	Flat 69KV Wood	Flat 161KV Wood	Flat 161KV Steel	Flat 500KV Steel	Rolling 69KV Wood	Rolling 161KV Wood	Rolling 161KV Steel	Rolling 500KV Steel	Mountain 69KV Wood	Mountain 161KV Wood	Mountain 161KV Steel	Mountain 500KV Steel
Structures	Ea.	13^1	11^6			10^2	9^2	6^9		8^2	8^2	6^9	
Excavation	C.Y.	–	–			–	–	120		–	–	120	
Concrete	C.Y.	–	–			–	–	10		–	–	10	
Steel Towers	Tons	–	–			–	–	32		–	–	32	
Poles	Ea.	13	11			20	18	–		16	16	–	
Crossarms	Ea.	26^3	33^7			10^4	9^8	–		8^4	8^8	–	
Conductor	Ft.	15,990	15,990			15,990	15,990	15,990		15,990	15,990	15,990	
Insulators[5]	Ea.	195	165			150	297	297		120	264	297	
Ground Wire	Ft.	5330	5330			10,660	10,660	10,660		10,660	10,660	10,660	

Conductor: 954,000 – Cir. Mil., 45/7 – ACSR

Item	Unit	Flat 69KV Wood	Flat 161KV Wood	Flat 161KV Steel	Flat 500KV Steel	Rolling 69KV Wood	Rolling 161KV Wood	Rolling 161KV Steel	Rolling 500KV Steel	Mountain 69KV Wood	Mountain 161KV Wood	Mountain 161KV Steel	Mountain 500KV Steel
Structures	Ea.	14^1	12^6		4^{11}	10^2	9^2	6^9	4^{11}	8^2	8^2	6^9	4^{13}
Excavation	C.Y.	–	–		200	–	–	125	214	–	–	125	233
Concrete	C.Y.	–	–		20	–	–	10	21	–	–	10	21
Steel Towers	Tons	–	–		57	–	–	33	57	–	–	33	63
Poles	Ea.	14	12		–	20	18	–	–	16	16	–	–
Crossarms	Ea.	28^{10}	36^7		–	10^4	9^8	–	–	8^4	8^8	–	–
Conductor	Ft.	15,990	15,990		$47,970^{12}$	15,990	15,990	15,990	$47,970^{12}$	15,990	15,990	15,990	$47,970^{12}$
Insulators[5]	Ea.	210	180		288	150	297	297	288	120	264	297	576
Ground Wire	Ft.	5330	5330		10,660	10,660	10,660	10,660	10,660	10,660	10,660	10,660	10,660

Conductor: 1,351,500 – Cir. Mil., 45/7 – ACSR

Item	Unit	Flat (centered)	Rolling (centered)
Structures	Ea.	8^{14}	8^{14}
Excavation	C.Y.	220	220
Concrete	C.Y.	28	28
Steel Towers	Ton	46	46
Conductor	Ft.	$31,680^{15}$	$31,680^{15}$
Insulators	Ea.	528	528
Ground Wire	Ft.	10,660	10,660

1. Single pole two-arm suspension type construction
2. Two-pole wood H-frame construction
3. 4¾" x 5¾" x 8' and 4¾" x 5¾" x 10' wood crossarm
4. 6" x 8" x 26'-0" wood crossarm
5. 5¾" x 10" disc insulator
6. Single pole construction with 3 fiberglass crossarms (5 fog- type insulators per phase)
7. 7'-0" fiberglass crossarms
8. 6" x 10" x 35'-0" wood crossarm
9. Laced steel tower, single circuit construction
10. 5" x 7" x 8' and 5" x 7" x 10' wood crossarm
11. Laced steel tower, single circuit 500-KV construction
12. Bundled conductor (3 sub-conductors per phase)
13. Laced steel tower, single circuit restrained phases (500-KV)
14. Laced steel tower, double circuit construction
15. Both sides of double circuit strung

Note: To allow for sagging, a mile (5280 Ft.) of transmission line uses 5330 Ft. of conductor per wire (called a wire mile).

Figure 21.1

conductor. For each mile, you will need 12 wood poles, 24 crossarms, 15,990 L.F. (3 wire miles) of conductor wire, 180 insulators, and 5,330 L.F. (1 wire mile) of ground wire. Transfer the quantities and use *Means Electrical Cost Data*, Division 169, for pricing and extensions.

Budget Estimates

For budget estimating purposes, we will use average transmission line material requirements (per mile) as a base, and the calculations as follows:

Digging holes in earth (12 EA. @ $199)	$ 2,388
Wood poles, material handling and spotting (12 EA. @ $269)	3,228
Erecting wood poles (12 EA. @ $1,600)	19,200
Crossarms, material handling and spotting (24 EA. @ $120)	2,880
Installing crossarms (24 EA. @ $740)	17,760
Conductors, primary, material handling and spotting (3 W. mile @ $510)	1,530
Conductors, 210 to 636 MCM (3 W. mile @ $8,150)	24,450
Overhead ground wire, material handling and spotting (1 W. mile @ $310)	310
Installing ground wire (1 W. mile @ $5,275)	5,275
Insulators and hardware, material handling and spotting (180 EA. @ $3.63)	653
Installing disk insulators (180 EA. @ $49.50)	8,910
	$86,584

Next, add sagging cost, disposal of surplus material, and contingency factors for unforeseen costs, for which the budget cost per mile will be approximately $90,000.

Steel Towers

For steel tower structures, the same procedures can be used, selecting Division 169-120, Line Towers and Fixtures, to arrive at an estimate. Another option is to employ a steel fabrication company that specializes in transmission poles, towers, substation and switchyard structures. Such companies can provide you with complete engineering and estimating services, and furnish accurate drawings for field construction purposes. The advantage of this approach is that it will save you a great deal of energy and will help to ensure the completion of the project on time and on budget.

Right of Way

The contractor clears the right of way to construct power transmission and distribution lines. All trees, brush, stumps, and other obstacles must be cleared before transmission lines can be installed. Restoration and seeding the right of way is done after installation. All units of measure are based on the acre; for estimating in metric units the square kilometer or hectare (10 000 m^2) is used.

Substation Equipment

The functions of substation equipment are high-voltage switching, control, interrupting, and protection of the transmission system. The major components of substation equipment are main conversion equipment; power circuit breakers; disconnect switches; instrument transformers; protective equipment; station service equipment and accessories; conduits; wires; manholes; and concrete foundation. The takeoff procedure and units for measure are similar to that discussed in Chapter 15 and Chapter 19, except that the units of measure are as follows: for power transformers, MVA (Million Volt Amperes); for station capacitors, MVAR (Million Volt

217

Amperes Reactance); and for control batteries, KAH (Thousand Amperes Hours), which are not counted as each (EA.).

Summary

The project size, scope of power transmission, and distribution will have a significant impact on cost. Besides the first construction costs, the operation and maintenance of the entire transmission system also affect the overall cost. The intent of Division 169 in *Means Electrical Cost Data* is to provide a benchmark cost so that owners, engineers, and electrical contractors will have a comfortable number with which to start a project. To finalize the project, it is sound practice to obtain a vendor's quote to meet all the requirements.

Chapter 22

Field
Fabrication

Field fabrication involves the construction of stands or supports for electrical equipment, conduits, or cable trays. Field fabrication is performed when there is no stock item available to conform to existing field conditions. This chapter describes both field fabrication and the appropriate estimating procedure for this aspect of electrical work.

In many instances, stands and supports for electrical equipment, conduits, or cable trays are not stock items. They must be shop or field fabricated to conform to existing field conditions.

Steel supports are fabricated of angles designated "L," channels "C," wide flange beams "W," American Standard beams "S," plates, rods, or bars. Steel members are usually priced per pound, so it is necessary to convert each component into weight before pricing. Beams, both "W" and "S," and channels "C" are designated by weight. "W 8 × 31" designates a nominal 8″ deep wide flange beam 31 pounds per foot; "S 5 × 14.75" refers to a 5″ deep American Standard beam (formerly called an "I beam") 14.75 pounds per foot; and "C 7 × 9.8" indicates a 7″ deep channel section 9.8 pounds per foot. (For any given size, the weight per foot is a function of the member's thickness and, therefore, is also indicative of its load capability.)

Angles are rolled with equal and unequal legs in various thicknesses and are designated "L 3 × 3 × 1/4" or "5 × 3 × 7/16."

The weight of angles, bars, rods, or plates is not usually shown on drawings. To convert linear footage to weight requires a handbook that lists the various members by size and weight. If a handbook is not readily available, one linear foot of 1″ × 1″ steel or 12 cubic inches of steel weighs 3.4 pounds. Therefore, one foot of a 4″ × 4″ × 1/4″ L weighs approximately 8″ × 1/4″ = 2 cu. in./ft. × 3.4 lbs. = 6.8 lbs./ft. The actual weight from a handbook lists a 4″ × 4″ × 1/4″ L as 6.6 pounds per foot, which includes the deductions for the radius at the toe of the legs. A plate 12″ × 1″ × 12″ would weigh 12 × 3.4 pounds = 40.8 pounds.

Large quantities of steel may be purchased from the mill cut to specified lengths; smaller quantities can be obtained from a warehouse at a higher price and in standard available lengths. If small quantities of shapes are to be purchased from a warehouse, allowance for waste must be included in the estimate.

The following example demonstrates the estimating process for a field-fabricated transformer stand:

Top:	2 @ 4' + 2 @ 2'	= 12.00 L.F.
Legs:	4 @ 3'-11-3/4″	= 15.92 L.F.
		27.92 L.F.

Angle is available from a warehouse in 5' increments. Buy 1 @ 20'-0″ and 1 @ 15'-0″.

Material: 35 L.F. × 6.6 lb./ft. =	
231 lb. @ $.72 =	$166.32
Fabricate: Cut to length 12 each × 1/4 hr. =	
3 hrs. @ $27.15 =	81.45
Weld: 4.5'/4 L.F./hr. = 1.125 hrs. @ $27.15 =	30.54
Torch Gas and Air: 3 hrs. @ $8.85 =	26.55
Welder (machine) 1.125 hrs. @ $6.60 =	7.43
Total:	$312.29

The estimate does not include overhead and profit. Painting is assumed to be performed by the painting contractor.

Estimates for most field-fabricated support structures may be broken down and priced utilizing cost manuals, such as *Means Building Construction Cost Data*.

Part 3

Sample Estimate

Chapter 23

How to Use Means Electrical Cost Data

Parts I and II of this book are directed to the principles of estimating—from an overview of the entire process to a detailed discussion of techniques for measuring and pricing individual components. Part III, the Sample Estimate, demonstrates these principles and techniques in practice. The prices used throughout the sample estimate are from *Means Electrical Cost Data*. This chapter describes the components and uses of this annual cost source, along with the methods by which these costs are obtained and organized.

Format and Data

Users of *Means Electrical Cost Data* are chiefly interested in obtaining quick, reasonable, average prices for electrical construction estimates. This is the primary purpose of the annual book—to eliminate guesswork when pricing individual items of an installation. Many people use the cost data—whether for bid verification, quotations, or budgets—without being fully aware of how the prices are obtained and derived. Without this understanding, the reader cannot use the cost data resource to fullest advantage. In addition to the basic cost data, the book also contains a wealth of information to aid the estimator, contractor, designer, and owner to better plan and manage electrical construction projects. For example, productivity data is provided to assist with scheduling; national labor rates are analyzed; and tables and charts for location and time adjustments are included to help the estimator tailor the nationally averaged prices to a specific project. The costs in *Means Electrical Cost Data* include over ten thousand unit price line items as well as thousands of electrical systems, or assembly price line items. This information can also provide an invaluable checklist to the construction professional to assure that all required items are included in a project.

The major portion of *Means Electrical Cost Data* is the Unit Price section. This data is organized according to the CSI MasterFormat (see the list of divisions on the following page). This format was developed by representatives of many parties concerned with the building construction industry. It has been accepted by the American Institute of Architects (AIA), the Associated General Contractors of America, Inc. (AGC), and the Construction Specifications Institute, Inc. (CSI). In *Means Electrical Cost Data*, relevant parts of other divisions are included along with Division 16—Electrical. Appropriate items from Divisions 1, 2, 3, 5, 6, 7, 10, 11, 13, and 15 appear prior to the Division 16 entries.

MasterFormat Divisions:

Division 1 — General Requirements
Division 2 — Site Work
Division 3 — Concrete
Division 4 — Masonry
Division 5 — Metals
Division 6 — Wood & Plastics
Division 7 — Thermal & Moisture Protection
Division 8 — Doors and Windows
Division 9 — Finishes
Division 10 — Specialties
Division 11 — Equipment
Division 12 — Furnishings
Division 13 — Special Construction
Division 14 — Conveying Systems
Division 15 — Mechanical
Division 16 — Electrical

In addition to the 16 CSI divisions of the Unit Price section, Division 17, Square Foot and Cubic Foot Costs, presents consolidated data from over 10,200 actual reported construction projects and provides information based on total project costs as well as costs for some major segments.

The Assemblies section contains thousands of costs for electrical and appropriate mechanical systems. Components of the systems are fully detailed and accompanied by illustrations.

The Reference section contains technical tables and reference information. It also provides estimating procedures for some types of work and explanations of cost development that support and supplement the unit price and systems cost data. Also included in the Reference section are the City Cost Indexes, representing the compilation of construction data for 209 major U.S. and Canadian cities. Cost adjustment factors are given for each city, by trade, relative to the national average.

The prices presented in *Means Electrical Cost Data* are national averages. Material and equipment costs are developed through continuous contact with manufacturers, dealers, distributors, and contractors throughout the United States. Means' staff of engineers is constantly updating prices and keeping abreast of changes and fluctuations within the industry. Labor wage rates are the national average of each trade as determined from union agreements from 30 major U.S. cities.

Following is a list of factors and assumptions on which the costs presented in *Means Electrical Cost Data* have been based:

Quality — The costs are based on methods, materials, and workmanship in accordance with U.S. Government standards and represent good, sound construction practice.

Overtime — The costs as presented include no allowance for overtime. If overtime or premium time is anticipated, labor costs must be adjusted accordingly.

Productivity — The unit labor-hour figures are based on an eight-hour workday, during daylight hours. The chart in Figure 11.7 shows that as the number of hours worked per day (over eight) increases, and as the days per week (over five) increase, production efficiency decreases. (See Chapter 11: Cost Control and Analysis.)

Size of Project — Costs in *Means Electrical Cost Data* are based on commercial and industrial buildings that cost $500,000 and up. This equates to an electrical construction package of about $45,000 to $50,000 and up. Large residential projects (e.g., apartment or condominium complexes) are also included.

Local Factors — Specific local conditions are not included in national averages. Weather conditions, season of the year, local union restrictions, and unusual building code requirements can all have a significant impact on construction costs. The availability of a skilled labor force, sufficient materials, and adequate energy and utilities are assumed. The lack of any of these will affect the project's costs. These factors vary in importance and are not dependent solely on location. They must be reviewed for each project in every area.

In presenting prices in *Means Electrical Cost Data,* certain rounding rules are employed to make the numbers easier to use without significantly affecting accuracy. The rules are used consistently and are as follows:

From	To	Rounded to nearest
$ 0.01	$ 5.00	0.01
5.01	20.00	0.05
20.01	100.00	.50
100.01	300.00	1.00
300.01	1,000.00	5.00
1,000.01	10,000.00	25.00
10,000.01	50,000.00	100.00
50,000.01	up	500.00

Unit Price Section

The Unit Price section of *Means Electrical Cost Data* contains a great deal of information in addition to the unit cost for each construction component. Figure 23.1 is a typical page, showing costs for transformers. Note that prices are included for several types of transformers, each in a wide range of capacity ratings. In addition, suggested crews of workers are indicated. These crews are the basis of the installed costs and man-hour units. The information and cost data is broken down and itemized in this way to provide for the most detailed pricing possible. Both the unit price and the systems sections include detailed illustrations for rapid location of components.

Within each individual line item, there is a description of the construction component, information regarding the typical crews as anticipated to perform the work, and productivity shown in man-hours (labor units). Costs are presented both as "bare," or unburdened, and with markups for overhead and profit. Figure 23.2 is a graphic representation of how to read a Unit Price page as presented in *Means Electrical Cost Data.*

Line Numbers

Every construction item in the Means unit price cost data books has a unique line number. This line number acts as an address so that each item can be quickly located and/or referenced. The numbering system is based on the CSI classification by division. In Figure 23.2, note the bold number in reverse type, "164". This number represents the major subdivision — in this case "Transformers & Bus Duct" — of the major CSI Division 16 — Electrical. All 16 CSI divisions are organized in this manner. Within each subdivision, the data are broken down into major classifications. These major classifications are organized alphabetically and are designated by bold type for both numbers and descriptions. Each item, or line, is further defined by an individual number. As shown in Figure 23.2, the full line

164 | Transformers and Bus Ducts

164 100 | Transformers

			CREW	DAILY OUTPUT	MAN-HOURS	UNIT	1995 BARE COSTS				TOTAL INCL O&P	
							MAT.	LABOR	EQUIP.	TOTAL		
140	0800	Operating room power & lighting, 8 circuit, 3 KVA	1 Elec	.58	13.793	Ea.	3,425	395		3,820	4,375	**140**
	1000	5 KVA		.54	14.815		3,475	420		3,895	4,450	
	1200	7.5 KVA		.52	15.385		3,950	440		4,390	5,000	
	1400	10 KVA		.44	18.182		4,075	520		4,595	5,250	
	1600	X-ray systems, 15 KVA, 90 amp		.44	18.182		8,800	520		9,320	10,500	
	1800	25 KVA, 125 amp		.36	22.222		9,050	635		9,685	10,900	
150	0010	**ISOLATING TRANSFORMER** R164-100										**150**
	0100	Single phase, 120/240 volt primary, 120/240 volt secondary										
	0200	0.50 KVA	1 Elec	4	2	Ea.	154	57		211	255	
	0400	1 KVA		2	4		217	114		331	410	
	0600	2 KVA		1.60	5		350	143		493	600	
	0800	3 KVA		1.40	5.714		380	163		543	665	
	1000	5 KVA		1.20	6.667		485	190		675	820	
	1200	7.5 KVA		1.10	7.273		645	207		852	1,025	
	1400	10 KVA		.80	10		800	285		1,085	1,300	
	1600	15 KVA		.60	13.333		1,200	380		1,580	1,900	
	1800	25 KVA		.50	16		1,425	455		1,880	2,250	
	1810	37.5 KVA	2 Elec	.80	20		1,550	570		2,120	2,550	
	1820	75 KVA	"	.65	24.615		2,425	700		3,125	3,725	
	1830	3 phase, 120/240 primary, 120/208V secondary, 112.5 KVA	R-3	.90	22.222		3,400	625	119	4,144	4,825	
	1840	150 KVA		.85	23.529		4,375	665	126	5,166	5,975	
	1850	225 KVA		.65	30.769		5,850	870	165	6,885	7,925	
	1860	300 KVA		.55	36.364		7,675	1,025	195	8,895	10,200	
	1870	500 KVA		.45	44.444		11,700	1,250	238	13,188	15,100	
	1880	750 KVA		.35	57.143		18,100	1,625	305	20,030	22,700	
160	0010	**OIL FILLED TRANSFORMER** Pad mounted, Primary delta or Y, R164-100										**160**
	0050	5 KV or 15 KV, with taps, 277/480 V secondary, 3 phase										
	0100	150 KVA	R-3	.65	30.769	Ea.	9,200	870	165	10,235	11,600	
	0110	225 KVA		.55	36.364		9,975	1,025	195	11,195	12,800	
	0200	300 KVA		.45	44.444		11,100	1,250	238	12,588	14,400	
	0300	500 KVA		.40	50		13,300	1,400	268	14,968	17,000	
	0400	750 KVA		.38	52.632		16,600	1,475	282	18,357	20,900	
	0500	1000 KVA		.26	76.923		19,700	2,175	410	22,285	25,400	
	0600	1500 KVA		.23	86.957		23,300	2,450	465	26,215	29,800	
	0700	2000 KVA		.20	100		29,400	2,825	535	32,760	37,200	
	0710	2500 KVA		.19	105		32,700	2,975	565	36,240	41,100	
	0720	3000 KVA		.17	117		34,300	3,325	630	38,255	43,400	
	0800	3750 KVA		.16	125		39,700	3,525	670	43,895	49,800	
170	0010	**TRANSFORMER, SILICON FILLED** Pad mounted										**170**
	0020	5 KV or 15 KV primary, 277/480 volt secondary, 3 phase										
	0050	225 KVA	R-3	.55	36.364	Ea.	17,200	1,025	195	18,420	20,700	
	0100	300 KVA		.45	44.444		18,300	1,250	238	19,788	22,300	
	0200	500 KVA		.40	50		21,500	1,400	268	23,168	26,100	
	0250	750 KVA		.38	52.632		26,300	1,475	282	28,057	31,500	
	0300	1000 KVA		.26	76.923		31,100	2,175	410	33,685	37,900	
	0350	1500 KVA		.23	86.957		39,900	2,450	465	42,815	48,100	
	0400	2000 KVA		.20	100		48,700	2,825	535	52,060	58,500	
	0450	2500 KVA		.19	105		56,000	2,975	565	59,540	66,500	
190	0010	**HANDLING** Add to normal labor cost in restricted areas										**190**
	5000	Transformers										
	5150	15 KVA, approximately 200 pounds	2 Elec	2.70	5.926	Ea.		169		169	255	
	5160	25 KVA, approximately 300 pounds		2.50	6.400			182		182	275	
	5170	37.5 KVA, approximately 400 pounds		2.30	6.957			198		198	299	
	5180	50 KVA, approximately 500 pounds		2	8			228		228	345	

Figure 23.1

IMPORTANT

PRICES ARE LISTED TWO WAYS, ONE WITH BARE COSTS,
THE OTHER INCLUDES THE SUBCONTRACTOR'S OVERHEAD & PROFIT

GENERAL RECOMMENDATION

When using total costs including Subcontractor's O & P, add 10%
[see "How to Use the Book: The Details"]

EXAMPLES OF HOW FIGURES ARE DEVELOPED
on Figure 23.1 under OIL FILLED TRANSFORMER, 150 KVA is shown as follows:

164 | Transformers and Bus Ducts

164 100 | Transformers

			CREW	DAILY OUTPUT	MAN-HOURS	UNIT	MAT.	LABOR	EQUIP.	TOTAL	TOTAL INCL O&P	
160	0010	OIL FILLED TRANSFORMER Pad mounted, Primary delta or Y,	R164 -100									160
	0050	5 KV or 15 KV, with taps, 277/480 V secondary, 3 phase										
	0100	150 KVA	R-3	.65	30.769	Ea.	9,200	870	165	10,235	11,600	
	0110	225 KVA		.55	36.364		9,975	1,025	195	11,195	12,800	

1995 BARE COSTS

General Meaning:
Crew R-3 will install A 150 KVA transformer using 30.8 Man Hours

Reference Number Information

Each

Crew R-3 is shown on page 388 as follows:

Crew R-3	Bare Costs Hr.	Daily	Incl. Subs O & P Hr.	Daily	Cost Per Man-Hour Bare Costs	Incl. O&P
1 Electrician Foreman	$29.00	$232.00	$43.70	$349.60	$28.23	$42.70
1 Electrician	28.50	228.00	42.95	343.60		
.5 Equip. Oper. (crane)	26.15	104.60	40.20	160.80		
.5 S.P. Crane, 5 Ton		107.10		117.80	5.36	5.89
20 M.H., Daily Totals		$671.70		$971.80	$33.59	$48.59

This figure represents the total cost per man-hour for labor.

This figure represents the total cost per man-hour for equipment.

Line number determination:

Major CSI subdivision = 164
(3 digits)

Major classification division = 160
(3 digits)

Item line number = 0100
(4 digits)

Complete line number = 164-160-0100

These figures are printed above:

BARE COSTS are developed as follows for line no. **164-160-0100**
MAT. is **BARE MATERIAL COST ($9,200)**
LABOR for Crew R-3 = Man-hour Cost ($28.23) × Man-hours (30.8) = $870
EQUIP. for Crew R-3 = Equip. Cost ($5.36) × Man-hours (30.8) = $165
TOTAL = **MAT. COST ($9,200)** + **LABOR COST ($870)** + **EQUIP. COST ($165)** = $10,235

(**Note:** Equipment and Labor costs are taken from the Crew Tables. See example at the top of this page.)

Only the total of these figures is printed above.

TOTAL COSTS INCLUDING O&P are developed as follows:
MAT. is **BARE MATERIAL COST** + 10% = $10,120
LABOR for Crew R-3 = Man-hour Cost ($42.70) × Man-hours (30.8) = $1,315
EQUIP. for Crew R-3 = Equip. Hour Cost ($5.89) × Man-hours (30.8) = $181
TOTAL = **MAT. COST** $10,120 + **LABOR COST** $1,315 + **EQUIP. COST** $181 = $11,616
(Rounded to $11,600)

Figure 23.2

number for each item consists of: a major CSI subdivision number, a major classification number, and an item line number. Each full line number describes a unique construction element. For example, in Figure 23.1, the line number for an oil-filled transformer, pad-mounted, primary delta or Y, 150 KVA is 164-160-0100.

Line Description

Each line has a text description of the item for which costs are listed. The description may be self-contained and all inclusive, as is line 164-150-0100 in Figure 23.1. If indented, the complete description for a line is dependent on the information provided above. All indented items are delineations (by size, color, material, etc.) or breakdowns of previously described items. It may be necessary to refer back one, two, three, or more successively indented headings to get the full description of a line item. An index is provided in the back of *Means Electrical Cost Data* to aid in locating particular items.

Crew

For each construction element (each line item), a minimum typical crew is designated as appropriate to perform the work. The crew may include one or more trades, foremen, craftsmen and helpers, and any equipment required for proper installation of the described item. If an individual trade installs the item using only hand tools, the smallest efficient number of tradespeople will be indicated ("1 Elec," "2 Elec," etc.). Most electrical items are based on a one-electrician crew. Abbreviations for trades are shown in Figure 23.3. If more than one trade is required to install the item and/or if powered equipment is needed, a crew number will be designated (B-5, D-3, etc.). A complete listing of crews is presented in the Reference Section of *Means Electrical Cost Data* (see Figure 23.4). On these pages, each crew is broken down into the following components:

1. Number and type of workers designated.
2. Number, size, and type of any equipment required.
3. Hourly labor costs listed two ways: "bare"—base rate including fringe benefits; and billing rate—including installing contractor's overhead and profit. (See Figure 23.3 from the inside back cover of *Means Electrical Cost Data* for labor rate information.)
4. Daily equipment costs, based on the weekly equipment rental cost divided by 5, plus the hourly operating cost, times 8 hours. This cost is listed two ways: as a bare cost and with a 10% markup to cover handling and management costs.
5. Labor and equipment are broken down further into cost per man-hour for labor, and cost per man-hour for the equipment.
6. The total daily man-hours for the crew.
7. The total bare costs per day for the crew, including equipment.
8. The total daily cost of the crew used to calculate the installing contractor's overhead and profit.

The total man-hour cost of the required crew is used to calculate the unit installation cost for each item (for both bare costs and cost including overhead and profit).

The crew designation does not mean that this is the only crew that can perform the work. Crew size and content have been developed and chosen based on practical experience and feedback from contractors. These designations represent a labor and equipment make-up commonly found in the industry. The most appropriate crew for a given task is best

Installing Contractor's Overhead & Profit

Below are the **average** installing contractor's percentage mark-ups applied to base labor rates to arrive at typical billing rates.

Column A: Labor rates are based on union wages averaged for 30 major U.S. cities. Base rates including fringe benefits are listed hourly and daily. These figures are the sum of the wage rate and employer-paid fringe benefits such as vacation pay, employer-paid health and welfare costs, pension costs, plus appropriate training and industry advancement funds costs.

Column B: Workers' Compensation rates are the national average of state rates established for each trade.

Column C: Column C lists average fixed overhead figures for all trades. Included are Federal and State Unemployment costs set at 7.3%; Social Security Taxes (FICA) set at 7.65%; Builder's Risk Insurance costs set at 0.34%; and Public Liability costs set at 1.55%. All the percentages except those for Social Security Taxes vary from state to state as well as from company to company.

Columns D and E: Percentages in Columns D and E are based on the presumption that the installing contractor has annual billing of $500,000 and up. Overhead percentages may increase with smaller annual billing. The overhead percentages for any given contractor may vary greatly and depend on a number of factors, such as the contractor's annual volume, engineering and logistical support costs, and staff requirements. The figures for overhead and profit will also vary depending on the type of job, the job location, and the prevailing economic conditions. All factors should be examined very carefully for each job.

Column F: Column F lists the total of Columns B, C, D, and E.

Column G: Column G is Column A (hourly base labor rate) multiplied by the percentage in Column F (O&P percentage).

Column H: Column H is the total of Column A (hourly base labor rate) plus Column G (Total O&P).

Column I: Column I is Column H multiplied by eight hours.

		A		B	C	D	E	F	G	H	I
		Base Rate Incl. Fringes		Workers' Comp. Ins.	Average Fixed Overhead	Overhead	Profit	Total Overhead & Profit		Rate with O & P	
Abbr.	Trade	Hourly	Daily					%	Amount	Hourly	Daily
Skwk	Skilled Workers Average (35 trades)	$25.35	$202.80	19.8%	16.8%	13.0%	10.0%	59.6%	$15.10	$40.45	$323.60
	Helpers Average (5 trades)	18.85	150.80	21.2		11.0		59.0	11.10	29.95	239.60
	Foreman Average, Inside ($.50 over trade)	25.85	206.80	19.8		13.0		59.6	15.40	41.25	330.00
	Foreman Average, Outside ($2.00 over trade)	27.35	218.80	19.8		13.0		59.6	16.30	43.65	349.20
Clab	Common Building Laborers	19.40	155.20	21.7		11.0		59.5	11.55	30.95	247.60
Asbe	Asbestos Workers	28.00	224.00	19.0		16.0		61.8	17.30	45.30	362.40
Boil	Boilermakers	29.30	234.40	12.1		16.0		54.9	16.10	45.40	363.20
Bric	Bricklayers	25.25	202.00	19.3		11.0		57.1	14.40	39.65	317.20
Brhe	Bricklayer Helpers	19.55	156.40	19.3		11.0		57.1	11.15	30.70	245.60
Carp	Carpenters	24.60	196.80	21.7		11.0		59.5	14.65	39.25	314.00
Cefi	Cement Finishers	23.90	191.20	12.4		11.0		50.2	12.00	35.90	287.20
Elec	Electricians	28.50	228.00	7.9		16.0		50.7	14.45	42.95	343.60
Elev	Elevator Constructors	29.05	232.40	9.2		16.0		52.0	15.10	44.15	353.20
Eqhv	Equipment Operators, Crane or Shovel	26.15	209.20	13.0		14.0		53.8	14.05	40.20	321.60
Eqmd	Equipment Operators, Medium Equipment	25.15	201.20	13.0		14.0		53.8	13.55	38.70	309.60
Eqlt	Equipment Operators, Light Equipment	24.15	193.20	13.0		14.0		53.8	13.00	37.15	297.20
Eqol	Equipment Operators, Oilers	21.40	171.20	13.0		14.0		53.8	11.50	32.90	263.20
Eqmm	Equipment Operators, Master Mechanics	26.85	214.80	13.0		14.0		53.8	14.45	41.30	330.40
Glaz	Glaziers	24.50	196.00	16.0		11.0		53.8	13.20	37.70	301.60
Lath	Lathers	24.30	194.40	13.9		11.0		51.7	12.55	36.85	294.80
Marb	Marble Setters	25.10	200.80	19.3		11.0		57.1	14.35	39.45	315.60
Mill	Millwrights	25.95	207.60	13.2		11.0		51.0	13.25	39.20	313.60
Mstz	Mosaic and Terrazzo Workers	24.55	196.40	11.0		11.0		48.8	12.00	36.55	292.40
Pord	Painters, Ordinary	22.60	180.80	16.4		11.0		54.2	12.25	34.85	278.80
Psst	Painters, Structural Steel	23.50	188.00	64.2		11.0		102.0	23.95	47.45	379.60
Pape	Paper Hangers	22.85	182.80	16.4		11.0		54.2	12.40	35.25	282.00
Pile	Pile Drivers	24.70	197.60	33.4		16.0		76.2	18.80	43.50	348.00
Plas	Plasterers	23.70	189.60	17.4		11.0		55.2	13.10	36.80	294.40
Plah	Plasterer Helpers	19.80	158.40	17.4		11.0		55.2	10.95	30.75	246.00
Plum	Plumbers	29.30	234.40	10.1		16.0		52.9	15.50	44.80	358.40
Rodm	Rodmen (Reinforcing)	27.10	216.80	36.1		14.0		76.9	20.85	47.95	383.60
Rofc	Roofers, Composition	22.05	176.40	36.4		11.0		74.2	16.35	38.40	307.20
Rots	Roofers, Tile and Slate	22.05	176.40	36.4		11.0		74.2	16.35	38.40	307.20
Rohe	Roofer Helpers (Composition)	15.60	124.80	36.4		11.0		74.2	11.60	27.20	217.60
Shee	Sheet Metal Workers	28.10	224.80	13.7		16.0		56.5	15.90	44.00	352.00
Spri	Sprinkler Installers	30.85	246.80	10.4		16.0		53.2	16.40	47.25	378.00
Stpi	Steamfitters or Pipefitters	29.25	234.00	10.1		16.0		52.9	15.45	44.70	357.60
Ston	Stone Masons	25.35	202.80	19.3		11.0		57.1	14.45	39.80	318.40
Sswk	Structural Steel Workers	27.15	217.20	44.4		14.0		85.2	23.15	50.30	402.40
Tilf	Tile Layers	24.45	195.60	11.0		11.0		48.8	11.95	36.40	291.20
Tilh	Tile Layer Helpers	19.95	159.60	11.0		11.0		48.8	9.75	29.70	237.60
Trlt	Truck Drivers, Light	20.00	160.00	16.9		11.0		54.7	10.95	30.95	247.60
Trhv	Truck Drivers, Heavy	20.35	162.80	16.9		11.0		54.7	11.15	31.50	252.00
Sswl	Welders, Structural Steel	27.15	217.20	44.4		14.0		85.2	23.15	50.30	402.40
Wrck	*Wrecking	19.40	155.20	44.4 ▼		11.0 ▼		82.2	15.95	35.35	282.80

*Not included in Averages.

Figure 23.3

Crews

Crew No.	Bare Costs		Incl. Subs O & P		Cost Per Man-Hour	
	Hr.	Daily	Hr.	Daily	Bare Costs	Incl. O&P
Crew R-3						
1 Electrician Foreman	$29.00	$232.00	$43.70	$349.60	$28.23	$42.70
1 Electrician	28.50	228.00	42.95	343.60		
.5 Equip. Oper. (crane)	26.15	104.60	40.20	160.80		
.5 S.P. Crane, 5 Ton		107.10		117.80	5.36	5.89
20 M.H., Daily Totals		$671.70		$971.80	$33.59	$48.59
Crew R-4	Hr.	Daily	Hr.	Daily	Bare Costs	Incl. O&P
1 Struc. Steel Foreman	$29.15	$233.20	$54.00	$432.00	$27.82	$49.57
3 Struc. Steel Workers	27.15	651.60	50.30	1207.20		
1 Electrician	28.50	228.00	42.95	343.60		
1 Gas Welding Machine		77.80		85.60	1.95	2.14
40 M.H., Daily Totals		$1190.60		$2068.40	$29.77	$51.71
Crew R-5	Hr.	Daily	Hr.	Daily	Bare Costs	Incl. O&P
1 Electrician Foreman	$29.00	$232.00	$43.70	$349.60	$25.04	$38.29
4 Electrician Lineman	28.50	912.00	42.95	1374.40		
2 Electrician Operators	28.50	456.00	42.95	687.20		
4 Electrician Groundmen	18.85	603.20	29.95	958.40		
1 Crew Truck		180.20		198.20		
1 Tool Van		327.20		359.90		
1 Pick-up Truck		120.60		132.65		
.2 Crane, 55 Ton		150.40		165.45		
.2 Crane, 12 Ton		83.76		92.15		
.2 Auger, Truck Mtd.		332.20		365.40		
1 Tractor w/Winch		282.40		310.65	16.78	18.46
88 M.H., Daily Totals		$3679.96		$4994.00	$41.82	$56.75
Crew R-6	Hr.	Daily	Hr.	Daily	Bare Costs	Incl. O&P
1 Electrician Foreman	$29.00	$232.00	$43.70	$349.60	$25.04	$38.29
4 Electrician Linemen	28.50	912.00	42.95	1374.40		
2 Electrician Operators	28.50	456.00	42.95	687.20		
4 Electrician Groundmen	18.85	603.20	29.95	958.40		
1 Crew Truck		180.20		198.20		
1 Tool Van		327.20		359.90		
1 Pick-up Truck		120.60		132.65		
.2 Crane, 55 Ton		150.40		165.45		
.2 Crane, 12 Ton		83.76		92.15		
.2 Auger, Truck Mtd.		332.20		365.40		
1 Tractor w/Winch		282.40		310.65		
3 Cable Trailers		418.20		460.00		
.5 Tensioning Rig		135.50		149.05		
.5 Cable Pulling Rig		809.00		889.90	32.27	35.49
88 M.H., Daily Totals		$5042.66		$6492.95	$57.31	$73.78
Crew R-7	Hr.	Daily	Hr.	Daily	Bare Costs	Incl. O&P
1 Electrician Foreman	$29.00	$232.00	$43.70	$349.60	$20.54	$32.24
5 Electrician Groundmen	18.85	754.00	29.95	1198.00		
1 Crew Truck		180.20		198.20	3.75	4.13
48 M.H., Daily Totals		$1166.20		$1745.80	$24.29	$36.37
Crew R-8	Hr.	Daily	Hr.	Daily	Bare Costs	Incl. O&P
1 Electrician Foreman	$29.00	$232.00	$43.70	$349.60	$25.37	$38.74
3 Electrician Linemen	28.50	684.00	42.95	1030.80		
2 Electrician Groundmen	18.85	301.60	29.95	479.20		
1 Pick-up Truck		120.60		132.65		
1 Crew Truck		180.20		198.20	6.27	6.89
48 M.H., Daily Totals		$1518.40		$2190.45	$31.64	$45.63

Crew No.	Bare Costs		Incl. Subs O & P		Cost Per Man-Hour	
	Hr.	Daily	Hr.	Daily	Bare Costs	Incl. O&P
Crew R-9						
1 Electrician Foreman	$29.00	$232.00	$43.70	$349.60	$23.74	$36.54
1 Electrician Lineman	28.50	228.00	42.95	343.60		
2 Electrician Operators	28.50	456.00	42.95	687.20		
4 Electrician Groundmen	18.85	603.20	29.95	958.40		
1 Pick-up Truck		120.60		132.65		
1 Crew Truck		180.20		198.20	4.70	5.17
64 M.H., Daily Totals		$1820.00		$2669.65	$28.44	$41.71
Crew R-10	Hr.	Daily	Hr.	Daily	Bare Costs	Incl. O&P
1 Electrician Foreman	$29.00	$232.00	$43.70	$349.60	$26.98	$40.91
4 Electrician Linemen	28.50	912.00	42.95	1374.40		
1 Electrician Groundman	18.85	150.80	29.95	239.60		
1 Crew Truck		180.20		198.20		
3 Tram Cars		492.00		541.20	14.00	15.40
48 M.H., Daily Totals		$1967.00		$2703.00	$40.98	$56.31
Crew R-11	Hr.	Daily	Hr.	Daily	Bare Costs	Incl. O&P
1 Electrician Foreman	$29.00	$232.00	$43.70	$349.60	$25.89	$39.49
4 Electricians	28.50	912.00	42.95	1374.40		
1 Helper	18.85	150.80	29.95	239.60		
1 Common Laborer	19.40	155.20	30.95	247.60		
1 Crew Truck		180.20		198.20		
1 Crane, 12 Ton		418.80		460.70	10.70	11.77
56 M.H., Daily Totals		$2049.00		$2870.10	$36.59	$51.26
Crew R-12	Hr.	Daily	Hr.	Daily	Bare Costs	Incl. O&P
1 Carpenter Foreman	$25.10	$200.80	$40.05	$320.40	$23.04	$37.26
4 Carpenters	24.60	787.20	39.25	1256.00		
4 Common Laborers	19.40	620.80	30.95	990.40		
1 Equip. Oper. (med.)	25.15	201.20	38.70	309.60		
1 Steel Worker	27.15	217.20	50.30	402.40		
1 Dozer, 200 H.P.		845.00		929.50		
1 Pick-up Truck		120.60		132.65	10.97	12.07
88 M.H., Daily Totals		$2992.80		$4340.95	$34.01	$49.33

Figure 23.4

determined based on particular project requirements. Unit costs may vary if actual crew sizes or content differ significantly.

Figure 23.5 is a page from Subdivision 016 of *Means Electrical Cost Data*. This type of page lists the equipment costs used in the presentation and calculation of the crew costs and unit price data. Rental costs are shown as daily, weekly, and monthly rates. The Hourly Operating Cost represents the cost of fuel, lubrication, and routine maintenance. Equipment costs used in the crews are calculated as follows:

Line Number	016-420-0400
Equipment	Diesel Engine, rotary screw, 250 C.F.M.
Rent per Week	$325.00
Hourly Operating Cost:	$5.45

$$\frac{\text{Weekly Rental}}{(5 \text{ days/week})} + (\text{Hourly Oper. Cost} \times 8 \text{ hrs./day}) = \text{Crew's Equipment Cost}$$

$$\frac{\$325}{5} + (\$5.45 \times 8) = \$108.60$$

Unit

The unit column (see Figures 23.1 and 23.2) defines the measurement parameter for which the costs have been calculated. It is this "unit of quantity" upon which Unit Price Estimating is based. The units as used represent standard estimating and quantity takeoff procedures. However, the estimator should always check to be sure that the units taken off match those priced. For example, the estimator may measure linear feet (L.F.), but the unit prices may be per each hundred linear feet (C.L.F.). A list of standard abbreviations is included in the Reference Section of *Means Electrical Cost Data*.

Bare Costs

The three columns listed under "Bare Costs"—"Material," "Installation," and "Total"—represent the actual cost of construction items to the contractor. In other words, bare costs are those which *do not* include the overhead and profit of the installing contractor (e.g., a subcontractor or a general contracting company using its own crews).

Material: Material costs are based on the national average contractor purchase price delivered to the job site. Delivered costs are assumed to be within a 20-mile radius of metropolitan areas. No sales tax is included in the material prices because of the variations from state to state. The prices are based on quantities that would normally be purchased for electrical installations of $45,000 to $50,000 and up. Prices for small quantities must be adjusted accordingly. If more current costs for materials are available for the appropriate location, it is recommended that adjustments be made to the unit costs to reflect any cost difference.

Installation: The unit cost for installation of an item is calculated by multiplying the total hourly cost rate of the designated crew by the number of man-hours required to install one unit of quantity. The resulting unit price for installation includes both labor and equipment costs (if any).

The labor rates used to determine the bare installation costs are shown for 35 standard skilled trades in the Labor Rates chart (Figure 23.3), under the column "Base Rate Including Fringes." This rate includes a worker's actual hourly wage plus employer-paid benefits (health insurance, vacation, pension, etc.). The labor rates used are *national average* union rates based on trade union agreements (as of January 1 of the current year) from

016 400 | Equipment Rental

			UNIT	HOURLY OPER. COST	RENT PER DAY	RENT PER WEEK	RENT PER MONTH	CREW EQUIPMENT COST	
408	0010	EARTHWORK EQUIPMENT RENTAL Without operators — R016 -410	Ea.	44.65	2,175	6,520	19,600	1,661	408
	0075	Auger, truck mounted, vertical drilling, to 25' depth							
	0100	Backhoe, diesel hydraulic, crawler mounted, 1/2 C.Y. cap.		10.75	405	1,215	3,650	329	
	0120	5/8 C.Y. capacity		15	450	1,350	4,050	390	
	0140	3/4 C.Y. capacity		16.50	525	1,570	4,700	446	
	0150	1 C.Y. capacity		21.30	625	1,875	5,625	545.40	
	0200	1-1/2 C.Y. capacity		25.30	835	2,505	7,525	703.40	
	0300	2 C.Y. capacity		42.50	1,050	3,120	9,350	964	
	0320	2-1/2 C.Y. capacity		57.60	2,100	6,305	18,900	1,722	
	0340	3-1/2 C.Y. capacity		76.20	2,600	7,765	23,300	2,163	
	0350	Gradall type, truck mounted, 3 ton @ 15' radius, 5/8 C.Y.		25.30	700	2,105	6,325	623.40	
	0370	1 C.Y. capacity		27.85	1,050	3,180	9,550	858.80	
	0400	Backhoe-loader, wheel type, 40 to 45 H.P., 5/8 C.Y. capacity		7	220	660	1,975	188	
	0450	45 H.P. to 60 H.P., 3/4 C.Y. capacity		8.20	233	700	2,100	205.60	
	0460	80 H.P., 1-1/4 C.Y. capacity		12.30	305	920	2,750	282.40	
	0470	112 H.P.,1-3/4 C.Y. loader, 1/2 C.Y. backhoe		14.75	335	1,000	3,000	318	
	0750	Bucket, clamshell, general purpose, 3/8 C.Y.		.75	53.50	160	480	38	
	0800	1/2 C.Y.		1	58.50	175	525	43	
	0850	3/4 C.Y.		1.05	71.50	215	645	51.40	
	0900	1 C.Y.		1.35	88.50	265	795	63.80	
	0950	1-1/2 C.Y.		1.60	115	345	1,025	81.80	
	1000	2 C.Y.		1.80	127	380	1,150	90.40	
	1200	Compactor, roller, 2 drum, 2000 lb., operator walking		1.75	117	350	1,050	84	
	1250	Rammer compactor, gas, 1000 lb. blow		.40	38.50	115	345	26.20	
	1300	Vibratory plate, gas, 13" plate, 1000 lb. blow		.50	30.50	92	276	22.40	
	1350	24" plate, 5000 lb. blow		1.75	55	165	495	47	
	3710	Screening plant 110 hp. w / 5' x 10' screen		15.45	415	1,240	3,725	371.60	
	3720	5' x 16' screen		16.50	480	1,445	4,325	421	
	4900	Trencher, chain, boom type, gas, operator walking, 12 H.P.		1.85	115	345	1,025	83.80	
	4910	Operator riding, 40 H.P.		6.10	240	720	2,150	192.80	
	5000	Wheel type, diesel, 4' deep, 12" wide		13.20	465	1,395	4,175	384.60	
	5100	Diesel, 6' deep, 20" wide		14.80	695	2,090	6,275	536.40	
	5150	Ladder type, diesel, 5' deep, 8" wide		8.95	325	980	2,950	267.60	
	5200	Diesel, 8' deep, 16" wide		16.90	565	1,700	5,100	475.20	
	5250	Truck, dump, tandem, 12 ton payload		17	330	995	2,975	335	
	5300	Three axle dump, 16 ton payload		19	430	1,295	3,875	411	
	5350	Dump trailer only, rear dump, 16-1/2 C.Y.		3.30	158	475	1,425	121.40	
	5400	20 C.Y.		3.30	160	480	1,450	122.40	
	5450	Flatbed, single axle, 1-1/2 ton rating		10.70	128	385	1,150	162.60	
	5500	3 ton rating		10.75	132	395	1,175	165	
	5550	Off highway rear dump, 25 ton capacity		18.85	775	2,320	6,950	614.80	
	5600	35 ton capacity		30.40	1,200	3,590	10,800	961.20	
420	0010	GENERAL EQUIPMENT RENTAL — R016 -410	Ea.	1.10	86.50	260	780	60.80	420
	0150	Aerial lift, scissor type, to 15' high, 1000 lb. cap., electric							
	0160	To 25' high, 2000 lb. capacity		1.65	133	400	1,200	93.20	
	0170	Telescoping boom to 40' high, 750 lb. capacity, gas		6.25	380	1,135	3,400	277	
	0180	2000 lb. capacity		8.05	480	1,445	4,325	353.40	
	0190	To 60' high, 750 lb. capacity		8.45	570	1,705	5,125	408.60	
	0200	Air compressor, portable, gas engine, 60 C.F.M.		5.10	51.50	155	465	71.80	
	0300	160 C.F.M.		6.80	68.50	205	615	95.40	
	0400	Diesel engine, rotary screw, 250 C.F.M.		5.45	108	325	975	108.60	
	0500	365 C.F.M.		9.35	190	570	1,700	188.80	
	0600	600 C.F.M.		16.20	238	715	2,150	272.60	
	0700	750 C.F.M.		17.65	243	730	2,200	287.20	
	0800	For silenced models, small sizes, add		3%	5%	5%	5%		
	0900	Large sizes, add		4%	7%	7%	7%		
	0920	Air tools and accessories							
	0930	Breaker, pavement, 60 lb.	Ea.	.10	24	72	216	15.20	

Figure 23.5

30 major cities in the United States. As new wage agreements are negotiated within a calendar year, labor costs should be adjusted. The equipment portion of installation costs is discussed earlier in this chapter.

Total Bare Costs: The "Total Bare Cost" column represents the arithmetic sum of the bare material and installation costs. This total is the average cost to the installing contractor for the particular item of construction, supplied and installed, or "in place." No overhead and/or profit are included.

Total Including Overhead and Profit

The price units in the "Total Including Overhead and Profit" column might also be called the "billing rate." These prices are, on the average, what the installing contractor would charge for the particular item of work.

The "Total Including Overhead and Profit" costs are determined by adding the following two calculations:

1. Bare materials—increased by 10% for profit. See Figure 23.2.
2. Bare installation costs—increased to include overhead and profit.

To increase the installation cost to include overhead and profit, labor and equipment costs are treated separately. Ten percent is added to the bare equipment cost for handling, management, etc. Labor costs are increased by percentages for overhead and profit, depending on the trade as shown in Figure 23.3. The resulting rates are listed in the right-hand columns of the same figure. Note that the percentage increase for overhead and profit for the average electrician is 50.7% of the base rate. The following items are included in the increase for overhead and profit, also shown in Figure 23.3:

Workers' Compensation and Employer's Liability: Workers' Compensation and Employer's Liability Insurance rates vary from state to state and are tied into the construction trade safety records in that particular state. Rates also vary by trade according to the hazard involved. (See Figures 23.6 and 23.7.) The proper authorities will most likely keep the contractor well informed of the rates and obligations.

State and Federal Unemployment Insurance: The employer's tax rate is adjusted by a merit-rating system according to the number of former employees applying for benefits. Contractors who find it possible to offer a maximum of steady employment can enjoy a reduction in the unemployment tax rate.

Employer-Paid Social Security (FICA): The tax rate is adjusted annually by the federal government. It is a percentage of an employee's salary up to a maximum annual contribution.

Builder's Risk and Public Liability: These insurance rates vary according to the trades involved and the state in which the work is done.

Overhead: The column listed as "Sub's Overhead" provides percentages to be added for office or operating overhead. This is the cost of doing business. The percentages are presented as national averages by trade as shown in Figure 23.3. Note that the operating overhead costs are applied to labor only in *Means Electrical Cost Data.*

Profit: The profit percentage is the fee added by the contractor to offer both a return on investment and an allowance to cover the risk involved in the type of construction being bid. The profit percentage may vary from

Workers' Compensation Insurance Rates by Trade

Trade	Insurance Rate (% Labor Cost)		% of Building Cost			Workers' Compensation		
	Range	Average	Office Bldgs.	Schools & Apts.	Mfg.	Office Bldgs.	Schools & Apts.	Mfg.
Excavation, Grading, etc.	5.5% to 49.4%	13.0%	4.8%	4.9%	4.5%	.62%	.64%	.59%
Piles & Foundations	9.0 to 80.1	33.4	7.1	5.2	8.7	2.37	1.74	2.91
Concrete	7.8 to 56.2	20.5	5.0	14.8	3.7	1.03	3.03	.76
Masonry	6.2 to 84.1	19.3	6.9	7.5	1.9	1.33	1.45	.37
Structural Steel	9.5 to 149.6	44.4	10.7	3.9	17.6	4.75	1.73	7.81
Miscellaneous & Ornamental Metals	4.6 to 42.0	14.9	2.8	4.0	3.6	.42	.60	.54
Carpentry & Millwork	8.4 to 69.3	21.7	3.7	4.0	0.5	.80	.87	.11
Metal or Composition Siding	5.2 to 32.9	19.4	2.3	0.3	4.3	.45	.06	.83
Roofing	9.5 to 116.9	36.4	2.3	2.6	3.1	.84	.95	1.13
Doors & Hardware	3.5 to 31.0	12.4	0.9	1.4	0.4	.11	.17	.05
Sash & Glazing	6.4 to 38.6	16.0	3.5	4.0	1.0	.56	.64	.16
Lath & Plaster	6.2 to 41.9	17.4	3.3	6.9	0.8	.57	1.20	.14
Tile, Marble & Floors	4.3 to 35.3	11.0	2.6	3.0	0.5	.29	.33	.06
Acoustical Ceilings	5.1 to 32.7	13.9	2.4	0.2	0.3	.33	.03	.04
Painting	4.9 to 50.8	16.4	1.5	1.6	1.6	.25	.26	.26
Interior Partitions	8.4 to 69.3	21.7	3.9	4.3	4.4	.85	.93	.95
Miscellaneous Items	2.9 to 183.7	21.0	5.2	3.7	9.7	1.09	.78	2.03
Elevators	2.9 to 24.1	9.2	2.1	1.1	2.2	.19	.10	.20
Sprinklers	3.3 to 21.8	10.4	0.5	–	2.0	.05	–	.21
Plumbing	3.2 to 24.2	10.1	4.9	7.2	5.2	.49	.73	.53
Heat., Vent., Air Conditioning	5.2 to 32.9	13.7	13.5	11.0	12.9	1.85	1.51	1.77
Electrical	3.1 to 15.4	7.9	10.1	8.4	11.1	.80	.66	.88
Total	2.9% to 183.7%	–	100.0%	100.0%	100.0%	20.04%	18.41%	22.33%
Overall Weighted Average 20.26%								

Figure 23.6

Workers' Compensation Insurance Rates by States

State	Weighted Average	Factor	State	Weighted Average	Factor	State	Weighted Average	Factor
Alabama	23.1%	117	Kentucky	18.6%	94	North Dakota	16.1%	81
Alaska	19.3	97	Louisiana	27.2	137	Ohio	13.2	67
Arizona	21.1	107	Maine	21.8	110	Oklahoma	21.9	111
Arkansas	14.7	74	Maryland	11.9	60	Oregon	23.6	119
California	18.6	94	Massachusetts	32.8	166	Pennsylvania	22.8	115
Colorado	26.4	133	Michigan	27.6	139	Rhode Island	19.1	96
Connecticut	24.6	124	Minnesota	42.5	215	South Carolina	15.4	78
Delaware	12.3	62	Mississippi	13.8	70	South Dakota	18.8	95
District of Columbia	29.2	147	Missouri	13.7	69	Tennessee	15.0	76
Florida	29.2	147	Montana	55.4	280	Texas	24.7	125
Georgia	20.9	106	Nebraska	16.6	84	Utah	12.9	65
Hawaii	17.6	89	Nevada	20.5	104	Vermont	17.3	87
Idaho	16.7	84	New Hampshire	23.8	120	Virginia	13.2	67
Illinois	33.0	167	New Jersey	11.2	57	Washington	14.3	72
Indiana	7.9	40	New Mexico	26.9	136	West Virginia	12.8	65
Iowa	14.2	72	New York	21.5	109	Wisconsin	17.3	87
Kansas	16.0	81	North Carolina	13.7	69	Wyoming	10.4	53
Weighted Average for U.S. is 20.3% of payroll = 100 %								

Figure 23.7

4% on large, straightforward projects to as much as 25% on smaller, high-risk jobs. Profit percentages are directly affected by economic conditions, the expected number of bidders, and the estimated risk involved in the project. For estimating purposes, *Means Electrical Cost Data* assumes 10% as a reasonable average profit factor.

Square Foot and Cubic Foot Costs

Division 17 in *Means Electrical Cost Data* has been developed to facilitate the preparation of rapid preliminary budget estimates. The cost figures in this division are derived from more than 10,200 actual building projects contained in the R.S. Means data bank of construction costs and include the contractor's overhead and profit. The prices shown *do not* include architectural fees or land costs. The files are updated each year with costs for new projects. In no case are all subdivisions of a project listed.

These projects were located throughout the United States and reflect differences in square foot and cubic foot costs resulting from both the variations in labor and material costs and the differences in the owners' requirements. For instance, a bank in a large city would have different features and costs than one in a rural area. This is true of all the different types of buildings analyzed. All individual cost items were computed and tabulated separately. Thus, the sum of the median figures for Plumbing, HVAC, and Electrical will not normally add up to the total Mechanical and Electrical costs arrived at by separate analysis and tabulation of the projects.

The data and prices presented on a Division 17 page (as shown in Figure 23.8) are listed both as square foot or cubic foot costs and as a percentage of total costs. Each category tabulates the data in a similar manner. The median, or middle figure, is listed (this is not the average cost). This means that 50% of all projects had a lower cost and 50% had a higher cost per unit than the median figure. Figures in the 1/4 column indicate that 25% of the projects had lower costs and 75% had higher costs. Similarly, figures in the 3/4 column indicate that 75% had lower costs and 25% of the projects had higher costs.

The costs and figures represent all projects and do not take into account project size. As a rule, larger buildings (of the same type and relative location) will cost less to build per square foot than similar buildings of a smaller size. This cost difference results from economies of scale as well as a lower exterior envelope-to-floor area ratio. From the electrical point of view, certain components are used only once within a wide range of building sizes. In such cases, the cost of these components will vary only slightly with the building size. A conversion is necessary to adjust project costs, when appropriate, based on size relative to the norm.

There are two stages of project development when square foot cost estimates are most useful. The first is during the conceptual stage when few, if any, details are available. At this time, square foot costs are appropriate for ballpark budget purposes. As soon as details become available in the project design, the square foot approach should be discontinued and the project priced more accurately. After the detailed unit price estimate is completed, square foot costs can be used again—this time for verification and as a check against gross errors.

When using the figures in Division 17, it is recommended that the median cost column be consulted for preliminary figures if no additional information is available. When costs have been converted for location (see City Cost Indexes), the median numbers (as shown in Figure 23.8) should provide a fairly accurate base figure. This figure should then be adjusted

		171 000 | S.F. & C.F. Costs	UNIT	UNIT COSTS			% OF TOTAL			
				1/4	MEDIAN	3/4	1/4	MEDIAN	3/4	
500	0100	Site work	S.F.	5.35	7.80	13.05	8%	11.60%	16.10%	500
	1800	Equipment		1.20	1.97	3.23	2.10%	2.90%	4.60%	
	2720	Plumbing		3.04	4.27	5.40	6.80%	9%	11.50%	
	2730	Heating, ventilating, air conditioning		1.62	3.15	3.36	4.20%	6%	6.40%	
	2900	Electrical		2.70	3.88	5.55	5%	6.50%	8.10%	
	3100	Total: Mechanical & Electrical	▼	8.15	11.75	16.15	15.60%	19.20%	23.50%	
	9000	Per apartment, total cost	Apt.	47,600	53,000	67,100				
	9500	Total: Mechanical & Electrical	"	7,800	10,700	13,400				
510	0010	**ICE SKATING RINKS**	S.F.	40.30	70.40	97.50				510
	0020	Total project costs	C.F.	2.81	2.88	3.32				
	2720	Plumbing	S.F.	1.43	2.27	2.68	3.10%	3.20%	5.60%	
	2900	Electrical		4.10	4.52	6.30	6.70%	10.10%	15%	
	3100	Total: Mechanical & Electrical	▼	7.25	10.45	13.05	9.90%	25.90%	29.80%	
520	0010	**JAILS**	S.F.	115	144	192				520
	0020	Total project costs	C.F.	10.70	12.70	17.20				
	1800	Equipment	S.F.	4.87	12.95	22.50	4%	8.90%	15.10%	
	2720	Plumbing		11.45	15.10	18.35	7%	8.90%	13.30%	
	2770	Heating, ventilating, air conditioning		10.50	14.30	26.50	7.40%	9.40%	17.70%	
	2900	Electrical		12.80	16.60	20.40	7.90%	11.30%	12.40%	
	3100	Total: Mechanical & Electrical	▼	30	43.30	57.15	24.30%	30.10%	31.70%	
530	0010	**LIBRARIES**	S.F.	69.55	87.70	109				530
	0020	Total project costs	C.F.	4.96	6	7.55				
	0500	Masonry	S.F.	3.91	7.15	13.75	4.50%	7.40%	10.70%	
	1800	Equipment		1	2.60	4.31	1.10%	2.80%	4.80%	
	2720	Plumbing		2.80	3.93	5.35	3.40%	4.60%	5.60%	
	2770	Heating, ventilating, air conditioning		6.20	10.20	13.25	8.70%	11%	14.60%	
	2900	Electrical		7.15	9.30	11.90	8.20%	10.90%	12.10%	
	3100	Total: Mechanical & Electrical	▼	14.85	19.55	28.75	17.10%	22%	28%	
550	0010	**MEDICAL CLINICS**	S.F.	68.10	84.15	106				550
	0020	Total project costs	C.F.	5.20	6.70	8.85				
	1800	Equipment	S.F.	1.82	3.88	5.85	1.80%	4.80%	6.80%	
	2720	Plumbing		4.71	6.50	8.70	6.10%	8.40%	10%	
	2770	Heating, ventilating, air conditioning		5.60	7.20	10.60	6.60%	9.20%	11.30%	
	2900	Electrical		5.95	8.30	11	8.10%	10%	11.90%	
	3100	Total: Mechanical & Electrical	▼	14.40	18.35	25.80	18.60%	23.60%	29.60%	
	3500	See also division 117-001								
570	0010	**MEDICAL OFFICES**	S.F.	63.35	79.60	98.20				570
	0020	Total project costs	C.F.	4.87	6.65	8.95				
	1800	Equipment	S.F.	2.15	4.26	6.05	3%	5.80%	7.10%	
	2720	Plumbing		3.69	5.65	7.65	5.60%	6.80%	8.60%	
	2770	Heating, ventilating, air conditioning		4.35	6.50	8.30	6.10%	8%	9.50%	
	2900	Electrical		5.15	7.55	10.50	7.60%	9.70%	11.60%	
	3100	Total: Mechanical & Electrical	▼	11.95	16.70	22.35	16.60%	21.20%	26%	
590	0010	**MOTELS**	S.F.	41.80	60.60	76.15				590
	0020	Total project costs	C.F.	3.59	5.06	8.30				
	2720	Plumbing	S.F.	4.17	5.20	6.35	9.40%	10.60%	12.50%	
	2770	Heating, ventilating, air conditioning		2.20	3.79	5.55	4.90%	5.60%	8.20%	
	2900	Electrical		3.88	4.90	6.35	7.10%	8.20%	10.40%	
	3100	Total: Mechanical & Electrical	▼	9.40	12.05	16.60	18.50%	23.10%	26.20%	
	5000									
	9000	Per rental unit, total cost	Unit	21,000	31,500	40,700				
	9500	Total: Mechanical & Electrical	"	4,025	5,700	6,150				

Figure 23.8

according to the estimator's experience, local economic conditions, code requirements, and the owner's particular project requirements. There is no need to factor the percentage figures, as these should remain relatively constant from city to city.

Repair and Remodeling

Cost figures in *Means Electrical Cost Data* are based on new construction utilizing the most cost-effective combination of labor, equipment, and material. The work is scheduled in the proper sequence to allow the various trades to accomplish their tasks in an efficient manner. Figure 23.9 (from Division 1 of *Means Electrical Cost Data*) shows factors that can be used to adjust figures in other sections of the book for repair and remodeling projects. For expanded coverage, see *Means' Repair and Remodeling Cost Data*.

Assemblies Section

Means' assemblies (systems) data are divided into twelve "UniFormat" divisions, which organize the components of construction into logical groupings. The Assemblies approach was devised to provide quick and easy methods for estimating even when only preliminary design data are available. The groupings, or assemblies, are presented in such a way that the estimator can easily vary components within the assemblies as well as substitute one assembly for another. This is extremely useful when adapting to budget, design, or other considerations. Figure 23.10 shows how the data are presented in the Assemblies section.

Each assembly is illustrated and accompanied by a detailed description. The book lists the components and sizes of each assembly, usually in the order of construction. Alternates for the most common variations are also listed. Each individual component is found in the Unit Price Section. If an alternate (not listed in Assemblies) is required, it can easily be derived.

Quantity: A unit of measure is established for each assembly. For example, lighting assemblies are measured by the square foot of floor area; motor assemblies are measured by "each"; generators are measured by kilowatt. Within each assembly, the components are measured by industry standard, using the same units as in the Unit Price Section.

Material: The cost of each component in the Material column is the "Bare Material Cost," plus 10% profit, for the unit and quantity as defined in the "Quantity" column.

Installation: Installation costs as listed in the Assemblies pages contain both labor and equipment costs. The labor rate includes the "Bare Labor Cost" plus the installing contractor's overhead and profit. These rates are shown in Figure 23.3. The equipment rate is the "Bare Equipment Cost" plus 10%.

171 | S.F., C.F. and % of Total Costs

		171 000 | S.F. & C.F. Costs	UNIT	UNIT COSTS			% OF TOTAL			
				1/4	MEDIAN	3/4	1/4	MEDIAN	3/4	
910	0010	**THEATERS**	S.F.	54.60	72.95	105				910
	0020	Total project costs	C.F.	2.62	3.86	5.70				
	2720	Plumbing	S.F.	1.76	2.04	6.15	2.90%	4.60%	6.10%	
	2770	Heating, ventilating, air conditioning		4.89	6.60	7.55	7.30%	11.60%	13.30%	
	2900	Electrical		4.94	6.65	12.95	8%	9.30%	12.20%	
	3100	Total: Mechanical & Electrical	↓	11.70	13.85	25.65	17.10%	24.90%	27.40%	
940	0010	**TOWN HALLS** City Halls & Municipal Buildings	S.F.	63.95	78.40	103				940
	0020	Total project costs	C.F.	4.34	6.75	8.65				
	2720	Plumbing	S.F.	2.24	4.39	7.65	4.20%	5.90%	7.90%	
	2770	Heating, ventilating, air conditioning		4.76	9.45	10.80	7%	9%	13.20%	
	2900	Electrical		5.05	7.50	10.70	7.90%	9.40%	11.60%	
	3100	Total: Mechanical & Electrical	↓	10.60	18.20	25.90	15.80%	22%	29.90%	
970	0010	**WAREHOUSES** And Storage Buildings	S.F.	23.10	32.55	50.50				970
	0020	Total project costs	C.F.	1.20	1.91	3.26				
	0100	Site work	S.F.	2.35	4.81	7.30	5.90%	12.50%	19.80%	
	0500	Masonry		1.46	3.34	7.20	5%	7.70%	13.10%	
	1800	Equipment		.38	.79	4.61	.90%	2.40%	6.50%	
	2720	Plumbing		.78	1.34	2.56	2.80%	4.70%	6.40%	
	2730	Heating, ventilating, air conditioning		.89	2.31	3.34	2.40%	5%	8.30%	
	2900	Electrical		1.40	2.62	4.31	4.90%	7.20%	10%	
	3100	Total: Mechanical & Electrical	↓	2.64	4.55	10	9.50%	15.40%	21.40%	

010 | Overhead and Miscellaneous Data

		010 000 | Overhead	CREW	DAILY OUTPUT	MAN-HOURS	UNIT	1995 BARE COSTS				TOTAL INCL O&P	
							MAT.	LABOR	EQUIP.	TOTAL		
032	0010	**FACTORS** To be added to construction costs for particular job										032
	0200											
	0500	Cut & patch to match existing construction, add, minimum				Costs	2%	3%				
	0550	Maximum					5%	9%				
	0800	Dust protection, add, minimum					1%	2%				
	0850	Maximum					4%	11%				
	1100	Equipment usage curtailment, add, minimum					1%	1%				
	1150	Maximum					3%	10%				
	1400	Material handling & storage limitation, add, minimum					1%	1%				
	1450	Maximum					6%	7%				
	1700	Protection of existing work, add, minimum					2%	2%				
	1750	Maximum					5%	7%				
	2000	Shift work requirements, add, minimum						5%				
	2050	Maximum						30%				
	2300	Temporary shoring and bracing, add, minimum				↓	2%	5%				
	2350	Maximum					5%	12%				

Figure 23.9

LIGHTING & POWER | A9.2-710 | Motor Installation

System 9.2-710 installed cost of motor wiring as per Table R160-030 using 50′ of rigid conduit and copper wire. **Cost and setting of motor not included.**

System Components	QUANTITY	UNIT	COST EACH MAT.	COST EACH INST.	COST EACH TOTAL
SYSTEM 9.2-710-0200					
MOTOR INSTALLATION, SINGLE PHASE, 115V, TO AND INCLUDING 1/3 HP MOTOR SIZE					
Wire 600V type THWN-THHN, copper solid #12	1.250	C.L.F.	7.94	38.75	46.69
Steel intermediate conduit, (IMC) 1/2″ diam	50.000	L.F.	56	172	228
Magnetic FVNR, 115V, 1/3 HP, size 00 starter	1.000	Ea.	133	86	219
Safety switch, fused, heavy duty, 240V 2P 30 amp	1.000	Ea.	69.50	98	167.50
Safety switch, non fused, heavy duty, 600V, 3 phase, 30 A	1.000	Ea.	80.50	107	187.50
Flexible metallic conduit, Greenfield 1/2″ diam	1.500	L.F.	.51	2.58	3.09
Connectors for flexible metallic conduit Greenfield 1/2″ diam	1.000	Ea.	1.10	4.30	5.40
Coupling for Greenfield to conduit 1/2″ diam flexible metalic conduit	1.000	Ea.	.76	6.85	7.61
Fuse cartridge nonrenewable, 250V 30 amp	1.000	Ea.	.87	6.85	7.72
TOTAL			350.18	522.33	872.51

9.2-710	Motor Installation	COST EACH MAT.	COST EACH INST.	COST EACH TOTAL
0200	Motor installation, single phase, 115V, to and including 1/3 HP motor size	350	520	870
0240	To and incl. 1 HP motor size	370	520	890
0280	To and incl. 2 HP motor size	400	555	955
0320	To and incl. 3 HP motor size	460	565	1,025
0360	230V, to and including 1 HP motor size	360	530	890
0400	To and incl. 2 HP motor size	380	530	910
0440	To and incl. 3 HP motor size	420	570	990
0520	Three phase, 200V, to and including 1-1/2 HP motor size	400	580	980
0560	To and incl. 3 HP motor size	430	630	1,060
0600	To and incl. 5 HP motor size	470	705	1,175
0640	To and incl. 7-1/2 HP motor size	485	720	1,205
0680	To and incl. 10 HP motor size	795	900	1,695
0720	To and incl. 15 HP motor size	1,075	1,000	2,075
0760	To and incl. 20 HP motor size	1,325	1,150	2,475
0800	To and incl. 25 HP motor size	1,350	1,150	2,500
0840	To and incl. 30 HP motor size	2,150	1,375	3,525
0880	To and incl. 40 HP motor size	2,600	1,625	4,225
0920	To and incl. 50 HP motor size	4,775	1,875	6,650
0960	To and incl. 60 HP motor size	4,900	2,000	6,900
1000	To and incl. 75 HP motor size	6,200	2,275	8,475
1040	To and incl. 100 HP motor size	13,000	2,675	15,675
1080	To and incl. 125 HP motor size	13,300	2,950	16,250
1120	To and incl. 150 HP motor size	15,700	3,475	19,175
1160	To and incl. 200 HP motor size	17,800	4,225	22,025
1240	230V, to and including 1-1/2 HP motor size	385	575	960
1280	To and incl. 3 HP motor size	420	625	1,045
1320	To and incl. 5 HP motor size	455	695	1,150
1360	To and incl. 7-1/2 HP motor size	455	695	1,150
1400	To and incl. 10 HP motor size	735	850	1,585
1440	To and incl. 15 HP motor size	820	930	1,750
1480	To and incl. 20 HP motor size	1,250	1,125	2,375
1520	To and incl. 25 HP motor size	1,325	1,150	2,475

Figure 23.10

Reference Section

Throughout the Unit Price and Assemblies sections are reference numbers highlighted with bold squares. These numbers serve as footnotes, referring the reader to illustrations, charts, and estimating reference tables in the Reference Section. Figure 23.11 shows an example reference number (for steel tubular scaffold) as it appears on a Unit Price page. Figure 23.12 shows the corresponding reference page from the Reference Section. The development of unit costs for many items is explained in these reference tables. Design criteria for many types of electrical systems are also included to aid the designer/estimator in making appropriate choices.

City Cost Indexes

The unit prices in *Means Electrical Cost Data* are national averages. When they are to be applied to a particular location, these prices must be adjusted to local conditions. R.S. Means has developed the City Cost Indexes for just that purpose. The Reference Section of *Means Electrical Cost Data* contains tables of indexes for 209 U.S. and Canadian cities based on a 30 major city average of 100. The figures are broken down into material and installation for the Electrical and Mechanical CSI divisions, as shown in Figure 23.13. Please note that for each city there is a weighted average based on total project costs. This average is based on the relative contribution of each division to the construction process as a whole.

In addition to adjusting the figures in *Means Electrical Cost Data* for particular locations, the City Cost Index can also be used to adjust costs from one city to another. For example, the price of the electrical work for a particular building type is known for City A. To budget the costs of the same building type in City B, the following calculation can be made:

$$\frac{\text{City B Index}}{\text{City A Index}} \times \text{City A Cost} = \text{City B Cost}$$

While City Cost Indexes provide a means to adjust prices for location, the Historical Cost Index (also included in *Means Electrical Cost Data* and shown in Figure 23.14) provides a means to adjust for time. Using the same principle as above, a time-adjustment factor can be calculated:

$$\frac{\text{Index for Year X}}{\text{Index for Year Y}} = \text{Time-adjustment Factor}$$

This time-adjustment factor can be used to determine the budget costs for a particular building type in Year X, based on costs for a similar building type known from Year Y. Used together, the two indexes allow for cost adjustments from one city during a given year to another city in another year (the present or otherwise). For example, an office building built in Los Angeles in 1974 *originally cost* $1,000,000. How much will a similar building cost in Phoenix in 1995? Adjustment factors are developed as shown above using data from Figures 23.13 and 23.14:

$$\frac{\text{Phoenix index}}{\text{Los Angeles index}} = \frac{91.1}{115.2} = 0.79$$

$$\frac{\text{1995 index}}{\text{1974 index}} = \frac{105.7}{41.4} = 2.55$$

Original cost $\times$ location adjustment $\times$ time adjustment = Proposed new cost

$$\$1,000,000 \times 0.79 \times 2.55 = \$2,014,500$$

Understanding how Means' prices are obtained and organized makes this annual cost book a more valuable tool for the estimating process. The Sample Estimate in the following chapter is based on prices in the 1995 edition of *Means Electrical Cost Data*.

015 250 | Construction Aids

			DAILY OUTPUT	MAN-HOURS	UNIT	1995 BARE COSTS				TOTAL INCL O&P	
		CREW				MAT.	LABOR	EQUIP.	TOTAL		
254	0010	**SCAFFOLD** Steel tubular, regular, buy									**254**
	0090	Building exterior, 1 to 5 stories	R015 -100	3 Carp	16.80	1.429	C.S.F.	31.50	35		66.50	90.50	
	0200	6 to 12 stories		4 Carp	15	2.133		31.50	52.50		84	118	
	0310	13 to 20 stories		5 Carp	16.75	2.388		31.50	59		90.50	128	
	0460	Building interior walls, (area) up to 16' high		3 Carp	22.70	1.057		31.50	26		57.50	76	
	0560	16' to 40' high			18.70	1.283		31.50	31.50		63	85	
	0800	Building interior floor area, up to 30' high			90	.267	C.C.F.	17.50	6.55		24.05	29.50	
	0900	Over 30' high		4 Carp	100	.320	"	17.50	7.85		25.35	32	
255	0011	**SCAFFOLDING SPECIALTIES**										**255**
	1500	Sidewalk bridge using tubular steel										
	1510	scaffold frames, including planking		3 Carp	45	.533	L.F.	3.50	13.10		16.60	25	
	1600	For 2 uses per month, deduct from all above						50%					
	1700	For 1 use every 2 months, add to all above						100%					
	1900	Catwalks, 32" wide, no guardrails, 6' span, buy					Ea.	115			115	127	
	2000	10' span, buy						180			180	198	
	3720	Putlog, standard, 8' span, with hangers, buy						55			55	60.50	
	3750	12' span, buy						83.50			83.50	92	
	3760	Trussed type, 14' span, buy						192			192 .	211	
	3790	20' span, buy						227			227	249	
	3795	Rent per month						30			30	33	
	3800	Rolling ladders with handrails, 30" wide, buy, 2 step						124			124	136	
	4000	7 step						360			360	400	
	4050	10 step						585			585	640	
	4100	Rolling towers, buy, 5' wide, 7' long, 9' high						1,075			1,075	1,175	
	4200	For 5' high added sections, add						180			180	198	
	4300	Complete incl. wheels, railings, etc.											
	4400	up to 20' high, rent per month					Ea.	110			110	121	
256	0010	**SWING STAGING**, 500 lb cap., 2' wide to 24' long, hand operated hoist											**256**
	0020	steel cable type, with 60' cables, buy					Ea.	3,950			3,950	4,350	
	0030	Rent per week					"	155			155	171	

015 300 | Barriers & Enclosures

				DAILY OUTPUT	MAN-HOURS	UNIT	MAT.	LABOR	EQUIP.	TOTAL	TOTAL INCL O&P	
302	0010	**BARRICADES** 5' high, 3 rail @ 2" x 8", fixed	2 Carp	30	.533	L.F.	10.30	13.10		23.40	32.50	**302**
	0150	Movable		20	.800		11.20	19.70		30.90	44	
	1000	Guardrail, wooden, 3' high, 1" x 6", on 2" x 4" posts		200	.080		1.60	1.97		3.57	4.90	
	1100	2" x 6", on 4" x 4" posts		165	.097		2.66	2.39		5.05	6.75	
	1200	Portable metal with base pads, buy					12.65			12.65	13.90	
	1250	Typical installation, assume 10 reuses	2 Carp	600	.027		1.50	.66		2.16	2.70	
304	0010	**FENCING** Chain link, 5' high	2 Clab	100	.160	L.F.	4.95	3.10		8.05	10.40	**304**
	0100	6' high		75	.213		5.55	4.14		9.69	12.70	
	0200	Rented chain link, 6' high, to 500'		100	.160		2.15	3.10		5.25	7.30	
	0250	Over 1000' (up to 12 mo.)		110	.145		1.75	2.82		4.57	6.45	
	0350	Plywood, painted, 2" x 4" frame, 4' high	A-4	135	.178		4.90	4.25		9.15	12.10	
	0400	4" x 4" frame, 8' high	"	110	.218		8.35	5.20		13.55	17.45	
	0500	Wire mesh on 4" x 4" posts, 4' high	2 Carp	100	.160		4.92	3.94		8.86	11.70	
	0550	8' high	"	80	.200		7	4.92		11.92	15.55	
306	0010	**WINTER PROTECTION** Reinforced plastic on wood										**306**
	0100	framing to close openings	2 Clab	750	.021	S.F.	.31	.41		.72	1	
	0200	Tarpaulins hung over scaffolding, 8 uses, not incl. scaffolding		1,500	.011		.16	.21		.37	.51	
	0300	Prefab fiberglass panels, steel frame, 8 uses		1,200	.013		.58	.26		.84	1.05	

015 500 | Access Roads

				DAILY OUTPUT	MAN-HOURS	UNIT	MAT.	LABOR	EQUIP.	TOTAL	TOTAL INCL O&P	
552	0010	**ROADS AND SIDEWALKS** Temporary										**552**
	0050	Roads, gravel fill, no surfacing, 4" gravel depth	B-14	715	.067	S.Y.	1.09	1.38	.29	2.76	3.70	

Figure 23.11

R015-100   Steel Tubular Scaffolding

On new construction, tubular scaffolding is efficient up to 60' high or five stories. Above this it is usually better to use a hung scaffolding if construction permits.

In repairing or cleaning the front of an existing building the cost of tubular scaffolding per S.F. of building front increases as the height increases above the first tier. The first tier cost is relatively high due to leveling and alignment. Swing scaffolding operations may interfere with tenants. In this case the tubular is more practical at all heights.

The minimum efficient crew for erection is three men. For heights over 50', a four-man crew is more efficient. Use two or more on top and two at the bottom for handing up or hoisting. Four men can erect and dismantle about nine frames per hour up to five stories. From five to eight stories they will average six frames per hour. With 7' horizontal spacing this will run about 300 S.F. and 200 S.F. of wall surface, respectively. Time for placing planks must be

added to the above. On heights above 50', five planks can be placed per man-hour.

The cost per 1,000 S.F. of building front in the table below was developed by pricing the materials required for a typical tubular scaffolding system eleven frames long and two frames high. Planks were figured five wide for standing plus two wide for materials.

Frames are 2', 4' and 5' wide and usually spaced 7' O.C. horizontally. Sidewalk frames are 6' wide. Rental rates will be lower for jobs over three months duration.

For jobs under twenty-five frames, figure rental at $6.00 per frame. For jobs over one hundred frames, rental can go as low as $2.65 per frame. These figures do not include accessories which are listed separately below. Large quantities for long periods can reduce rental rates by 20%.

Item	Unit	Purchase, Each		Monthly Rent, Each		Per 1,000 S. F. of Building Front	
		Regular	Heavy Duty	Regular	Heavy Duty	No. of Frames	Rental per Mo.
5' Wide Frames, 3' High	Ea.	$ 59.00	–	$ 4.00	$ 4.00	–	–
*5'-0" High		75.00	–	4.00	4.00	–	–
*6'-4" High		90.00	–	4.00	4.00	24	$ 96.00
2' & 4' Wide, 5' High		–	$ 80.00	4.00	4.00	–	–
6'-0" High		–	91.00	4.00	4.00	–	–
6' Wide Frame, 7'-6" High (Canopy Frames)		138.00	165.00	–	7.45	–	–
Outrigger Bracket, 20"		20.00	–	3.20	–	–	–
Guardrail Post		16.00	–	1.20	–	12	14.40
Guardrail, 7' section		7.00	–	.85	–	11	9.35
Cross Braces		15.00	17.00	.85	.85	44	37.40
Screw Jacks & Plates		22.00	33.00	2.00	2.50	24	60.00
8" Casters		50.00	–	6.00	–	–	–
16' Plank, 2" x 10"		22.00	–	5.10	–	35	178.50
8' Plank, 2" x 10"		11.00	–	3.75	–	7	26.25
1' to 6' Extension Tube	▼	–	70.00	–	2.50	–	–
Shoring Stringers, steel, 10' to 12' long	L.F.	–	7.00	–	.40	–	–
Aluminum, 12' to 16' long		–	16.00	–	.60	–	–
Aluminum joists with nailers, 10' to 22' long	▼	–	12.50	–	.50	–	–
16' Powered Swing Staging (with accessories)	Ea.	–	–	650.00	–	–	–
						Total	$421.90
						2 Use/Mo.	$210.95

*Most commonly used

Scaffolding is often used as falsework over 15' high during construction of cast-in-place concrete beams and slabs. Two ft. wide scaffolding is generally used for heavy beam construction. The span between frames depends upon the load to be carried with a maximum span of 5'.

Heavy duty scaffolding with a capacity of 10,000#/leg can be spaced up to 10' O. C. depending upon form support design and loading.

Scaffolding used as horizontal shoring requires less than half the material required with conventional shoring.

On new construction, erection is done by carpenters.

Rolling towers supporting horizontal shores can reduce labor and speed the job. For maintenance work, catwalks with spans up to 70' can be supported by the rolling towers.

Figure 23.12

City Cost Indexes

UNITED STATES / ALABAMA

DIVISION		30 CITY AVERAGE			BIRMINGHAM			HUNTSVILLE			MOBILE			MONTGOMERY			TUSCALOOSA		
		MAT.	INST.	TOTAL	MAT.	INST.	TOTAL	MAT.	INST.	TOTAL	MAT.	INST.	TOTAL	MAT.	INST.	TOTAL	MAT.	INST.	TOTAL
2	SITE WORK	100.0	100.0	100.0	89.4	91.8	91.3	88.4	91.9	91.1	99.3	86.2	89.3	99.8	85.7	89.0	88.8	91.1	90.6
031	CONCRETE FORMWORK	100.0	100.0	100.0	95.8	66.2	70.8	97.6	63.8	69.1	97.6	68.0	72.6	94.8	60.6	65.9	97.5	49.5	57.0
032	CONCRETE REINFORCEMENT	100.0	100.0	100.0	90.3	70.2	79.0	90.3	67.7	77.6	93.3	64.9	77.3	93.3	69.5	79.9	90.3	69.9	78.8
033	CAST IN PLACE CONCRETE	100.0	100.0	100.0	85.7	63.9	76.2	80.0	64.8	73.4	81.7	67.3	75.5	83.7	59.8	73.3	83.7	56.9	72.1
3	CONCRETE	100.0	100.0	100.0	83.6	67.9	75.7	81.1	66.7	73.9	82.3	68.9	75.5	83.0	63.9	73.4	82.9	58.2	70.4
4	MASONRY	100.0	100.0	100.0	78.1	63.8	69.2	77.4	58.5	65.7	77.3	64.7	69.5	78.2	44.8	57.4	77.6	47.2	58.7
5	METALS	100.0	100.0	100.0	98.4	92.5	96.1	98.0	92.4	95.8	96.9	91.3	94.7	97.1	91.1	94.8	97.1	91.7	95.0
6	WOOD & PLASTICS	100.0	100.0	100.0	96.7	67.1	82.1	95.6	63.6	79.8	95.6	69.4	82.7	92.1	63.6	78.0	95.6	50.4	73.3
7	THERMAL & MOISTURE PROTECTION	100.0	100.0	100.0	96.5	64.1	81.4	96.5	62.6	80.6	96.4	65.2	81.8	96.3	57.6	78.2	96.5	56.0	77.6
8	DOORS & WINDOWS	100.0	100.0	100.0	96.3	66.3	89.1	96.3	61.7	88.0	96.3	66.0	89.1	96.3	63.4	88.4	96.3	57.2	87.0
092	LATH, PLASTER & GYPSUM BOARD	100.0	100.0	100.0	104.6	66.7	79.3	104.6	63.0	76.9	104.6	69.0	80.9	104.6	63.0	76.9	104.6	49.4	67.8
095	ACOUSTICAL TREATMENT & WOOD FLOORING	100.0	100.0	100.0	98.1	66.7	77.9	98.1	63.0	75.5	98.1	69.0	79.4	98.1	63.0	75.5	98.1	49.4	66.7
096	FLOORING & CARPET	100.0	100.0	100.0	97.8	67.4	90.7	97.8	58.3	88.5	106.3	73.1	98.5	106.3	37.8	90.2	97.8	55.4	87.9
099	PAINTING & WALL COVERINGS	100.0	100.0	100.0	88.0	62.2	73.1	88.0	61.0	72.4	88.7	70.6	78.2	88.7	69.3	77.5	88.0	59.7	71.6
9	FINISHES	100.0	100.0	100.0	98.3	66.2	82.0	98.3	62.2	79.9	102.3	69.5	85.6	102.4	57.2	79.4	98.3	51.2	74.4
10-14	TOTAL DIV. 10-14	100.0	100.0	100.0	91.9	76.3	88.5	100.0	76.1	94.8	100.0	76.4	94.9	100.0	73.1	94.2	100.0	69.7	93.4
15	MECHANICAL	100.0	100.0	100.0	100.1	61.9	83.5	100.1	62.6	83.8	100.1	67.0	85.7	100.1	56.4	81.1	100.1	49.6	78.2
16	ELECTRICAL	100.0	100.0	100.0	97.3	62.6	74.2	97.3	75.6	82.9	97.3	65.8	76.3	97.3	53.2	68.0	97.2	62.6	74.2
1-16	WEIGHTED AVERAGE	100.0	100.0	100.0	94.7	70.0	82.8	94.9	70.9	83.3	95.7	71.5	84.0	95.8	62.9	79.9	95.0	62.0	79.1

ALASKA / ARIZONA / ARKANSAS / CALIFORNIA

DIVISION		ANCHORAGE			PHOENIX			TUCSON			FORT SMITH			LITTLE ROCK			ANAHEIM		
		MAT.	INST.	TOTAL	MAT.	INST.	TOTAL	MAT.	INST.	TOTAL	MAT.	INST.	TOTAL	MAT.	INST.	TOTAL	MAT.	INST.	TOTAL
2	SITE WORK	123.8	140.3	136.5	73.2	98.8	92.9	70.4	98.6	92.1	76.4	82.5	81.1	76.0	82.5	81.0	87.2	114.6	108.3
031	CONCRETE FORMWORK	125.2	123.3	123.6	96.8	83.1	85.2	97.7	82.9	85.2	97.9	54.8	61.5	92.1	60.3	65.3	100.7	128.0	123.7
032	CONCRETE REINFORCEMENT	146.6	142.4	144.3	101.3	81.9	90.4	100.3	81.8	89.9	99.2	65.8	80.4	99.5	63.3	79.1	111.0	112.8	112.0
033	CAST IN PLACE CONCRETE	184.9	117.3	155.5	92.7	83.0	88.5	88.4	82.9	86.0	83.5	57.4	72.2	83.5	57.5	72.2	100.5	127.5	112.2
3	CONCRETE	156.9	123.9	140.3	100.1	82.5	91.2	98.0	82.4	90.1	83.1	58.7	70.8	82.7	60.7	71.6	120.7	123.8	122.3
4	MASONRY	161.3	130.1	141.9	86.7	79.9	82.5	89.2	79.9	83.4	92.3	59.0	71.6	91.8	59.0	71.4	88.7	132.5	116.0
5	METALS	130.7	115.8	124.9	102.0	79.9	93.5	101.4	79.7	93.0	98.7	73.7	89.0	98.7	73.0	88.7	112.2	103.4	108.8
6	WOOD & PLASTICS	120.8	121.3	121.0	98.8	82.5	90.8	99.8	82.5	91.2	96.7	55.0	76.1	92.5	62.2	77.6	98.2	125.8	111.8
7	THERMAL & MOISTURE PROTECTION	199.0	118.9	161.6	110.3	84.4	98.2	111.6	81.4	97.5	90.4	58.2	75.3	89.7	58.9	75.3	121.8	125.4	123.5
8	DOORS & WINDOWS	129.5	123.7	128.1	102.2	83.9	97.8	100.9	83.9	96.8	98.1	54.7	87.8	98.1	58.5	88.7	106.7	119.9	109.9
092	LATH, PLASTER & GYPSUM BOARD	137.9	121.9	127.2	87.1	81.9	83.6	87.5	81.9	83.7	94.5	54.6	67.9	94.5	62.1	72.9	96.4	126.7	116.6
095	ACOUSTICAL TREATMENT & WOOD FLOORING	149.5	121.9	131.7	97.0	81.9	87.2	98.5	81.9	87.8	96.3	54.6	69.4	96.3	62.1	74.2	139.0	126.7	131.0
096	FLOORING & CARPET	137.7	142.8	138.9	89.3	85.1	88.3	88.5	75.1	85.4	121.4	66.8	108.6	123.1	66.8	109.9	134.4	128.0	132.9
099	PAINTING & WALL COVERINGS	128.9	126.2	127.4	100.8	74.3	85.5	98.6	73.1	83.9	99.2	43.8	67.2	99.2	60.5	76.8	123.0	121.9	122.4
9	FINISHES	153.4	127.4	140.2	87.9	82.6	85.2	87.8	80.3	84.0	103.9	55.7	79.4	104.4	61.8	82.7	125.5	127.3	126.4
10-14	TOTAL DIV. 10-14	100.0	118.7	104.1	100.0	87.9	97.4	100.0	87.9	97.4	100.0	69.1	93.3	100.0	70.0	93.5	100.0	122.4	104.9
15	MECHANICAL	108.9	114.5	111.3	99.8	85.3	93.5	99.7	79.1	90.8	100.0	51.0	78.8	100.0	58.1	81.8	100.2	130.1	113.1
16	ELECTRICAL	159.2	125.2	136.6	116.7	69.9	85.6	110.2	74.8	86.7	95.1	64.6	74.8	97.2	67.0	77.1	91.2	117.5	108.6
1-16	WEIGHTED AVERAGE	134.2	123.9	129.3	99.3	82.4	91.1	98.4	81.6	90.3	96.2	61.8	79.5	96.2	64.7	81.0	106.7	122.2	114.2

CALIFORNIA

DIVISION		BAKERSFIELD			FRESNO			LOS ANGELES			OXNARD			RIVERSIDE			SACRAMENTO		
		MAT.	INST.	TOTAL	MAT.	INST.	TOTAL	MAT.	INST.	TOTAL	MAT.	INST.	TOTAL	MAT.	INST.	TOTAL	MAT.	INST.	TOTAL
2	SITE WORK	93.7	111.3	107.2	93.7	111.1	107.1	86.4	115.5	108.8	94.5	108.9	105.6	86.3	112.1	106.2	92.8	110.4	106.3
031	CONCRETE FORMWORK	90.8	126.8	121.2	97.6	121.5	117.8	102.8	127.8	123.9	97.7	128.0	123.3	101.8	127.8	123.8	104.1	121.7	118.9
032	CONCRETE REINFORCEMENT	110.6	112.3	111.6	111.0	112.3	111.7	113.1	112.8	112.9	110.6	112.3	111.5	109.6	112.4	111.1	108.6	112.4	110.7
033	CAST IN PLACE CONCRETE	95.7	125.9	108.8	95.7	120.1	106.3	100.2	124.3	110.7	102.0	126.5	112.7	100.5	127.5	112.2	102.4	120.3	110.2
3	CONCRETE	117.6	122.6	120.1	118.2	118.3	118.2	122.2	122.4	122.3	121.1	123.3	122.2	120.6	123.6	122.1	122.7	118.4	120.6
4	MASONRY	112.6	125.8	120.9	113.7	121.3	118.5	116.5	132.3	126.4	118.3	122.1	120.7	89.2	124.1	110.9	113.9	121.3	118.5
5	METALS	106.6	101.4	104.4	108.5	102.0	106.0	103.4	101.0	102.5	106.0	102.3	104.6	112.1	102.7	108.5	104.9	102.5	104.0
6	WOOD & PLASTICS	85.6	125.9	105.5	99.4	119.1	109.2	93.7	125.4	109.3	95.6	125.9	110.5	98.2	125.8	111.8	104.9	118.8	111.8
7	THERMAL & MOISTURE PROTECTION	104.5	112.5	108.2	100.6	114.2	107.0	110.1	125.8	117.5	109.7	121.8	115.4	121.2	122.7	121.9	115.2	120.0	117.4
8	DOORS & WINDOWS	105.4	116.3	108.0	105.4	113.3	107.3	104.2	119.7	107.9	103.9	120.0	107.8	106.7	119.9	109.9	106.0	113.7	107.8
092	LATH, PLASTER & GYPSUM BOARD	96.4	126.7	116.6	95.8	119.7	111.7	96.2	126.7	116.5	96.4	126.7	116.6	96.4	126.7	116.6	94.1	119.3	110.9
095	ACOUSTICAL TREATMENT & WOOD FLOORING	139.0	126.7	131.0	139.0	119.7	126.5	140.5	126.7	131.6	139.0	126.7	131.0	139.0	126.7	131.0	139.0	119.3	126.3
096	FLOORING & CARPET	130.1	85.0	119.5	130.1	98.9	122.8	125.9	128.0	126.4	130.1	128.0	129.6	134.4	128.0	132.9	123.9	119.9	123.0
099	PAINTING & WALL COVERINGS	125.6	119.6	122.2	125.6	102.0	111.9	125.5	125.2	125.3	125.6	114.1	118.9	123.0	121.9	122.4	125.2	115.6	119.6
9	FINISHES	127.4	119.3	123.3	127.3	114.6	120.8	122.2	127.3	124.8	127.2	126.5	126.8	125.4	127.3	126.4	125.1	120.2	122.6
10-14	TOTAL DIV. 10-14	100.0	122.7	104.9	100.0	140.5	108.8	100.0	121.3	104.6	100.0	122.8	104.9	100.0	122.4	104.9	100.0	140.4	108.8
15	MECHANICAL	100.2	105.4	102.4	100.2	121.6	109.5	100.1	130.0	113.1	100.2	130.1	113.2	100.2	130.1	113.1	100.2	122.7	109.9
16	ELECTRICAL	90.6	106.4	101.1	90.3	102.7	98.5	107.3	128.2	121.2	95.2	115.3	108.6	91.2	106.5	101.3	96.1	93.7	94.5
1-16	WEIGHTED AVERAGE	106.4	112.9	109.6	106.8	114.2	110.4	107.3	123.6	115.2	107.5	120.0	113.5	106.7	119.2	112.7	107.6	113.8	110.6

Figure 23.13

Year	Quarterly City Cost Index Jan. 1, 1993 = 100		Current Index Based on Jan. 1, 1995 = 100		Year	Quarterly City Cost Index Jan. 1, 1993 = 100	Current Index Based on Jan. 1, 1995 = 100		Year	Quarterly City Cost Index Jan. 1, 1993 = 100	Current Index Based on Jan. 1, 1995 = 100	
	Est.	Actual	Est.	Actual		Actual	Est.	Actual		Actual	Est.	Actual
Oct 1995					July 1980	62.9	59.5		July 1962	20.2	19.1	
July 1995					1979	57.8	54.7		1961	19.8	18.7	
April 1995					1978	53.5	50.6		1960	19.7	18.6	
Jan 1995	105.7		100.0	100.0	1977	49.5	46.8		1959	19.3	18.3	
July 1994		104.4	98.8		1976	46.9	44.4		1958	18.8	17.8	
1993		101.7	96.2		1975	44.8	42.4		1957	18.4	17.4	
1992		99.4	94.1		1974	41.4	39.2		1956	17.6	16.7	
1991		96.8	91.6		1973	37.7	35.7		1955	16.6	15.7	
1990		94.3	89.2		1972	34.8	32.9		1954	16.0	15.1	
1989		92.1	87.2		1971	32.1	30.4		1953	15.8	14.9	
1988		89.9	85.0		1970	28.7	27.2		1952	15.4	14.6	
1987		87.7	83.0		1969	26.9	25.4		1951	15.0	14.2	
1986		84.2	79.7		1968	24.9	23.6		1950	13.7	13.0	
1985		82.6	78.2		1967	23.5	22.2		1949	13.3	12.6	
1984		82.0	77.5		1966	22.7	21.5		1948	13.3	12.6	
1983		80.2	75.8		1965	21.7	20.5		1947	12.1	11.4	
1982		76.1	72.0		1964	21.2	20.1		1946	10.1	9.6	
▼ 1981		70.0	66.2		▼ 1963	20.7	19.6		▼ 1945	8.8	8.3	

Figure 23.14

Chapter 24

A Sample Estimate

This chapter contains a complete sample estimate for the electrical portion of an office building. In this step-by-step example, forms are filled out and calculations made according to the techniques described in Parts I and II. For this example, let us assume that an electrical contractor has received a request for quote. The request is from the construction management company of an office building to be built in the local area.

Project Description

The project selected for the sample estimate is a three-story office building with a basement parking garage. The building will have a composite steel frame with a curtain wall system. Plans for the electrical work are shown in Figures 24.1 through 24.6. These plans, representing the major features of the electrical installation, are provided for illustrative purposes only. In actuality, such a building would require additional drawings with more plans, details, sections, and elevations. A full set of specifications would also be provided. The quantities, as given in the sample estimate, represent realistic conditions. Assumptions have been made for some items not shown that could normally be included.

This estimate may not necessarily be complete in every detail. Telephone systems, for example, are assumed to be outside the scope of the contract. Nevertheless, the estimate demonstrates techniques and approaches that can be used to solve real estimating problems.

Getting Started

A good estimator must be able to visualize the proposed electrical installation from source (service) to end use (fixtures or devices). This process helps to identify each component needed to make the system work. Before starting the takeoff, the estimator should follow some basic steps:
- Read the electrical specifications thoroughly.
- Scan the electrical plans; check other sections of the plans and specifications for their potential effect on electrical work (special attention should be given to mechanical and site work).
- Check the architectural and structural plans for unique or atypical requirements.
- Check and become familiar with the fixture and power symbols.
- Clarify with the architect or engineer any unclear areas, ensuring that the scope of work is understood. Addenda may be

Figure 24.1

ELECTRICAL LAYOUT

PARKING GARAGE PLAN

Note:
1. All conduit to be 1/2" EMT with compression type coupling unless otherwise indicated
2. All wire to be #12 THHN-THWN copper unless otherwise indicated

Note:
These drawings are diagrammatic only and not to scale.

Figure 24.2

247

TYPICAL ELECTRICAL LAYOUT

FIRST FLOOR PLAN

Note:
These drawings are diagrammatic only and not to scale

Note:
1. All fixtures type A unles otherwise indicated
2. All conduit to be 1/2" EMT above drop ceiling unless otherwise indicated
3. Fixture whips to be 3/8" Greenfield with 2 #12 THHN conductors
4. All stairway lighting from panel LP-1 in garage area

Figure 24.3

248

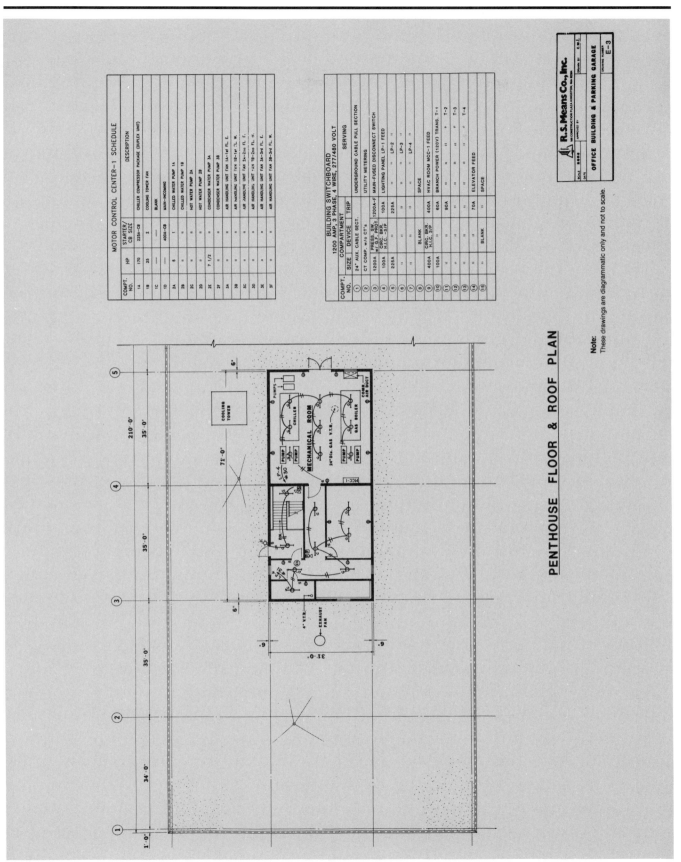

MOTOR CONTROL CENTER-1 SCHEDULE

COMPT. NO.	HP	STARTER/ CB SIZE	DESCRIPTION
1A	170	225A-CB	CHILLER COMPRESSOR PACKAGE (DUPLEX UNIT)
1B	25	2	COOLING TOWER FAN
1C	—		BLANK
1D	—	400A-CB	MAIN-INCOMING
2A	5	1	CHILLED WATER PUMP 1A
2B	"	"	CHILLED WATER PUMP 1B
2C	"	"	HOT WATER PUMP 2A
2D	"	"	HOT WATER PUMP 2B
3E	7 1/2	"	CONDENSER WATER PUMP 3A
3F	"	"	CONDENSER WATER PUMP 3B
3A	"	"	AIR HANDLING UNIT 7AH 1A-1st FL. E.
3B	"	"	AIR HANDLING UNIT 7AH 1B-1st FL. W.
3C	"	"	AIR HANDLING UNIT 7AH 2A-2ND FL. E.
3D	"	"	AIR HANDLING UNIT 7AH 7B-2ND FL. W.
3X	"	"	AIR HANDLING UNIT 7AH 3A-3rd FL. E.
3F	"	"	AIR HANDLING UNIT 7AH 3B-3rd FL. W.

BUILDING SWITCHBOARD
1200 AMP, 3 PHASE, 4 WIRE, 277/480 VOLT

COMPT. NO.	COMPARTMENT		SERVING
	SIZE	DEVICE / TRIP	
①	24" AUX. CABLE SECT.		UNDERGROUND CABLE PULL SECTION
②	CT COMP. w/o CT's		UTILITY METERING
③	1200A	FUSED SW. w/ G.F. PROT.	1200A-F	MAIN-FUSED DISCONNECT SWITCH
④	100A	CIRC. BKR. H.I.C. -3/P	100A	LIGHTING PANEL LP-1 FEED
⑤	225A	"	225A	LP-2
⑥	"	"	"	LP-3
⑦	"	"	"	LP-4
⑧		BLANK		SPACE
⑨	400A	CIRC. BKR. H.I.C. 3/P	400A	HVAC ROOM MCC-1 FEED
⑩	100A	"	60A	BRANCH POWER (120V) TRANS. T-1
⑪	"	"	90A	"	"	T-2
⑫	"	"	"	"	"	T-3
⑬	"	"	"	"	"	T-4
⑭	"	"	70A	ELEVATOR FEED
⑮	"	BLANK		SPACE

PENTHOUSE FLOOR & ROOF PLAN

R.S. Means Co., Inc.
100 CONSTRUCTION PLAZA KINGSTON, MA 02364

SCALE | APPROVED BY | DRAWN BY | C.W.I.
DATE

OFFICE BUILDING & PARKING GARAGE

DRAWING NUMBER E-3

Note:
These drawings are diagrammatic only and not to scale.

Figure 24.4

Figure 24.5

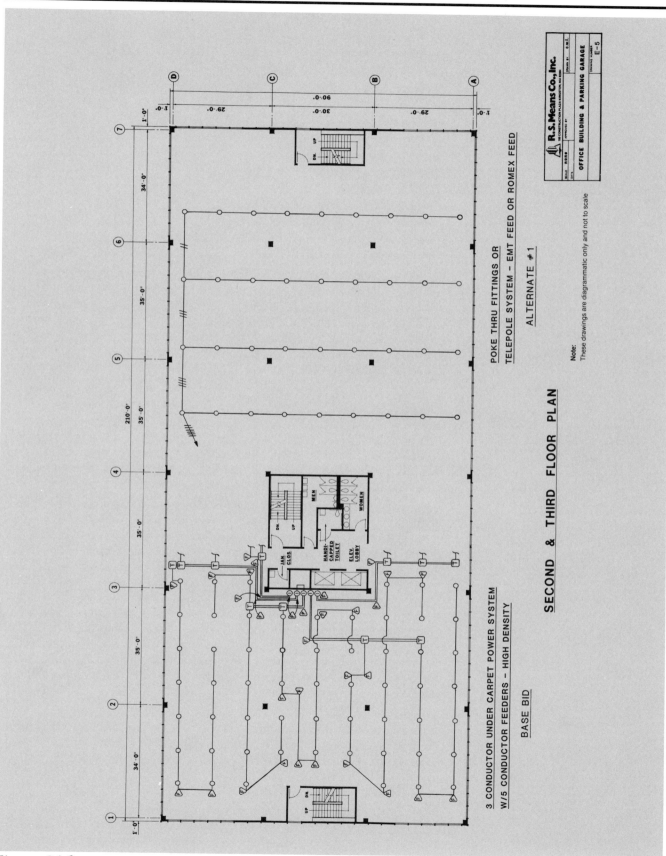

Figure 24.6

necessary to clarify certain items of work so that the responsibility for the performance of all work is defined.

- Immediately contact suppliers, manufacturers, and subsystem specialty contractors to get their quotations, sub-bids, and drawings.

Certain information should be taken from complete plans and specifications if the electrical portion of the work is to be properly estimated. In addition to floor plans, other sources of information are:

- Power riser diagram
- Panelboard schedule
- Fixture schedule
- Electrical symbol legend
- Reflected ceiling plans
- Branch circuit plans
- Fire alarm and telephone riser diagrams
- Special systems

Selecting a starting point can be difficult when a large-scale project is involved. Lighting is often a good place to begin for the following reasons: First, lighting is an item common to nearly all projects. Second, it represents a large, if not the largest, cost center for most projects. Third, when doing the lighting takeoff, the estimator is also taking a complete "tour" of the building. The resulting overview enables the estimator to select the order in which the remainder of the estimate should be carried out.

Lighting

The lighting takeoff should begin with a counting of all the various fixtures. A fixture schedule may be provided in the drawings or listed in the specifications. Figure 24.7 shows a fixture schedule for this type of building. A copy of this schedule should be fixed to a wall or desk top for handy reference throughout the lighting takeoff. The legend of drawing symbols (see Figure 24.5) should be posted with the schedule.

To organize the lighting takeoff information, use a form such as the "Lighting Schedule" form shown in Figure 24.8. Enter each fixture type with a brief description. Enter the symbol of each fixture as it will appear on the drawings. Note any special requirements or addenda; for example, an amendment to use Type C fixtures in lieu of Type F. Begin counting in an organized, systematic fashion. Arrange the schedule in such a way as to allow space for recording basement fixtures, followed by the fixtures for each of the other levels. Count carefully. Create columns for necessary components and count these components for each floor or area as you go. Included in this category are such items as raceways, fixture whips, boxes, and switches. To save time, take advantage of any symmetry or repetition on different floors. When all floors or areas are taken off, subtotal the columns. Make any needed adjustments and then calculate the total. It is a generally accepted practice to add 5% to conduit totals.

Wire is usually figured by multiplying the conduit footages times the overall average of the number of wires contained in all the conduit runs. In this example, allow three conductors per foot of conduit. Since wire length must exceed conduit lengths to make connections and terminations, add 10% to the wire totals.

Transfer the totals to a cost analysis form for pricing and extensions. "Pricing" refers to the process of assigning units of cost and/or hours to each activity code. "Extension" refers to the process of multiplying the value per unit times the total quantity of each item to get a total cost per item. See Figures 24.9 and 24.10.

Arrange the items on the cost analysis sheets into topical groupings, as much as is practical; this method can save time when researching the unit pricing. If changes must be made later, the affected items will be easier to locate.

It is a good idea to note the source of the unit costs used for pricing. Since we will be using *Means Electrical Cost Data* (1995 edition) for this estimate, the line number from the book will be the source description.

From the perspective of an electrical contractor, the man-hours needed to install the work as well as the costs for material and labor are listed. The column headings for each item include the man-hours, material cost (bare), and installation cost (bare). (Markups for overhead and profit will be added at the "bottom line" of the estimate.) Refer to Figure 24.9.

In the normal estimating process, the entire job takeoff is completed before the cost analysis sheets are priced. However, for the purpose of this example estimate, pricing and extending each segment of the job are discussed with that segment's takeoff.

Type	Manufacturer & Catalog #	Fixture	Type	Lamps Qty.	Volts	Watts	Mounting	Remarks
A	Meansco #7054	2' x 4' Lay-In	F-40 CW	4	277	40	Recessed	Acrylic Lens
B	Meansco #7055	1' x 4' Lay-In	F-40 CW	2	277	40	Recessed	Acrylic Lens
C	Meansco #7709	6" x 4'	F-40 CW	1	277	40	Surface	Acrylic Wrap
D	Meansco #7710	6" x 8' Strip	F96T12 CW	1	277	75	Surface	
E	Meansco #7900A	6" x 4'	F-40	1	277	40	Surface	Mirror Light
F	Kingston #100A	6" x 4'	F-40	1	277	40	Surface	Acrylic Wrap
G	Kingston #110C	4' Strip	F-40 CW	1	277	40	Surface	2' Below Fascia
H	Kingston #3752	Wallpack, Ext.	HPS	1	277	150	Bracket	
J	Kingston #201-202	Floodlight, Ext.	HPS	1	277	400	Surface	2' Below Fascia
K	Kingston #203	Wallpack, Ext	HPS	1	277	70	Wall Bracket	
L	Meansco #8100	Exit Light	1-13W CW	1	120	13	Surface	
		Single, Face	T6-1/2	2	6-1/2	20		
M	Meansco #9000	Battery Unit	Sealed Beam	2	6V	18	Wall Mount	6 V, Lead-Acid
N	Meansco #9001	Remote Head	Sealed Beam	1	6V	18	Wall Mount	

Figure 24.7

LIGHTING SCHEDULE

JOB NO. **E4-33**
JOB DESCRIPTION **Office Bldg.**
OWNER **R.S. Means Company, Inc.**
LOCATION **Kingston, MA**

ESTIMATE NO. **4-33**
SHEET **1** OF **19**
SCALE **1/4 = 1**
TAKE OFF BY **MEL**
CHECKED BY **SP**
DATE **1-2-95**

FIXTURES: Type F deleted — Use Type C

SYSTEM	A 2'x4' Troffer 4L	B 1'x4' Troffer 3L	C 4'x4' Acrylic	D Strip	E 6'x8' mirror Light	G 4' Strip surface mt	H 150w Wall Pack	K 70w Wall Pack	L Fluor. Elect Light	m Battery Emerg Light	n Em. Lt Remote Head	EMT 1/2	Conn. 1/2" Set Screw Type	Conn. 1/2" Comp. Type	Whips 6' #6/3W THHN	O 4" Round Box	4" Round Cover	S₁ 1gang Switch Box	S₁ S.P. Switch 20A	4" Sq. Box	Sw. Cover Plate	4" Plaster Ring	THHN #12
Basmnt	-	6	4	53	-	6	-	1	6	3	1	1480 LF	190	18	6	8	8	1	1	6	1	6	4440 LF
1st Fl	237	10	9	-	3	1	2	1	8	3	1	2070 LF	244	26	247	128	128	5	5	8	5	8	6210 LF
2nd Fl	244	6	8	-	3	1	-	-	4	3	1	1880 LF	242	24	250	129	129	5	5	4	5	4	5040 LF
3rd Fl	244	6	8	-	3	1	-	-	4	3	1	1880 LF	242	24	250	129	129	6	5	4	5	4	5040 LF
Pnt Hs	-	-	-	-	-	18	-	1	1	1	1	940 LF	114	12	-	-	-	4	4	1	4	1	2820 LF
Sub Tl												8250 LF +5%											24,750 LF +10%
Adjust												413 LF											2475 LF
Total	725	28	29	53	9	27	2	3	23	13	4	8663 LF	1052	104	753	394	394	20	20	23	20	23	273 CLF

Round up to 8676 LF

COST ANALYSIS

PROJECT: Office Building		Lighting						SHEET NO.	2 of 19			
LOCATION:				ARCHITECT:				ESTIMATE NO:	4 - 33			
TAKE OFF BY: VP	QUANTITIES BY: VP	PRICES BY: MJM		EXTENSIONS BY: MJM				DATE:	1 / 8 / 95			
								CHECKED BY:	MJM			

DESCRIPTION	SOURCE/DIMENSIONS			QUANTITY	UNIT	MAN-HOURS		MATERIAL		LABOR	
						COS	TOTAL	COST	TOTAL	COS	TOTAL
Fixtures											
Type A, 2' x 4', Lay-in, 4 lamp	166	130	0600	725	Ea.	1.702	1234	70.00	50,750	48.50	35,163
Type B, 1' x 4', Lay-in, 2 lamp	166	130	0200	28	Ea.	1.404	39	50.50	1414	40.00	1120
Type C, 6" x 4", Acrylic wrap, 1 lamp	166	130	2020	29	Ea.	1.000	29	46.50	1349	28.50	827
Type D, 8' Strip, 1 lamp	166	130	2600	53	Ea.	1.190	63	50.00	2650	34.00	1802
Type E, 6" x 4", Mirror lt., 1 lamp	166	130	6910	9	Ea.	1.000	9	65.00	585	28.50	257
Type G, 4" Strip, surface mt, 1 lamp	166	130	2200	27	Ea.	0.941	25	29.00	783	27.00	729
Type H, 150 W, Wall pack, Ext.	166	115	1170	2	Ea.	2.000	4	330.00	660	57.00	114
Type K, 70 W, Wall pack, Ext.	166	115	1160	3	Ea.	2.000	6	300.00	900	57.00	171
Type L, Fluorescent, Ext. lt, S face	166	110	0150	23	Ea.	1.000	23	139.00	3197	28.50	656
Type M, Battery unit emergency lt.	166	110	0500	13	Ea.	2.000	26	258.00	3354	57.00	741
Type N, Emergency lt., Remote, 1 lamp	166	110	0780	4	Ea.	0.300	1	20.50	82	8.55	34
Raceway											
1/2" EMT	160	205	5000	8670	LF	0.047	407	0.40	3468	1.34	11,618
Fixture Whips											
3/8" x 6', 3 wire, #14, THHN	166	125	0300	753	Ea.	0.250	188	8.95	6739	7.15	5384
Wire											
# 12 THWN, Solid	161	165	0940	273	CLF	0.727	198	5.75	1570	20.50	5597
Page 2 Subtotal							2,252		$77,501		$64,210

Figure 24.9

COST ANALYSIS

PROJECT: Office Building   Lighting

ARCHITECT:

LOCATION:

TAKE OFF BY: VP   QUANTITIES BY: VP   PRICES BY: MJM   EXTENSIONS BY: MJM   CHECKED BY: MJM

DESCRIPTION	SOURCE/DIMENSIONS			QUANTITY	UNIT	MAN-HOURS		MATERIAL		LABOR	
						COST	TOTAL	COST	TOTAL	COST	TOTAL
Boxes and Devices											
4" Octagon box	162	110	0020	394	Ea.	0.400	158	1.25	493	11.40	4492
4" Octagon blank cover	162	110	0060	394	Ea.	0.125	49	0.53	209	3.56	1403
4" Square box	162	110	0150	23	Ea.	0.400	9	1.60	37	11.40	262
Plaster rings	162	110	0300	23	Ea.	0.125	3	0.94	22	3.56	82
Switch box	162	110	0650	20	Ea.	0.296	6	1.60	32	8.45	169
S. P. Switch - 20 A	162	320	0500	20	Ea.	0.296	6	5.65	113	8.45	169
Switch plate - 1 gang	162	320	2600	20	Ea.	0.100	2	1.85	37	2.85	57
Page 3 Subtotal							233		942		6633
Page 2 Subtotal							2,252		77,501		64,210
Lighting Total							2,485		$78,442		$70,844

Figure 24.10

Complete the pricing and extensions and subtotal each sheet. When each segment of the estimate is complete, combine the subtotals to get a category total. In this case, the "totals" (Figure 24.10) are for the lighting work. It is not necessary to combine material and labor costs yet.

Service and Distribution Equipment

After the lighting takeoff is complete, the next logical step is to take off the service entrance equipment and distribution feeders. This segment of the work is appropriately listed early in the takeoff because it represents the source of all power for the building. In addition, the equipment is located in the basement level and can be approached in the same bottom-to-top order as was used for lighting. Furthermore, service and distribution equipment usually represents the second largest cost segment (after lighting) for this type of project.

The equipment, conduit, cable, and destination equipment are represented in diagrams on the electric riser drawing (Figure 24.5). When using the riser diagram to organize the takeoff sheets, remember that it is a "not to scale" drawing. To estimate the conduit lengths, fittings, and cable lengths, it will be necessary to use the plan and elevation drawings. Relevant information that does not appear on the drawings might instead be found in the specifications. Some information may appear in both locations. For example, the specifications might inform the contractor that "the elevator equipment, including controls, will be furnished and installed by others. The electrical contractor shall furnish and install two feeders with safety disconnects to be mounted within sight of the elevator equipment." Items of this kind must be noted by the estimator when reading the specifications. In this way, the estimate can be done correctly as the takeoff is performed.

Begin the riser diagram takeoff by filling in a feeder schedule to tabulate each conduit and cable run (see Figures 24.11 and 24.12). Enter each circuit number along with its origin and destination. Using the riser legend (Figure 24.5), enter the given information for each circuit, such as conduit size, number of conductors, and size of conductors. Referring to the plan and elevation drawings, carefully determine the length of each conduit run. Count and list any extra items, such as wireway or conduit nipples. Add 5% for each conduit run as a tolerance and then total.

The next step is calculating the "run" length of each circuit by using the measured conduit length—plus any length required at the equipment. For example, the wires entering the top of a switchboard may need to reach a circuit breaker located at the bottom; therefore, add five feet to each cable run entering this board. Multiply the length of each run by the number of wires to arrive at the linear feet of each wire for each circuit. Finally, add 10% to the wire lengths as a tolerance.

Since the service and distribution equipment is clearly and simply represented on the riser drawing, it may be practical to take off this equipment directly, using a cost analysis sheet (see Figures 24.13, 24.14, and 24.15). Additional information, such as the panelboard schedule (Figure 24.16), may help to complete this takeoff.

Transfer the quantities from the feeder schedule to the cost analysis sheets. It is often convenient to summarize like quantities at the bottom of the feeder schedule before transferring those totals. Refer to the bottom of Figure 24.12.

FEEDER SCHEDULE
Riser Diagram

JOB NO.
OWNER:
JOB DESCRIPTION: Office Building
SCALE:

ADDRESS:
DRAWING NO.: E-4
TAKE OFF BY: PHD

PANEL NO.	CIRCUIT NO.	FROM	TO	AMPS	RACEWAY								WIRE						
					SIZE	TYPE	LF	TERM	+5%	6"nipl	Elbow	Endbl	Conn	NO.	SIZE	TYPE	VOLT	RUN	LF	+10%
SWBD.	1	Pad Mnt Xfmr	Main Swchbrd	1200	4"	PVC	4x200 =800	24	840		8	8		4 x 3	750 MCM	Cu. USE	480	4Trip @200'	2400	26.4
SWBD	4	SWBD	LP-1	100	1 1/2"	EMT	5		5				2	4	#1 AWG	Cu. THWN	480	10	40	.4
SWBD	5	SWBD	LP-2	225	2 1/2"	EMT	50		55					4	300 MCM	Cu. THWN	480	55	220	2.4
SWBD	6	SWBD	LP-3	225	2 1/2"	EMT	65		70					4	300 MCM	Cu. THWN	480	70	280	3.1
SWBD	7	SWBD	LP-4	225	2 1/2"	EMT	80		85					4	300 MCM	Cu. THWN	480	85	340	3.7
SWBD	9	SWBD	MCC-1	400	3"	EMT	85		90					4	500 MCM	Cu. THWN	480	90	360	4.0
SWBD	10	SWBD	T-1	60	3/4"	EMT	15		15				2	4	#6 AWG	Cu. THWN	480	20	80	.9
SWBD	10 A	T-1	PP-1	125	1 1/2"	EMT	5		5				2	4	#1 AWG	Cu. THWN	480	5	20	.2
SWBD	11	SWBD	T-2	90	1 1/4"	EMT	20		20					4	#3 AWG	Cu. THWN	480	25	100	1.1
SWBD	11 A	T-2	Disc. Sw. T-2	225	2 1/2"	RGS				1				4	300 MCM	Cu. THWN	480	2	8	.1
SWBD	11 B	Disc. Sw. T-2	PP-2	225	2 1/2"	EMT	50		55					4	300 MCM	Cu. THWN	480	50	200	2.2

Figure 24.11

FEEDER SCHEDULE

Riser Diagram

JOB NO.:			ADDRESS:	
OWNER:			DRAWING NO.: E-4	SHEET NO. 5 of 19
JOB DESCRIPTION: Office Building			TAKE OFF BY: PHD	ESTIMATE NO: 4-33
SCALE:			CHECKED BY: MJM	DATE: 1/2/95

PANEL NO.	CIRCUIT NO.	FROM	TO	AMPS	RACEWAY								WIRE						
					SIZE	TYPE	LF	TERM +5%	6"nipl	6x6wr way	6x6en caps	Conn	NO.	SIZE	TYPE	VOLT	RUN	LF	+10% CLF
SWBD.	12	SWBD	T-3	90	1 1/4"	EMT	20	20				2	4	#3 AWG	Cu. THWN	480	25	100	1.1
SWBD	12 A	T-3	Disc. Sw. T-3	225	2 1/2"	RGS	-		1				4	300 MCM	Cu. THWN	480	2	8	.1
SWBD	12 B	Disc. Sw. T-3	PP-3	225	2 1/2"	EMT	65	70					4	300 MCM	Cu. THWN	480	65	260	2.9
SWBD	13	SWBD	T-4	90	1 1/4"	EMT	25	25				2	4	#3 AWG	Cu. THWN	480	30	120	1.3
SWBD	13 A	T-4	Disc. Sw. T-4	225	2 1/2"	RGS	-		1				4	300 MCM	Cu. THWN	480	2	8	.1
SWBD	13 B	Disc. Sw. T-4	PP-4	225	2 1/2"	EMT	80	85					4	300 MCM	Cu. THWN	480	85	340	3.7
SWBD	14	SWBD	Elev. Dis. Sw. A&B	70	1"	EMT	25	25	2 RGS	4'	2	2	4	#4 AWG	Cu. THWN	480	30	120	1.3
SWBD	14 A	Elev. Disc. A	Elev. A Equip.	35	3/4"	EMT	10	10				2	4	#10 AWG	Cu. THWN	480	15	60	.7
SWBD	14 B	Elev. Disc. B	Elev. B Equip.	35	3/4"	EMT	15	15				2	4	#10 AWG	Cu. THWN	480	20	80	.9

Figure 24.12

259

COST ANALYSIS

PROJECT: Office Building   Riser Diagram and Feeder Schedule

LOCATION: ARCHITECT:

TAKE OFF BY: VP   QUANTITIES BY: VP PRICES BY: MJ   EXTENSIONS BY: MJM   CHECKED BY: MJM

DESCRIPTION	SOURCE/DIMENSIONS			QUANTITY	UNIT	MAN-HOURS		MATERIAL		LABOR	
						COST	TOTAL	COST	TOTAL	COST	TOTAL
Switchboard											
Main pressure switch and CT Compt., w / Ground fault, 1200 A, 480 V	163	260	3600	1	Ea.	24.240	24	12,100	12,100	690	690
Distribution section, 277/480 V, 1200 A	163	264	0500	2	Ea.	22.220	44	2075	4150	635	1270
Branch circuit breakers, HIC, Group mtd., 100 A, 3 P	163	266	1180	6	Ea.	-	-	415	2490	-	-
											-
225 A, 3 P	163	266	1220	3	Ea.	-	-	1550	4650	-	-
											-
400 A, 3 P	163	266	1260	1	Ea.	-	-	2050	2050	-	-
Panelboards with breakers											
120/208 V, 3 P - 4 W, 100 A, with 24 circuits and main	163	245	2050	1	Ea.	17.020	17	800	800	485	485
120/208 V, 3 P - 4 W, 225 A, with 42 circuits without main	163	245	1000	3	Ea.	23.530	71	890	2670	670	2010
277/480 V, 3 P - 4 W, 100 A, with 20 circuits without main	163	245	1300	1	Ea.	13.330	13	1225	1225	380	380
277/480 V, 3 P - 4 W, 225 A, with 42 circuits without main	163	245	1500	3	Ea.	26.670	80	2150	6450	760	2280
Safety Switches											
H. D. Fused, 60 A - 3 P, 600 V	163	360	4380	2	Ea.	3.480	7	169	338	99	198
H. D. Fused, 400 A - 3 P, 240 V	163	360	3700	3	Ea.	8.890	27	910	2730	253	759
							-----------		-----------		-----------
Page 6 Subtotal							283		$39,653		$8,072

Figure 24.13

COST ANALYSIS

PROJECT: Office Building			Riser Diagram and Feeder Schedule					**SHEET NO.** 7 of 19			
LOCATION:			**ARCHITECT:**					**ESTIMATE NO:** 4 - 33			
TAKE OFF BY: VP	**QUANTITIES BY:** VP	**PRICES BY:** MJM		**EXTENSIONS BY:** MJM				**DATE:** 1 / 8 / 95			
								CHECKED BY: MJM			

DESCRIPTION	SOURCE/DIMENSIONS			QUANTITY	UNIT	MAN-HOURS		MATERIAL		LABOR	
						COST	TOTAL	COST	TOTAL	COST	TOTAL
Transformers											
45 KVA, 3 P-240/480-120/208 Ventltd.	164	120	3500	1	Ea.	20.000	20	1525.00	1525	570.00	570
75 KVA, 3 P-240/480-120/208 Ventltd.	164	120	3700	3	Ea.	22.900	69	2300.00	6900	650.00	1950
Grounding and Wire											
4/0 Bare copper	161	810	1000	0.2	CLF	2.810	1	175.00	35	80.00	16
Cadweld 4/0 to Bldg. steel	161	810	2740	2	Ea.	1.140	2	6.65	13	32.50	65
Cable terminals 4/0 Cu.	161	520	3000	2	Ea.	0.727	1	4.00	8	20.50	41
750 MCM, USE, Cu.	161	165	5800	26.4	CLF	7.270	192	750.00	19800	207.00	5465
500 MCM, THWN, Cu.	161	165	2800	4	CLF	5.000	20	410.00	1640	143.00	572
300 MCM, THWN, Cu.	161	165	2400	18.3	CLF	4.210	77	260.00	4758	120.00	2196
#1 THWN, Cu.	161	165	1550	0.6	CLF	2.000	1	84.00	50	57.00	34
#3 THWN, Cu.	161	165	1450	3.5	CLF	1.600	6	49.00	172	45.40	159
#4 THWN, Cu.	161	165	1400	1.3	CLF	1.510	2	38.50	50	43.00	56
#6 THWN, Cu.	161	165	1350	0.9	CLF	1.230	1	24.50	22	35.00	32
#10 THWN, Cu. (Stranded)	161	165	1250	1.6	CLF	0.800	1	11.35	18	23.00	37
Raceways											
6" x 6" Wireway	160	150	0400	4	LF	0.267	1	12.95	52	7.60	30
6" x 6" End caps	160	150	4000	2	Ea.	0.444	1	4.35	9	12.65	25
Page 7 Subtotal							395		$35,052		$11,248

Figure 24.14

COST ANALYSIS

PROJECT: Office Building   Riser Diagram and Feeder Schedule

LOCATION: ARCHITECT:

TAKE OFF BY: VP   QUANTITIES BY: VP   PRICES BY: MJM   EXTENSIONS BY: MJM

ESTIMATE NO: 4 - 33

DATE: 1 / 8 / 95

CHECKED BY: MJM

DESCRIPTION	SOURCE/DIMENSIONS			QUANTITY	UNIT	MAN-HOURS		MATERIAL		LABOR	
						COST	TOTAL	COST	TOTAL	COST	TOTAL
Raceways (cont'd)											
4" PVC-Undergrnd duct bank(4@210')	167	110	5600	210	LF	0.200	42	3.80	798	5.70	119
4" PVC Elbows	167	110	8400	8	Ea.	0.667	5	15.20	122	19.00	15
4" PVC End bells	167	110	9800	8	Ea.	0.667	5	4.62	37	19.00	15
2 Qt. PVC Cement	167	110	9950	2	Ea.	-	-	8.40	17	-	-
Trenching, Backfill and Concrete ---By Others											
3" EMT	160	205	5140	90	LF	0.160	14	5.50	495	4.56	410
3" EMT Elbow	160	205	5800	3	Ea.	0.889	3	29.50	89	25.50	77
2-1/2" EMT	160	205	5120	420	LF	0.133	56	4.37	1835	3.80	1596
2-1/2" Set screw conn.	160	205	6620	4	Ea.	0.222	1	17.20	69	6.35	25
2-1/2" EMT Elbow	160	205	5780	6	Ea.	0.667	4	19.80	119	19.00	114
1-1/2" EMT	160	205	5080	10	LF	0.089	1	1.43	14	2.53	25
1-1/2" EMT Set screw conn.	160	205	6580	4	Ea.	0.133	1	3.84	15	3.80	15
1-1/4" EMT	160	205	5060	65	LF	0.080	5	1.21	79	2.28	148
1-1/4" EMT Set screw conn.	160	205	6560	4	Ea.	0.114	0	2.65	11	3.26	13
1" EMT	160	205	5040	25	LF	0.070	2	0.82	21	1.98	50
1" EMT Set screw conn.	160	205	6540	2	Ea.	0.089	0	1.35	3	2.53	5
3/4" EMT	160	205	5020	40	LF	0.062	2	0.55	22	1.75	70
3/4" Set screw conn.	160	205	6520	6	Ea.	0.073	0	0.77	5	2.07	12
2-1/2" x 6" RGS Nipple	160	220	3720	2	Ea.	0.615	1	24.00	48	17.55	35
1" x 6" RGS Nipple	160	220	2920	2	Ea.	0.348	1	4.20	8	9.90	20
Page 8 Subtotal							144		$3,805		$4,117
Subtotal page 6							283		39,653		8,072
Subtotal page 7							395		35,052		11,248
Subtotal page 8							144		3,805		4,117
							----------		----------		----------
Riser Total							823		$78,510		$23,437

Figure 24.15

To complete this segment of the work, price and extend these cost analysis sheets. Careful attention must be paid no matter what the price source, to assure that the unit of measure is compatible with those used in the takeoff.

Occasionally, the exact work item may not appear in the reference source; in such cases, common sense judgments must be made by selecting the similar task item, overwriting the descriptions, labor-hours, and material costs, and then creating a suitable estimate to meet project requirements.

Motor Control Center and Motor Feeders

Since motor control centers and motor feeders are taken off in a manner similar to that used for service and distribution equipment, this segment of the work is a logical choice for the next category in the estimate. The motor control center (MCC) appears on the penthouse floor plan drawing (Figure 24.4). The same drawing also shows an elevation of the MCC and a schedule of the MCC's circuits. Again, use a feeder schedule form (Figure 24.17) to tabulate the conduit and wire requirements. Enter each circuit from the MCC and list its destination.

In this case, the designer has provided only the horsepower of the motor being fed. Conduit and wire sizes are not given; this information must be determined by the estimator.

To complete this information, proceed according to the following steps:

1. Knowing the motor's horsepower and operating voltage (460V, 3 phase), we can refer to a table to find the amperage required. The reference table (from *Means Electrical Cost Data*) is "Ampere Values Determined By Horsepower, Voltage, and Phase Values," and appears in the Appendix of this book. Enter the HP and amp values on the feeder schedule.

Panelboard Schedule

Panel	Main Breaker	Main	Lugs	Amps	Circ.	Breakers #	Type	Location	Volts
PP-1	Yes	3-P	Wire	100	24	(24)	1P 20 A	Basement	120/208
PP-2	No	3-P	4 Wire	225	42	(42)	1P 20 A	1st Floor	120/208
PP-3	No	3-P	4 Wire	225	42	(42)	1P 20 A	2nd Floor	120/208
PP-4	No	3-P	4 Wire	225	42	(42)	1P-20 A	3rd Floor	120/208
LP-1	No	3-P	4 Wire	100	20	(20)	1P-20 A	Basement	277/480
LP-2	No	3-P	4 Wire	225	42	(42)	1P-20 A	1st Floor	277/480
LP-3	No	3-P	4 Wire	225	42	(42)	1P-20 A	2nd Floor	277/480
LP-4	No	3-P	4 Wire	225	42	(42)	1P-20 A	3rd Floor	277/480

Figure 24.16

FEEDER SCHEDULE

MCC - 1

JOB NO.
OWNER:
JOB DESCRIPTION: Office Building
SCALE:

ADDRESS:
DRAWING NO.: E - 4
TAKE OFF BY: PHD

PANEL NO.	CIRCUIT NO.	FROM	TO	HP/ AMPS		RACEWAY							WIRE					
					SIZE	TYPE	LF	TERM +5%	LB's	T's	Motor terms.	NO.	SIZE	TYPE	VOLT	RUN	LF	+10%
MCC - 1	1A	MCC	Chiller compres.	170 / 221	2"	RGS	30	30	1		1	3	300 MCM	THWN	480	35	105	115
MCC - 1	1B	MCC	Cooling tower fan	25 / 34	1/2"	RGS	80	85	2		1	3	#8	THWN	480	85	255	280
MCC - 1	2A	MCC	Chill wtr. pump 1A	5 / 7.6	1/2"	RGS	40	40	1		1	3	#12	THWN	480	45	135	150
MCC - 1	2B	MCC	Chill wtr. pump 1B	5 / 7.6	1/2"	RGS	40	40	1		1	3	#12	THWN	480	45	135	150
MCC - 1	2C	MCC	Hot wtr. pump 2A	5 / 7.6	1/2"	RGS	20	20	1		1	3	#12	THWN	480	25	75	85
MCC - 1	2D	MCC	Hot wtr. pump 2B	5 / 7.6	1/2"	RGS	20	20	1		1	3	#12	THWN	480	25	75	85
MCC - 1	2E	MCC	Cool twer. pump 3A	7.5 / 11	1/2"	RGS	50	55	1		1	3	#12	THWN	480	55	165	180
MCC - 1	2F	MCC	Cool twer. pump 3B	7.5 / 11	1/2"	RGS	50	55	1		1	3	#12	THWN	480	55	165	180
MCC - 1	3A	MCC	A H U fan 1A	7.5 / 11	1/2"	RGS	45	45	2		1	3	#12	THWN	480	50	150	165
MCC - 1	3B	MCC	A H U fan 1B	7.5 / 11	1/2"	RGS	20	20	1		1	3	#12	THWN	480	55	165	180
MCC - 1	3C	MCC	A H U fan 2A	7.5 / 11	1/2"	RGS	60	65	2		1	3	#12	THWN	480	65	195	215
MCC - 1	3D	MCC	A H U fan 2B	7.5 / 11	1/2"	RGS	20	20	1		1	3	#12	THWN	480	70	210	230

Figure 24.17

2. With the amperages known, the size of the conductors can be found based on a table (from *Means Electrical Cost Data*), "Minimum Copper and Aluminum Wire Sizes Allowed for Various Types of Insulation," which also appears in the Appendix of this book. Enter the copper wire size under the proper column on the feeder schedule. (When sizing wire for motor feeders, it is often appropriate to use #12 AWG as a *minimum*.)

3. The size of the conduit can now be listed from the table (*Means Electrical Cost Data*), "Maximum Number of Wires for Various Conduit Sizes" (see Appendix).

Although sizing wires and conduits in this manner may not be precise, it is generally accurate enough for estimating purposes.

Conduit and wire lengths are measured and calculated in the same manner as the distribution feeders. The conduit connection to each motor should allow for three feet of flexible metallic conduit (or sealtite) with connectors. Also, the power leads to the motors will require termination lugs for each conductor.

Next, the MCC and its components can be taken off directly onto the cost analysis sheets (see Figures 24.18 and 24.19).

Price and extend these items after transferring the quantities from the feeder schedule to the cost analysis sheets.

Branch Wiring

The "owner" in the sample estimate is considering two alternative methods for branch power receptacles: an undercarpet cable system (type FCC) and poke-through receptacles. A bid proposal is required for each system.

Fixed Receptacles: A portion of the branch wiring system is fixed to the structure walls and columns. The estimating process may be simplified if this portion is taken off separately from the undercarpet system or the poke-through system. The fixed receptacles are taken off as shown in Figure 24.20. Note that 5% is added to the conduit total and 10% to the wire total. The wire total is based on three wires per foot of conduit. The wire total is then changed from linear feet (L.F.) to hundred linear feet (C.L.F.) to match the cost units. The takeoff quantities are then transferred from the quantity sheet to the cost analysis sheet (Figure 24.21), priced, and extended.

Undercarpet System: A composite drawing showing typical representations of both systems is shown in Figure 24.6. The items for the undercarpet branch power system are taken off and extended according to the methods used for the fixed receptacles discussed above (see Figure 24.22). The quantities are transferred to the cost analysis sheet (Figure 24.23) and the items are priced and extended.

Poke-through System—Alternate: The poke-through system will be the option. Since the two systems are being considered as equal alternatives, it must be assumed that the same density of receptacles will be needed for each system. The poke-through devices come as an assembled unit; as a result, fewer components need to be listed and priced. The takeoff for this system is shown in Figure 24.24.

COST ANALYSIS

PROJECT: Office Building M C C-1 & Feeders

LOCATION: ARCHITECT:

TAKE OFF BY: VP QUANTITIES BY: VP PRICES BY: MJM EXTENSIONS BY: MJM

DESCRIPTION	SOURCE/DIMENSIONS			QUANTITY	UNIT	MAN-HOURS		MATERIAL		LABOR	
						COST	TOTAL	COST	TOTAL	COST	TOTAL
Motor Control Center, Factory assembled											
Sections, 72" high, NEMA 1	163	110	0900	3	Ea.	10.00	30	1250.00	3750	285.00	855
Copper bus, add	163	110	1100	3	Ea.	-	-	147.00	441	-	-
Pilot lights, add	163	110	1700	15	Ea.	-	-	96.50	1448	-	-
Pushbuttons, add	163	110	1800	15	Ea.	-	-	61.00	915	-	-
Size 1 Starters, FVNR, Type A, Circuit breakers	163	120	0120	12	Ea.	-	-	555.00	6660	-	-
Size 2 Starters, FVNR, Type A, Circuit breakers	163	120	1120	1	Ea.	-	-	690.00	690	-	-
225 A Feed. circuit breaker	163	120	6960	1	Ea.	-	-	895.00	895	-	-
400 A Inc. circuit breaker	163	120	7660	1	Ea.	-	-	3375.00	3375	-	-
Conduit											
2" RGS	160	205	1870	30	LF	0.178	5	4.25	128	5.05	152
2" LB Fitting	160	250	2370	1	Ea.	1.600	2	35.00	35	45.50	46
1/2" RGS	160	205	1750	565	LF	0.089	50	1.27	718	2.53	1429
1/2" LB Fitting	160	250	2280	17	Ea.	0.500	9	6.30	107	14.25	242
1/2" T Fitting	160	250	2420	3	Ea.	0.667	2	7.60	23	19.00	57
Page 10 Subtotal							98		$19,183		$2,781

Figure 24.18

COST ANALYSIS

PROJECT: Office Building	M C C-1 & Feeders			SHEET NO. 11 of 19

PROJECT: Office Building   M C C-1 & Feeders   SHEET NO.   11 of 19
LOCATION: ESTIMATE NO: 4 - 33
                            ARCHITECT: DATE: 1 / 8 / 95
TAKE OFF BY: VP   QUANTITIES BY: VP   PRICES BY: MJM   EXTENSIONS BY: MJM   CHECKED BY: MJM

DESCRIPTION	SOURCE/DIMENSIONS			QUANTITY	UNIT	MAN-HOURS		MATERIAL		LABOR	
						COST	TOTAL	COST	TOTAL	COST	TOTAL
Wire pulling											
#12 THWN, Cu.	161	165	1200	21.7	CLF	0.727	16	6.90	150	20.50	445
#8 THWN, Cu.	161	165	1300	2.8	CLF	1.000	3	17.80	50	28.50	80
300 MCM THWN, Cu.	161	165	2400	1.2	CLF	4.210	5	260.00	312	120.00	144
Motor Connections											
170 HP (as 200 HP)	160	275	1620	1	Ea.	5.330	5	84.00	84	152.00	152
25 HP	160	275	1530	1	Ea.	1.330	1	5.95	6	38.00	38
7-1/2 HP (as 10 HP)	160	275	1520	8	Ea.	1.000	8	3.75	30	28.50	228
5 HP	160	275	1500	4	Ea.	1.000	4	3.75	15	28.50	114
							--------		----------		----------
Page 11 Subtotal							42		$647		$1,201
Subtotal page 10							98		19,183		2,781
							--------		----------		----------
M C C Total							140		$19,830		$3,981

Figure 24.19

267

QUANTITY SHEET

PROJECT: Office Building
LOCATION:
TAKE OFF BY:
QUANTITIES BY: PHD
EXTENSIONS BY: MJM

SHEET NO. 12 of 19
ESTIMATE NO: 4-33
DATE: 1/2/95
CHECKED BY: MJM

Fixed Receptacles, Branch Wiring
ARCHITECT:

DESCRIPTION	SYMBOL	DIMENSIONS	Garage	UNIT	1st Floor	UNIT	2nd Floor	UNIT	3rd Floor	UNIT	Penthouse	UNIT	Totals +5% Cond +10% Wire	UNIT
Branch Wiring for Receptacles														
Cast box – FD, 1/2" Hub, 1 Gang			5	Ea.	2	Ea.							7	Ea.
W.P. Receptacle cover	WP		5	Ea.	2	Ea.							7	Ea.
GFI Receptacle	GF		1	Ea.	3	Ea.	1	Ea.	1	Ea.			6	Ea.
Duplex Receptacle	⏀		5	Ea.	80	Ea.	80	Ea.	80	Ea.	12	Ea.	257	Ea.
Handy box			1	Ea.							12	Ea.	13	Ea.
Receptacle cover			1	Ea.							12	Ea.	13	Ea.
4" Sq. Boxes					86	Ea.	81	Ea.	81	Ea.			248	Ea.
4" Sq. Plaster ring					81	Ea.	75	Ea.	75	Ea.			231	Ea.
Receptacle cover – S.S.			-	Ea.	81	Ea.	75	Ea.	75	Ea.			231	Ea
1/2" EMT			310	LF	1120	LF	1060	LF	1060	LF	180	LF	3920	LF
1/2" EMT Connector – compression			5	Ea.	2	Ea.							7	Ea.
1/2" EMT Connector – set screw			5	Ea.	160	Ea.	148	Ea.	146	Ea.	24	Ea.	483	Ea.
#12 Wire THHN – Solid			930	LF	3360	LF	3180	LF	3180	LF	540	LF	12310 or 124	LF CLF

Figure 24.20

COST ANALYSIS

PROJECT: Office Building   Fixed receptacles, Branch Wiring

LOCATION:

TAKE OFF BY: VP   QUANTITIES BY: VP PRICES BY: MJM EXTENSIONS BY: MJM

ARCHITECT:

DESCRIPTION	SOURCE/DIMENSIONS			QUANTITY	UNIT	MAN-HOURS		MATERIAL		LABOR	
						COST	TOTAL	COST	TOTAL	COST	TOTAL
Boxes & Wiring Devices											
Cast box - FD, 1/2" Hub, 1 Gang	162	110	1420	7	Ea.	0.667	5	10.00	70	19.00	133
WP Receptacle cover	162	110	1600	7	Ea.	0.125	1	9.45	66	3.56	25
GFI Receptacle, 15 A	162	320	2480	6	Ea.	0.296	2	29.00	174	8.45	51
Duplex Receptacle, 20 A	162	320	2470	257	Ea.	0.296	76	5.40	1388	8.45	2172
Handy box	162	110	0550	13	Ea.	0.296	4	1.33	17	8.45	110
Cover, receptacle	162	110	0560	13	Ea.	0.125	2	0.47	6	3.56	46
4" Sq. Boxes	162	110	0150	248	Ea.	0.400	99	1.60	397	11.40	2827
4" Sq. Plaster ring	162	110	0300	231	Ea.	0.125	29	0.94	217	3.56	822
Receptacle cover, - S.S.	162	320	2600	231	Ea.	0.100	23	1.85	427	2.85	658
Conduit											
1/2" EMT	160	205	5000	3920	LF	0.047	184	0.40	1568	1.34	5253
Wire											
#12 THWN - Solid	161	165	0940	124	CLF	0.727	90	5.75	713	20.50	2542
							--------------		--------------		-----------
Page 13 Fixed receptacle Totals							514		$5,044		$14,639

Figure 24.21

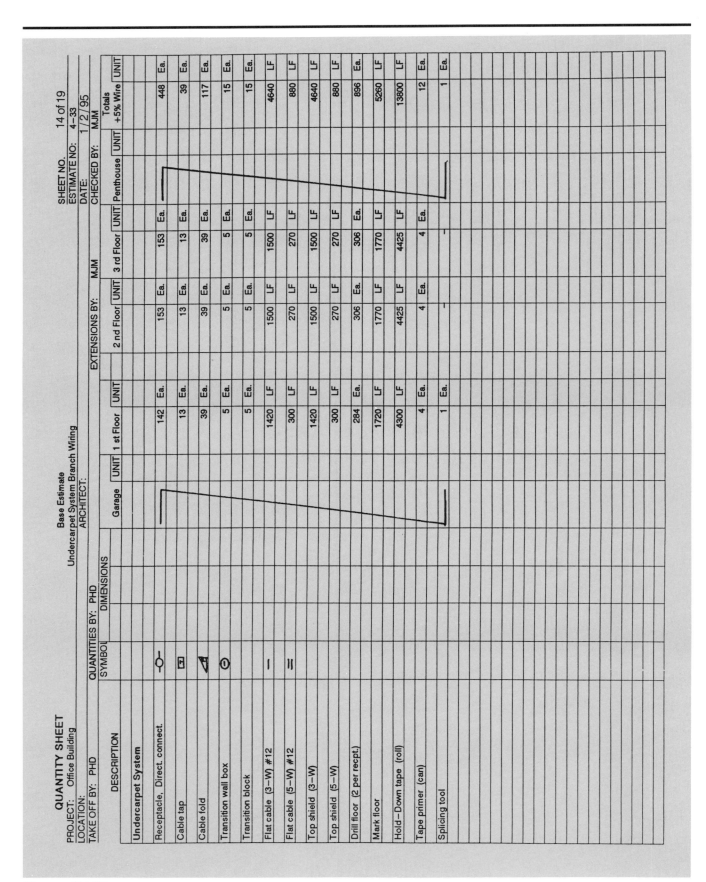

Figure 24.22

COST ANALYSIS

PROJECT: Office Building	Base Estimate		SHEET NO.	15 of 19

PROJECT: Office Building **Base Estimate** **Undercarpet Branch Wiring** **SHEET NO.** 15 of 19
LOCATION: **ARCHITECT:** **ESTIMATE NO:** 4 - 33 **DATE:** 1 / 8 / 95
TAKE OFF BY: VP **QUANTITIES BY:** VP **PRICES BY:** MJM **EXTENSIONS BY:** MJM **CHECKED BY:** MJM

DESCRIPTION	SOURCE/DIMENSIONS			QUANTITY	UNIT	MAN-HOURS		MATERIAL		LABOR	
						COST	TOTAL	COST	TOTAL	COST	TOTAL
Undercarpet Power System											
Receptacle, Direct conn. (single)	161	160	0860	448	Ea.	0.320	143	63.00	28,224	9.10	4077
Cable Tap 3/c	161	160	0350	39	Ea.	0.200	8	13.80	538	5.70	222
Insulating patch, tap, end	161	160	0400	78	Ea.	0.167	13	31.50	2457	4.75	371
Cable fold	161	160	0450	117	Ea.	0.035	4	-	-	0.99	116
Top shield, tap fold	161	160	0500	156	Ea.	0.083	13	0.95	148	2.38	371
Transition wall box	161	160	1000	15	Ea.	0.400	6	38.00	570	11.40	171
Transition block	161	160	0700	15	Ea.	0.104	2	25.00	375	2.96	44
Flat cable 3/c #12	161	160	0100	4640	LF	0.008	37	3.35	15544	0.23	1067
Flat cable 5/c #12	161	160	1450	880	LF	0.010	9	5.65	4972	0.28	246
Top shield (3/c)	161	160	0200	4640	LF	0.005	23	3.55	16472	0.13	603
Top shield (5/c)	161	160	1550	880	LF	0.005	4	5.60	4928	0.13	114
Mark, layout floor	161	160	8200	5260	LF	0.005	26	-	-	0.14	736
Drill floor	161	160	8100	896	Ea.	0.050	45	1.35	1210	1.43	1281
Tape, primer, can (500')	161	160	8350	12	Ea.	0.083	1	20.00	240	2.38	29
Splicing tool	161	160	8400	1	Ea.	-	-	195.00	195	-	-
Hold down tape	161	160	8300	13800	LF	0.001	14	0.13	1794	0.04	552
							---------------		---------------		---------------
Undercarpet Branch Wiring Total							348		$77,667		$10,002

Figure 24.23

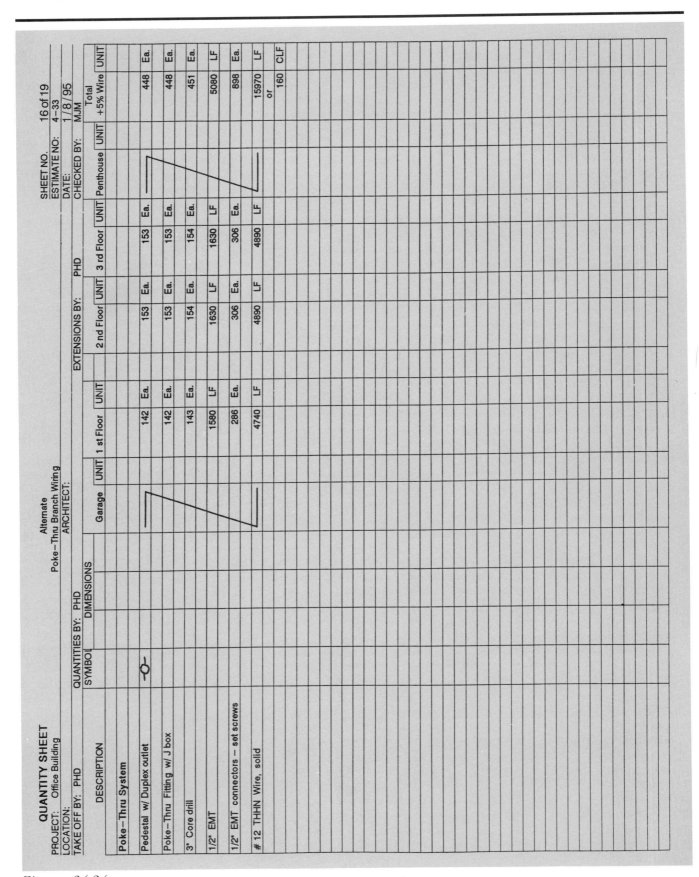

Figure 24.24

The cost analysis sheet for the poke-through system is shown in Figure 24.25. When pricing and extending this sheet note the third item—"Core 3 inch hole." Costs are taken from line 020-125-0300 of *Means Electrical Cost Data* (see Figure 24.26). A substantial portion of the crew cost will be for equipment. See crew B-89A in Figure 24.27. This crew includes costs for the drill, bit, and associated equipment.

Fire Detection Systems

There are several special systems that could be included in a building of this type. Telephone, burglar alarm, heat tracing, and sound systems are among them. For the purpose of this sample estimate, all of these systems are either furnished and installed by others or not used at all. Only the fire detection system is included in the scope of work.

Although some items of a fire detection system are shown in Figure 24.3, a full set of drawings would have additional details and specifications. Figure 24.28 shows the takeoff for this system. To maintain consistency, this takeoff sheet is arranged in a fashion similar to that of the branch wiring takeoff, i.e., by floors from the basement to the penthouse.

The quantities are transferred to the cost analysis sheet in Figure 24.29, where they are priced and extended. These special systems conclude the takeoff phase of the sample estimate.

The Estimate Summary

The Recap Sheet: It is generally a good practice to list the cost totals from each segment of the work onto one sheet of paper often called a "Recap." This procedure will allow the estimator to review all the segments and to add them into a total contractor's cost. Any alternates are usually listed and calculated on this sheet, as shown in Figure 24.30. The scheduling estimate can be drawn up from this recap sheet.

The Project Schedule: When the work for all sections is priced, the estimator should complete the Project Schedule so that time-related costs in the Project Overhead Summary can be determined. When preparing the schedule, the estimator must visualize the entire construction process to determine the correct sequence of work. Certain tasks must be completed before others are begun. Different trades will work simultaneously. Material deliveries will also affect scheduling. All such variables must be incorporated into the Project Schedule. An example is shown in Figure 24.31. The labor-hour figures, which have been calculated for each section, are used to assist with scheduling. The estimator must be careful to not only use the labor-hours for each section independently, but to coordinate each section with related work.

The schedule shows that the project will last approximately one year. The duration of the electrical work will be about six months. Time-dependent items, such as equipment rental and superintendent costs, can be included in the Project Overhead Summary. Some items, such as permits and insurance, are dependent on total job costs. The total direct costs for the project can be determined as shown in the Estimate Summary (Figures 24.32 and 24.33). All costs can now be included.

273

The Bottom Line: The estimator is now able to complete the Estimate Summary as shown. Appropriate contingency, sales tax, and overhead and profit costs must be added to the direct costs of the project. Ten percent is added to material. The overhead and profit percentage of 50.7% for labor is obtained from Figure 6.1 as the average markup for electricians. Contractors should determine appropriate markups for their own companies as discussed in Chapter 7: Indirect Costs. Finally, the totals represent national average prices, and should be adjusted with the City Cost Index for your locality.

COST ANALYSIS

PROJECT: Office Building	Alternate Poke-Thru Branch Wiring		SHEET NO. 17 of 19

LOCATION: ARCHITECT: ESTIMATE NO: 4 - 33

TAKE OFF BY: VP QUANTITIES BY: VP PRICES BY: MJM EXTENSIONS BY: MJM DATE: 1 / 8 / 95 CHECKED BY: MJM

DESCRIPTION	SOURCE/DIMENSIONS			QUANTITY	UNIT	MAN-HOURS		MATERIAL		LABOR	
						COST	TOTAL	COST	TOTAL	COST	TOTAL
Poke-Thru Components											
Pedestal w/ Duplex outlet	162	110	2140	448	Ea.	1.600	717	84.50	37,856	45.50	20,384
Poke-Thru Fitting w/ J box	162	110	2000	448	Ea.	1.180	529	70.00	31,360	33.50	15,008
Cutting & Drilling											
Core hole 3"	020	125	0300	451	Ea.	0.400	180	4.75	2142	8.95	4036
Core equipment	020	125	0300	451	Ea.	-	-	1.38	622	-	-
Conduit											
1/2" EMT	160	205	5000	5080	LF	0.047	238	0.40	2032	1.34	6807
Wire											
# 12 THHN - solid	161	165	0940	160	CLF	0.727	116	5.75	920	20.50	3280
Poke-Thru Wiring Total							1779		$74,933		$49,516

Figure 24.25

018 | Maintenance

018 000 | Facilities Maintenance

		CREW	DAILY OUTPUT	MAN-HOURS	UNIT	1995 BARE COSTS				TOTAL INCL O&P	
						MAT.	LABOR	EQUIP.	TOTAL		
160	3060	Up to 3/4 HP	1 Elec	4	2	Ea.		57		57	86	160
	3070	Up to 10 HP		3	2.667			76		76	115	
	3080	Megger test motor windings		5.33	1.501			43		43	64.50	
	3082	Motor vibration check		16	.500			14.25		14.25	21.50	
	3084	Oil motor bearings		25	.320			9.10		9.10	13.75	
	3086	Run test emergency generator for 30 minutes		11	.727			20.50		20.50	31	
	3090	Rewind motor, up to 1/4 HP		3	2.667			76		76	115	
	3100	Up to 3/4 HP		2	4			114		114	172	
	3110	Up to 10 HP		1.50	5.333			152		152	229	
	3150	Generator, repair or replace part		4	2			57		57	86	
	3160	Repair DC generator		2	4			114		114	172	
	4000	Stub pole, install or remove		3	2.667			76		76	115	
	4500	Transformer maintenance up to 15KVA	▼	2.70	2.963	▼		84.50		84.50	127	

020 | Subsurface Investigation and Demolition

020 120 | Std Penetration Tests

		CREW	DAILY OUTPUT	MAN-HOURS	UNIT	1995 BARE COSTS				TOTAL INCL O&P	
						MAT.	LABOR	EQUIP.	TOTAL		
125	0010	DRILLING, CORE Reinforced concrete slab, up to 6" thick slab										125
	0020	Including layout and set up										
	0100	1" diameter core	B-89A	48	.333	Ea.	2.14	7.45	1.15	10.74	15.50	
	0150	Each added inch thick, add		400	.040		.36	.90	.14	1.40	1.98	
	0300	3" diameter core		40	.400		4.75	8.95	1.38	15.08	21	
	0350	Each added inch thick, add		267	.060		.79	1.34	.21	2.34	3.24	
	0500	4" diameter core		37	.432		6.35	9.70	1.49	17.54	24	
	0550	Each added inch thick, add		242	.066		1.06	1.48	.23	2.77	3.78	
	0700	6" diameter core		29	.552		7.75	12.35	1.90	22	30.50	
	0750	Each added inch thick, add		200	.080		1.28	1.79	.28	3.35	4.57	
	0900	8" diameter core		21	.762		10.60	17.05	2.63	30.28	41.50	
	0950	Each added inch thick, add		133	.120		1.77	2.69	.42	4.88	6.70	
	1100	10" diameter core		19	.842		14.30	18.85	2.91	36.06	49	
	1150	Each added inch thick, add		114	.140		2.38	3.14	.48	6	8.15	
	1300	12" diameter core		16	1		17.25	22.50	3.45	43.20	58.50	
	1350	Each added inch thick, add		96	.167		2.88	3.73	.58	7.19	9.75	
	1500	14" diameter core		13.80	1.159		21	26	4	51	69	
	1550	Each added inch thick, add		80	.200		3.56	4.48	.69	8.73	11.85	
	1700	18" diameter core		6.80	2.353		27	52.50	8.10	87.60	122	
	1750	Each added inch thick, add	▼	40	.400		4.77	8.95	1.38	15.10	21	
	1760	For horizontal holes, add to above				▼				30%	30%	
	1770	Prestressed hollow core plank, 6" thick										
	1780	1" diameter core	B-89A	65	.246	Ea.	1.38	5.50	.85	7.73	11.25	
	1790	Each added inch thick, add		432	.037		.22	.83	.13	1.18	1.70	
	1800	3" diameter core		66	.242		3.13	5.45	.84	9.42	13	
	1810	Each added inch thick, add		296	.054		.53	1.21	.19	1.93	2.72	
	1820	4" diameter core		63	.254		4.17	5.70	.88	10.75	14.60	
	1830	Each added inch thick, add		271	.059		.70	1.32	.20	2.22	3.10	
	1840	6" diameter core		52	.308		5.05	6.90	1.06	13.01	17.70	
	1850	Each added inch thick, add		222	.072		.84	1.61	.25	2.70	3.76	
	1860	8" diameter core		37	.432		6.90	9.70	1.49	18.09	24.50	
	1870	Each added inch thick, add	▼	147	.109	▼	1.14	2.44	.38	3.96	5.55	

Figure 24.26

Crews

Crew B-86B

Crew No.	Bare Costs Hr.	Daily	Incl. Subs O & P Hr.	Daily	Cost Per Man-Hour Bare Costs	Incl. O&P
1 Equip. Oper. (medium)	$25.15	$201.20	$38.70	$309.60	$25.15	$38.70
1 Dozer, 200 H.P.		845.00		929.50	105.63	116.19
8 M.H., Daily Totals		$1046.20		$1239.10	$130.78	$154.89

Crew B-87

Crew No.	Bare Costs Hr.	Daily	Incl. Subs O & P Hr.	Daily	Cost Per Man-Hour Bare Costs	Incl. O&P
1 Laborer	$19.40	$155.20	$30.95	$247.60	$24.00	$37.15
4 Equip. Oper. (med.)	25.15	804.80	38.70	1238.40		
2 Feller Bunchers, 50 H.P.		704.40		774.85		
1 Log Chipper, 22" Tree		2034.00		2237.40		
1 Dozer, 105 H.P.		280.00		308.00		
1 Chainsaw, Gas, 36" Long		47.80		52.60	76.66	84.32
40 M.H., Daily Totals		$4026.20		$4858.85	$100.66	$121.47

Crew B-88

Crew No.	Bare Costs Hr.	Daily	Incl. Subs O & P Hr.	Daily	Cost Per Man-Hour Bare Costs	Incl. O&P
1 Laborer	$19.40	$155.20	$30.95	$247.60	$24.33	$37.59
6 Equip. Oper. (med.)	25.15	1207.20	38.70	1857.60		
2 Feller Bunchers, 50 H.P.		704.40		774.85		
1 Log Chipper, 22" Tree		2034.00		2237.40		
2 Log Skidders, 50 H.P.		703.20		773.50		
1 Dozer, 105 H.P.		280.00		308.00		
1 Chainsaw, Gas, 36" Long		47.80		52.60	67.31	74.04
56 M.H., Daily Totals		$5131.80		$6251.55	$91.64	$111.63

Crew B-89

Crew No.	Bare Costs Hr.	Daily	Incl. Subs O & P Hr.	Daily	Cost Per Man-Hour Bare Costs	Incl. O&P
1 Equip. Oper. (light)	$24.15	$193.20	$37.15	$297.20	$22.08	$34.05
1 Truck Driver (light)	20.00	160.00	30.95	247.60		
1 Truck, Stake Body, 3 Ton		165.00		181.50		
1 Concrete Saw		104.60		115.05		
1 Water Tank, 65 Gal.		7.20		7.90	17.30	19.03
16 M.H., Daily Totals		$630.00		$849.25	$39.38	$53.08

Crew B-89A

Crew No.	Bare Costs Hr.	Daily	Incl. Subs O & P Hr.	Daily	Cost Per Man-Hour Bare Costs	Incl. O&P
1 Skilled Worker	$25.35	$202.80	$40.45	$323.60	$22.38	$35.70
1 Laborer	19.40	155.20	30.95	247.60		
1 Core Drill (large)		55.20		60.70	3.45	3.80
16 M.H., Daily Totals		$413.20		$631.90	$25.83	$39.50

Crew B-90

Crew No.	Bare Costs Hr.	Daily	Incl. Subs O & P Hr.	Daily	Cost Per Man-Hour Bare Costs	Incl. O&P
1 Labor Foreman (outside)	$21.40	$171.20	$34.15	$273.20	$21.08	$33.04
3 Laborers	19.40	465.60	30.95	742.80		
2 Equip. Oper. (light)	24.15	386.40	37.15	594.40		
2 Truck Drivers (heavy)	20.35	325.60	31.50	504.00		
1 Road Mixer, 310 H.P.		977.00		1074.70		
1 Dist. Truck, 2000 Gal.		315.40		346.95	20.19	22.21
64 M.H., Daily Totals		$2641.20		$3536.05	$41.27	$55.25

Crew B-90A

Crew No.	Bare Costs Hr.	Daily	Incl. Subs O & P Hr.	Daily	Cost Per Man-Hour Bare Costs	Incl. O&P
1 Labor Foreman	$21.40	$171.20	$34.15	$273.20	$22.97	$35.84
2 Laborers	19.40	310.40	30.95	495.20		
4 Equip. Oper. (medium)	25.15	804.80	38.70	1238.40		
2 Graders, 30,000 Lbs.		1065.60		1172.15		
1 Roller, Steel Wheel		227.80		250.60		
1 Roller, Pneumatic Wheel		224.40		246.85	27.10	29.81
56 M.H., Daily Totals		$2804.20		$3676.40	$50.07	$65.65

Crew B-90B

Crew No.	Bare Costs Hr.	Daily	Incl. Subs O & P Hr.	Daily	Cost Per Man-Hour Bare Costs	Incl. O&P
1 Labor Foreman	$21.40	$171.20	$34.15	$273.20	$22.61	$35.36
2 Laborers	19.40	310.40	30.95	495.20		
3 Equip. Oper. (medium)	25.15	603.60	38.70	928.80		
1 Roller, Steel Wheel		227.80		250.60		
1 Roller, Pneumatic Wheel		224.40		246.85		
1 Road Mixer, 310 H.P.		977.00		1074.70	29.78	32.75
48 M.H., Daily Totals		$2514.40		$3269.35	$52.39	$68.11

Crew B-91

Crew No.	Bare Costs Hr.	Daily	Incl. Subs O & P Hr.	Daily	Cost Per Man-Hour Bare Costs	Incl. O&P
1 Labor Foreman (outside)	$21.40	$171.20	$34.15	$273.20	$22.64	$35.29
2 Laborers	19.40	310.40	30.95	495.20		
4 Equip. Oper. (med.)	25.15	804.80	38.70	1238.40		
1 Truck Driver (heavy)	20.35	162.80	31.50	252.00		
1 Dist. Truck, 3000 Gal.		344.60		379.05		
1 Aggreg. Spreader, S.P.		628.00		690.80		
1 Roller, Pneu. Tire, 12 Ton		224.40		246.85		
1 Roller, Steel, 10 Ton		227.80		250.60	22.26	24.49
64 M.H., Daily Totals		$2874.00		$3826.10	$44.90	$59.78

Crew B-92

Crew No.	Bare Costs Hr.	Daily	Incl. Subs O & P Hr.	Daily	Cost Per Man-Hour Bare Costs	Incl. O&P
1 Labor Foreman (outside)	$21.40	$171.20	$34.15	$273.20	$19.90	$31.75
3 Laborers	19.40	465.60	30.95	742.80		
1 Crack Cleaner, 25 H.P.		78.80		86.70		
1 Air Compressor		71.80		79.00		
1 Tar Kettle, T.M.		18.80		20.70		
1 Flatbed Truck, 3 Ton		165.00		181.50	10.45	11.50
32 M.H., Daily Totals		$971.20		$1383.90	$30.35	$43.25

Crew B-93

Crew No.	Bare Costs Hr.	Daily	Incl. Subs O & P Hr.	Daily	Cost Per Man-Hour Bare Costs	Incl. O&P
1 Equip. Oper. (med.)	$25.15	$201.20	$38.70	$309.60	$25.15	$38.70
1 Feller Buncher, 50 H.P.		352.20		387.40	44.03	48.43
8 M.H., Daily Totals		$553.40		$697.00	$69.18	$87.13

Crew B-94

Crew No.	Bare Costs Hr.	Daily	Incl. Subs O & P Hr.	Daily	Cost Per Man-Hour Bare Costs	Incl. O&P
1 Laborer	$19.40	$155.20	$30.95	$247.60	$19.40	$30.95
8 M.H., Daily Totals		$155.20		$247.60	$19.40	$30.95

Crew B-94A

Crew No.	Bare Costs Hr.	Daily	Incl. Subs O & P Hr.	Daily	Cost Per Man-Hour Bare Costs	Incl. O&P
1 Laborer	$19.40	$155.20	$30.95	$247.60	$19.40	$30.95
1 Diaph. Water Pump, 2"		20.60		22.65		
1-20 Ft. Suction Hose, 2"		4.60		5.05		
2-50 Ft. Disch. Hoses, 2"		7.00		7.70	4.03	4.43
8 M.H., Daily Totals		$187.40		$283.00	$23.43	$35.38

Crew B-94B

Crew No.	Bare Costs Hr.	Daily	Incl. Subs O & P Hr.	Daily	Cost Per Man-Hour Bare Costs	Incl. O&P
1 Laborer	$19.40	$155.20	$30.95	$247.60	$19.40	$30.95
1 Diaph. Water Pump, 4"		56.80		62.50		
1-20 Ft. Suction Hose, 4"		11.80		13.00		
2-50 Ft. Disch. Hoses, 4"		13.20		14.50	10.23	11.25
8 M.H., Daily Totals		$237.00		$337.60	$29.63	$42.20

Crew B-94C

Crew No.	Bare Costs Hr.	Daily	Incl. Subs O & P Hr.	Daily	Cost Per Man-Hour Bare Costs	Incl. O&P
1 Laborer	$19.40	$155.20	$30.95	$247.60	$19.40	$30.95
1 Centr. Water Pump, 3"		32.20		35.40		
1-20 Ft. Suction Hose, 3"		7.40		8.15		
2-50 Ft. Disch. Hoses, 3"		9.20		10.10	6.10	6.71
8 M.H., Daily Totals		$204.00		$301.25	$25.50	$37.66

Figure 24.27

QUANTITY SHEET

PROJECT: Office Building
LOCATION:
TAKE OFF BY: PHD
QUANTITIES BY: PHD

Fire Detection Alarm System
ARCHITECT:
EXTENSIONS BY: PHD

DESCRIPTION	SYMBOL	DIMENSIONS	BASEMNT	UNIT	1st Floor	UNIT	2nd Floor	UNIT	3rd Floor	UNIT	Penthouse	UNIT	Totals +5% Cond +10% Wire	UNIT
Fire Alarm Components														
Control panel	☐		1	Ea.									1	Ea.
Break–glass Station			1	Ea.	3	Ea.	3	Ea.	3	Ea.	1	Ea.	11	Ea.
Light & Horn			1	Ea.	3	Ea.	3	Ea.	3	Ea.	1	Ea.	11	Ea.
Master box					1	Ea.							1	Ea.
Annunciator					1	Ea.							1	Ea.
Smoke detector			6	Ea.	24	Ea.	24	Ea.	24	Ea.	5	Ea.	83	Ea.
Raceways & Boxes														
1/2" EMT			250	LF	920	LF	920	LF	920	LF	110	LF	3280	LF
1/2" EMT Connectors – compr.			18	Ea.	64	Ea.	60	Ea.	60	Ea.	14	Ea.	216	Ea.
4" Sq. Box			9	Ea.	32	Ea.	30	Ea.	30	Ea.	7	Ea.	108	Ea.
4" Sq. Plaster rings			9	Ea.	32	Ea.	30	Ea.	30	Ea.	7	Ea.	108	Ea.
Conductors														
Fire alarm, #18, 2 Pair			30	LF	1000	LF	1000	LF	1000	LF	350	LF	3720 or 37	LF CLF
Fire alarm, #18, 6 Pair			280	LF	500	LF	250	LF	280	LF	60	LF	1510 or 15	LF CLF

Figure 24.28

278

COST ANALYSIS

PROJECT: Office Building	Special Systems	SHEET NO. 19 of 19
LOCATION:	Fire Detection	ESTIMATE NO: 4 - 33
	ARCHITECT:	DATE: 1 / 8 / 95
TAKE OFF BY: VP QUANTITIES BY: VP PRICES BY: MJM EXTENSIONS BY: MJM		CHECKED BY: MJM

DESCRIPTION	SOURCE/DIMENSIONS			QUANTITY	UNIT	MAN-HOURS		MATERIAL		LABOR	
						COST	TOTAL	COST	TOTAL	COST	TOTAL
Fire Alarm Components											
Control panel, 12 zone	168	120	4000	1	Ea.	12.120	12	1725.00	1725	345.00	345
Battery & Rack	168	120	4200	1	Ea.	2.000	2	630.00	630	57.00	57
Battery charger	168	120	4400	1	Ea.	1.000	1	425.00	425	28.50	29
Break-glass station	168	120	7000	11	Ea.	1.000	11	47.50	523	28.50	314
Light & Horn	168	120	5600	11	Ea.	1.510	17	100.00	1100	43.00	473
Master box	168	120	6800	1	Ea.	2.960	3	2000.00	2000	84.50	85
Annunciator, 12 zone	168	120	8000	1	Ea.	6.150	6	295.00	295	175.00	175
Smoke detector	168	120	5200	83	Ea.	1.290	107	61.50	5105	37.00	3071
Raceways & Boxes											
1/2" EMT	160	205	5000	3280	LF	0.047	154	0.40	1312	1.34	4395
1/2" EMT Connectors - compr.	160	205	8800	216	Ea.	0.067	14	1.25	270	1.90	410
4" Sq. Box	162	110	0150	108	Ea.	0.400	43	1.60	173	11.40	1231
4" Sq. Plaster ring	162	110	0300	108	Ea.	0.125	14	0.94	102	3.56	384
Conductors											
Fire alarm, #18, 2 Pair	161	155	1900	37	CLF	1.230	46	122.00	4514	35.00	1295
Fire alarm, #18, 6 Pair	161	155	2000	15	CLF	2.000	30	244.00	3660	57.00	855
							------------		------------		------------
Fire Alarm Total							460		$21,832		$13,119

Figure 24.29

DESCRIPTION	SOURCE/DIMENSIONS			SHEET NO.	UNIT	MAN-HOURS		MATERIAL		LABOR	
						COST	TOTAL	COST	TOTAL	COST	TOTAL
BASE ESTIMATE -- UNDERCARPET											
Lighting				3			2,485		78,442		70,844
Service & Distribution (Riser)				8			823		78,510		23,437
M C C & Feeders				11			140		19,830		3,981
Branch Power Wiring, Fixed Receptacles				13			514		5,044		14,639
Undercarpet Receptacles				15			348		77,667		10,002
Fire dection				19			460		21,832		13,119
							------------		------------		------------
Total w/Undercarpet							4,770		281,325		136,022
ALTERNATE #1 POKE -- THRU											
Alternate Poke-Thru											
Deduct Undercarpet				15			348		77,667		10,002
Add Poke-Thru				17			1,779		74,933		49,516
							------------		------------		------------
Total w/Poke-Thru							6201		$278,590		$175,536

COST ANALYSIS
PROJECT: Office Building   RECAP
LOCATION: ARCHITECT:
TAKE OFF BY: VP   QUANTITIES BY: VP   PRICES BY: MJ   EXTENSIONS BY: MJM

SHEET NO.   Recap Sheet
ESTIMATE NO: 4 - 33
DATE: 1 / 8 / 95
CHECKED BY: MJM

Figure 24.30

Figure 24.31

COST ANALYSIS		Base Estimate						SHEET NO.		Estimate Summary	
PROJECT: Office Building		Estimate Summary						ESTIMATE NO:		4 - 33	

LOCATION:　　　　　　　　　ARCHITECT:　　　　　　　　　　DATE: 1 / 8 / 95

TAKE OFF BY: VP　　QUANTITIES BY: VP　PRICES BY: MJM　EXTENSIONS BY: MJM　CHECKED BY: MJM

DESCRIPTION	SOURCE/DIMENSIONS			QUANITY	UNIT	MATERIAL		LABOR		TOTAL	
						COST	TOTAL	COST	TOTAL	COST	TOTAL
UNDERCARPET SYSTEM											
Direct cost from recap							$281,325		$136,022		
Micellaneous											
Storage trailer	015	904	1250	6	Mo.	85	510				
Small tools	010	082	0100	Labor	%	2	2720				
Toilets	016	420	6410	2 for 6	Mo.	81	972				
Pick-up truck	016	420	7100	6	Mo.	585	3510				
Material Subtotal							$289,037				
Sales Tax				Material	%	5	14,452				
Material Markup				Material	%	10	28,904				
Material Total							$332,393				
Contractor O & P				Labor	%			50.7	68,963		
Labor Total									$204,985		
Material & Labor Total (National average)											$537,378
City Adjustment (Boston)						0.998	$332,393	1.351	$204,985		
Total Estimate w/ Undercarpet for Boston							$331,728		$276,935		$608,663

Figure 24.32

COST ANALYSIS				Alternate # 1						SHEET NO. Alternate Est. Summary		
PROJECT: Office Building				Alternate Estimate Summary						ESTIMATE NO: 4 - 33		
LOCATION:						ARCHITECT:				DATE:	1 / 8 / 95	
TAKE OFF BY: VP	QUANTITIES BY: VP		PRICES BY: MJM		EXTENSIONS BY: MJM					CHECKED BY:	MJM	

DESCRIPTION	SOURCE/DIMENSIONS			QUANITY	UNIT	MATERIAL		LABOR		TOTAL	
						COST	TOTAL	COST	TOTAL	COST	TOTAL
UNDERCARPET SYSTEM											
Direct cost from recap							$278,590		$175,536		
Micellaneous											
Storage trailer	015	904	1250	6	Mo.	85	510				
Small tools	010	082	0100	Labor	%	2	3511				
Toilets	016	420	6410	2 for 6	Mo.	81	972				
Pick-up truck	016	420	7100	6	Mo.	585	3510				

Material Subtotal							$287,093				
Sales Tax				Material	%	5	14,355				
Material Markup				Material	%	10	28,709				

Material Total							$330,157				
Contractor O & P				Labor	%			50.7	88,997		

Labor Total									$264,533		
Material & Labor Total (National average)											$594,689
City Adjustment (Boston)						0.998	$330,157	1.351	$264,533		
							-----------		-----------		
Total Estimate w/ Undercarpet for Boston							$329,496		$357,384		$686,880

Figure 24.33

Appendix

Appendix

Frequently, drawings and specifications do not contain complete, detailed information for the estimator. The design must be interpreted as to sizes, capacities, and/or equipment requirements to identify and select unit prices for the estimate.

This section contains the following reference information as an aid to the electrical estimator.

Appendix A — Symbols and Abbreviations
These designations are commonly used and accepted on electrical plan drawings, schematic diagrams, wiring diagrams, and takeoff forms.

Appendix B — Reference Tables
These determine weights and volumes, ampacities, and conduit and wire sizes.

Appendix C — NEMA Enclosures
A listing of NEMA enclosure requirement designations for various environments.

Appendix D — Forms
The electrical pages from R.S. Means' "Spec-Aid," reproduced as an example form for surveying the scope of work.

Trade Specific Symbols

Lighting Outlets

○   Ceiling Surface Incandescent Fixture

⊢○   Wall Surface Incandescent Fixture

®   Ceiling Recess Incandescent Fixture

⊢®   Wall Recess Incandescent Fixture

ᴬ○₃ᵦ   Standard Designation for All Lighting Fixtures – A = Fixture Type, 3 = Circuit Number, b = Switch Control

Ⓑ   Ceiling Blanked Outlet

⊢Ⓑ   Wall Blanked Outlet

Ⓔ   Ceiling Electrical Outlet

⊢Ⓔ   Wall Electrical Outlet

Ⓙ   Ceiling Junction Box

⊢Ⓙ   Wall Junction Box

Ⓛ₉ₛ   Ceiling Lamp Holder with Pull Switch

⊢Ⓛ₉ₛ   Wall Lamp Holder with Pull Switch

Ⓛ   Ceiling Outlet Controlled by Low Voltage Switching when Relay is Installed in Outlet Box

⊢Ⓛ   Wall Outlet – Same as Above

◇   Outlet Box with Extension Ring

[EX]→   Exit Sign with Arrow as Indicated

[○]   Surface Fluorescent Fixture

[○] P   Pendant Fluorescent Fixture

[OR]   Recessed Fluorescent Fixture

[○]   Wall Surface Fluorescent Fixture

─━┤- - -┤━─   Channel Mounted Fluorescent Fixture

[●▮   ▮]   Surface or Pendant Continous Row Fluorescent Fixtures

[OR▮   ▮]   Recessed Continuous Row Fluorescent Fixtures

●   Incandescent Fixture on Emergency Circuit

[●]   Fluorescent Fixture on Emergency Circuit

Receptacle Outlets

⊢⊖   Single Receptacle Outlet

⊢⊖   Duplex Receptacle Outlet

⊢ˣ⊖   Duplex Receptacle Outlet "X" Indicates above Counter Max. Height = 42″ or above Counter

⊢⊖ᵂᴾ   Weatherproof Receptacle Outlet

⊢⊕   Triplex Receptacle Outlet

⊢⊕   Quadruplex Receptacle Outlet

⊢⊖   Duplex Receptacle Outlet – Split Wired

⊢⊕   Triplex Receptacle Outlet – Split Wired

⊢△   Single Special Purpose Receptacle Outlet

⊢△   Duplex Special Purpose Receptacle Outlet

⊢⊖ᴿ   Range Outlet

⊢▲ᴰᵂ   Special Purpose Connection – Dishwasher

⊢⊖ˣᴾ   Explosion-proof Receptacle Outlet Max. Height = 36″ to ℄

⊢⊕ˣ   Multi-outlet Assembly

Ⓒ   Clock Hanger Receptacle

Ⓕ   Fan Hanger Receptacle

⊟   Floor Single Receptacle Outlet

Receptacle Outlets (Cont).

⊖ Floor Duplex Receptacle Outlet

△ Floor Special Purpose Outlet

◀ Floor Telephone Outlet – Public

◁ Floor Telephone Outlet – Private

  Underfloor Duct and Junction Box for Triple, Double, or Single Duct System as Indicated by Number of Parallel Lines

⊞ Cellular Floor Header Duct

Switch Outlets

S Single Pole Switch
Max. Height = 42" to $\mathbb{C}$

S₂ Double Pole Switch

S₃ Three-way Switch

S₄ Four-way Switch

S_D Automatic Door Switch

S_K Key Operated Switch

S_P Switch & Pilot Lamp

S_CB Circuit Breaker

S_WCB Weatherproof Circuit Breaker

S_MC Momentary Contact Switch

S_RC Remote Control Switch (Receiver)

S_WP Weatherproof Switch

S_F Fused Switch

S_L Switch for Low Voltage Switching System

S_LM Master Switch for Low Voltage Switching System

S_T Time Switch

S_TH Thermal Rated Motor Switch

S_DM Incandescent Dimmer Swtich

S_FDM Fluorescent Dimmer Switch

⊢⊖_S Switch & Single Receptacle

⊢⊖_S Switch & Double Receptacle

⊢⊖_A
S_A   } Special Outlet Circuits

Institutional, Commercial, & Industrial System Outlets

⊢⬡ Nurses Call System Devices – any Type

⊢◇ Paging System Devices – any Type

⊢☐ Fire Alarm System Devices – any Type

☐F Fire Alarm Manual Station – Max. Height = 48" to $\mathbb{C}$

◁F Fire Alarm Horn with Integral Warning Light

⊗ Fire Alarm Thermodetector, Fixed Temperature

Ⓢ Smoke Detector

⊗ Fire Alarm Thermodetector, Rate of Rise

⌂F Fire Alarm Master Box – Max. Height per Fire Department

H Magnetic Door Holder

[ANN] Fire Alarm Annunciator

⊢◇ Staff Register System – any Type

⊢◷ Electrical Clock System Devices – any Type

⊢◀ Public Telephone System Devices

Institutional, Commercial, & Industrial System Outlets (Cont).

+◁ Private Telephone System Devices

+⌂ Watchman System Devices

+◁(L) Sound System, L = Speaker, V = Volume Control

+⊙ Other Signal System Devices – CTV = Television Antenna, DP = Data Processing

[|SC|] Signal Central Station

◤ Telephone Interconnection Box

(PE) Pneumatic/Electric Switch

(EP) Electric/Pneumatic Switch

[GP] Operating Room Grounding Plate

[P]₆ Patient Ground Point – 6 = Number of Jacks

Panelboards

⊢▬⊣ Flush Mounted Panelboard & Cabinet

⊢▬⊣ Surface Mounted Panelboard & Cabinet

▬ Lighting Panel

▨ Power Panel

▭ Heating Panel

⊠ Controller (Starter)

⊐ Externally Operated Disconnect Switch

Busducts & Wireways

▥▥▥ Trolley Duct

▥▥▥ Busway (Service, Feeder, or Plug-in)

▥▥▥ Cable through Ladder or Channel

▥▥▥ Wireway

[J] Bus Duct Junction Box

Electrical Distribution or Lighting System, Aerial, Lightning Protection

○ Pole

✕— Street Light & Bracket

△ Transformer

——— Primary Circuit

- - - - Secondary Circuit

—·—·— Auxiliary System Circuits

——→ Down Guy

——•— Head Guy

——○→ Sidewalk Guy

⊂— Service Weather Head

⊙ Lightning Rod

—L— Lightning Protection System Conductor

Residential Signaling System Outlets

[•] Push Botton

□◣ Buzzer

◁□ Bell

◁□◣ Bell and Buzzer Combination

—◇ Annunciator

◀ Outside Telephone

◁ Interconnecting Telephone

◀ Telephone Switchboard

[BT] Bell Ringing Transformer

Residential Signaling System Outlets (Cont).

| D | Electric Door Opener |

| M | Maid's Signal Plug |

| R | Radio Antenna Outlet |

| CH | Chime |

| TV | Television Antenna Outlet |

| T | Thermostat |

Underground Electrical Distribution or Lighting System

| M | Manhole |

| H | Handhole |

| TM | Transformer – Manhole or Vault |

| TP | Transformer Pad |

– – – – Underground Direct Burial Cable

Underground Duct Line

Street Light Standard Fed from Underground Circuit

Panel Circuits & Miscellaneous

– – – – Conduit Concealed in Floor or Walls

- - - - - - Wiring Exposed

Home Run to Panelboard – Number of Arrows Indicate Number of Circuits

Home Run to Panelboard – Two-Wire Circuit

Home Run to Panelboard – Number of Slashes Indicate Number of Wires (When more than Two)

LS-L1,3,5 Home Run to Panelboard – 'LS' Indicates Panel Designation; LI, 3, 5, Indicates Circuit Breaker No.

—C— Clock Circuit, Conduit and Wire

—E— Emergency Conduit and Wiring

—T— Telephone Conduit and Wiring

——— Feeders

———o Conduit Turned Up

———• Conduit Turned Down

(G) Generator

(M) Motor

(5) Motor – Numeral Indicates Horsepower

(I) Instrument (Specify)

| T | Transformer |

Remote Start-Stop Push Button Station

Remote Start-Stop Push Button Station w/Pilot Light

| HTR | Electric Heater Wall Unit

Common Abbreviations on Drawings

EWC	Electric Water Cooler
EDH	Electric Duct Heater
AFF	Above Finished Floor
UH	Unit Heater
GFI	Ground Fault Interrupter
GFP	Ground Fault Protector
GFCB	Ground Fault Circuit Breaker
EC	Empty Conduit
WP	Weatherproof

Common Abbreviations on Drawings (Cont).

VP	Vaporproof	**ATS**	Automatic Transfer Switch
EXP	Explosion-proof	**IS**	Isolating Switch
AD	Auto Damper	**FATC**	Fire Alarm Terminal Cabinet
LP	Lighting Panel	**FA**	Fire Alarm
PP	Power Panel	**CAM**	Closed Circuit TV Camera
IP	Isolation Panel	**MON**	Closed Circuit TV Monitor
MC	Motor Controller	**MG**	Motor-Generator Set
MCC	Motor Control Center		

A	Area Square Feet; Ampere	B.F.	Board Foot	Circ.	Circuit
ABS	Acrylonitrile Butadiene Styrene; Asbestos-Bonded Steel	Bg. Cem.	Bag of Cement	C.L.	Carload Lot
		BHP	Brake Horsepower	Clab.	Common Laborer
		BI	Black Iron	C.L.F.	Hundred Linear Feet
AC	Alternating Current; Air Conditioning; Asbestos Cement; Armored Cable	Bit.; Bitum.	Bituminous	CLF	Current-Limiting Fuse
		Bk.	Backed	CLP	Cross-Linked Polyethylene
		Bkrs.	Breakers		
		Bldg.	Building	cm	Centimeter
ACI	American Concrete Institute	Blk.	Block	CMP	Corrugated Metal Pipe
		BM.	Beam	C.M.U.	Concrete Masonry Unit
ADA	Americans with Disabilities Act	Boil.	Boilermaker	C.O.D.	Cash on Delivery
		B.P.M.	Blows per Minute	Col.	Column
Addit.	Additional	BR	Bedroom	CO_2	Carbon Dioxide
Adj.	Adjustable	Brg.	Bearing	Comb.	Combination
af	Audio-frequency	Brhe.	Bricklayer Helper	Compr.	Compressor
A.G.A.	American Gas Association	Bric.	Bricklayer	Conc.	Concrete
		Brk.	Brick	Cont.	Continuous; Continued
Agg.	Aggregate	Brng.	Bearing	Corr	Corrugated
A.H.	Ampere Hours	Brs.	Brass	Cos	Cosine
A hr	Ampere-hour	Brz.	Bronze	Cot	Cotangent
A.I.A.	American Institute of Architects	Bsn.	Basin	Cov.	Cover
		Btr.	Better	CPA	Control Point Adjustment
AIC	Ampere Interrupting Capacity	Btu	British Thermal Unit		
		BTUH	Btu per Hour	Cplg.	Coupling
Allow.	Allowance	BX	Interlocked Armored Cable	CPM	Critical Path Method
Alt	Altitude			CPVC	Chlorinated Polyvinyl Chloride
AL; Alum.	Aluminum	c	Conductivity		
a.m.	ante meridiem	C	Hundred; Centigrade; Celsius	C.Pr.	Hundred Pair
Amp.	Ampere			CRC	Cold Rolled Channel
Approx.	Approximate	C/C	Center to Center	Creos.	Creosote
Apt.	Apartment	Cab.	Cabinet	Crpt.	Carpet & Linoleum Layer
Asb.	Asbestos	Cair.	Air Tool Laborer		
ASBC	American Standard Building Code	Calc.	Calculated	CRT	Cathode Ray Tube
		Cap.	Capacity	CS	Carbon Steel
Asbe.	Asbestos Worker	Carp.	Carpenter; Carpentry	Csc	Cosecant
ASHRAE	American Society of Heating, Refrigeration, and Air Conditioning Engineers	C.B.	Circuit Breaker	C.S.F.	Hundred Square Feet
		C.C.F.	Hundred Cubic Feet	CSI	Construction Specifications Institute
		cd	Candela		
		cd/sf	Candela per Square Foot	CT	Current Transformer
ASME	American Society of Mechanical Engineers	CD	Grade of Plywood Face & Back	CTS	Copper Tube Size
				Cu	Cubic
ASTM	American Society for Testing and Materials	CDX	Plywood, grade C & D, exterior glue	CU	Copper
				Cu. Ft.	Cubic Foot
Attchmt.	Attachment	Cefi.	Cement Finisher	cw	Continuous Wave
Avg.	Average	Cem.	Cement	C.W.	Cool White
AWG	American Wire Gauge	CF	Hundred Feet	Cwt.	100 Pounds
Bbl.	Barrel	C.F.	Cubic Feet	C.W.X.	Cool White Deluxe
B&B	Grade B and Better; Balled and Burlapped	CFM	Cubic Feet per Minute	C.Y.	Cubic Yard (27 cubic feet)
		c.g.	Center of Gravity	C.Y./Hr.	Cubic Yards per Hour
B&S	Bell and Spigot	CHW	Commercial Hot Water	Cyl.	Cylinder
B&W	Black and White	C.I.	Cast Iron	d	Penny (nail size)
b.c.c.	Body-centered cubic	C.I.P.	Cast in Place		

D	Deep; Depth; Discharge; Diameter	Eqlt.	Equipment Operator, Light	F.R.	Fire Rating
Dis.; Disch.	Discharge	Eqmd.	Equipment Operator, Medium	FRK	Foil Reinforced Kraft
Db	Decibel			FRP	Fiberglass Reinforced Plastic
Dbl.	Double	Eqmm.	Equipment Operator, Master Mechanic	FS	Forged Steel
DC	Direct Current			FSC	Cast Body; Cast Switch Box
Demob.	Demobilization	Eqol.	Equipment Operator, Oilers		
d.f.u.	Drainage Fixture Units			Ft.	Foot; Feet
D.H.	Double Hung	Equip.	Equipment	Ftng.	Fitting
DHW	Domestic Hot Water	ERW	Electric Resistance Welded	Ftg.	Footing
Diag.	Diagonal			Ft. Lb.	Foot Pound
Diam.	Diameter	Est.	Estimated	Furn.	Furniture; Furnish; Furnished
Dist.	Distance	esu	Electrostatic Unit		
Distri.	Distribution	EW	Each Way	FVNR	Full Voltage Non-Reversing
Dk.	Deck	EWT	Entering Water Temperature		
D.L.	Dead Load; Diesel			FVR	Full Voltage Reversing
Do.	Ditto	Excav.	Excavation	FXM	Female by Male
Dp.	Depth	Exp.	Expansion	Fy.	Minimum Yield Stress of Steel
DPST	Double Pole, Single Throw	Ext.	Exterior		
		Extru	Extrusion	g	Gram
Dr.	Driver	f.	Fiber stress	G	Gauss
Drink.	Drinking	F	Fahrenheit; Female; Fill	Ga.	Gauge
DS	Double Strength			Gal.	Gallon
DSA	Double Strength A Grade	Fab.	Fabricated	Gal./Min.	Gallon per Minute
		FBGS	Fiberglass	Galv	Galvanized
DSB	Double Strength B Grade	F.C., f.c.	Footcandles; Compressive Stress in Concrete; Extreme Compressive Stress	Gen.	General
				Glaz.	Glazier
Dty.	Duty			GPD	Gallons per Day
DWV	Drain Waste Vent			GPH	Gallons per Hour
DX	Deluxe White; Direct Expansion	f.c.c.	Face-centered cubic	GPM	Gallons per Minute
		FCC	Flat Conductor Cable	GR	Grade
dyn	Dyne	F.E.	Front End	Gran	Granular
e	Eccentricity	FEP	Fluorinated Ethylene Propylene (Teflon)	Grnd	Ground
E	Equipment Only; East			H	High; High Strength Bar Joist; Henry
Ea.	Each	F.G.	Flat Grain		
Econ.	Economy	FHA	Federal Housing Administration	H.C.	High Capacity
EDP	Electronic Data Processing			H.D.	Heavy Duty; High Density
		Fig.	Figure		
EDR	Equivalent Direct Radiation	Fin.	Finish; Finished	H.D.O.	High Density Overlaid
		Fixt.	Fixture	Hdr.	Header
Eq.	Equation	Fl. Oz.	Fluid Ounce	Hdwe.,	Hardware
Elec.	Electrician; Electrical	Flr.	Floor	Hdwr.	
Elev.	Elevator; Elevating; Elevator Constructor	F.M.	Frequency Modulation; Factory Mutual	Help.	Helper average
				HEPA	High Efficiency Particulate Air
EMT	Electrical Metallic Conduit; Thin Wall Conduit	Fmg.	Framing		
		Fndtn.	Foundation	Hg	Mercury
		FOB	Free on Board	HID	High-Intensity Discharge
Eng.	Engine	Fori.	Foreman, inside		
EPDM	Ethylene Propylene Diene Monomer	Foro.	Foreman, outside	HO	High Output
		Fount.	Fountain	Horiz.	Horizontal
Eqhv.	Equipment Operator, Heavy	fpm	Feet per Minute	HP	Horsepower; High Pressure
		FPT	Female Pipe Thread		
		Fr	Frame	H.P.F.	High Power Factor

Hr.	Hour	kVA	Kilovolt Ampere	Mach.	Machine
Hrs./Day	Hours per Day	kVAR	Kilovar (Reactance)	Mag. Str.	Magnetic Starter
HSC	High Short Circuit	kW	Kilowatt	Maint.	Maintenance
Ht.	Height	kWh	Kilowatt-hour	Marb.	Marble Setter
Htg.	Heating	L	Labor Only; Length;	Mat.	Material
Htrs.	Heaters		Long	Mat'l.	Material
HVAC	Heating, Ventilating,	Lab.	Labor	Max.	Maximum
	and Air Conditioning	lat	Latitude	MBF	Thousand Board Feet
Hvy.	Heavy	Lath.	Lather	MBH	Thousand Btu's per
HW	Hot Water	Lav.	Lavatory		Hour
Hyd.; Hydr.	Hydraulic	Lb; #	Pound	MC	Metal Clad
Hz	Hertz (cycles)	LB	Load Bearing; L	MCC	Motor Control Center
I.	Moment of Inertia		Conduit Body	M.C.F.	Thousand Cubic Feet
IC	Interrupting Capacity	L. & E.	Labor and Equipment	M.C.F.M.	Thousand Cubic Feet
ID	Inside Diameter; Inside	lb./hr.	Pounds per Hour		per Minute
	Dimension;	lb./L.F.	Pounds per Linear	MCM	Thousand Circular Mils
	Identification		Foot	MCP	Motor Circuit Protector
IF	Inside Frosted	lbf/sq.in.	Pound-force per Square	MD	Medium Duty
IMC	Intermediate Metallic		Inch	M.D.O.	Medium Density
	Conduit	LCL	Less than Carload Lot		Overlaid
In.	Inch	Ld	Load	Med.	Medium
Incan.	Incandescent	L.F.	Linear Foot	MF	Thousand Feet
Incl.	Included; Including	Lg.	Long; Length; Large	M.F.B.M.	Thousand Feet Board
Ins.	Insurance	L. & H.	Light and Heat		Measure
Int.	Interior	L.H.	Long Span High	Mfg.	Manufacturing
Inst.	Installation		Strength Bar Joist;	Mfrs.	Manufacturers
Insul.	Insulation; Insulate		Labor Hour	mg	Milligram
Inter.	Interior	L.J.	Long Span Standard	MGD	Million Gallons per
IP	Iron Pipe		Strength Bar Joist		Day
IPS	Iron Pipe Size	LL	Live Load	MGPH	Thousand Gallons per
IPT	Iron Pipe Threaded	LLD	Lamp Lumen		Hour
J	Joule		Depreciation	MH	Manhole; Metal Halide,
J.I.C.	Joint Industrial Council	lm	Lumen		Man Hour
K	Thousand; Thousand	lm/sf	Lumen per Square	MHz	Megahertz
	Pounds		Foot	Mi.	Mile
KAH	Thousand Ampere	lm/W	Lumen per Watt	M.I.	Malleable Iron; Mineral
	Hours	L.O.A.	Length Overall		Insulated
kcmil	Thousand Circular Mils	log	Logarithm	mm	Millimeter
KDAT	Kiln Dried After	LP	Liquefied Petroleum;	Mill.	Millwright
	Treatment		Low Pressure	Min.	Minimum; Minute
kg	Kilogram	LPF	Low Power Factor	Misc.	Miscellaneous
k	Kilogauss	LPS	Low-pressure Sodium	ml	Milliliter
kgf	Kilogram Force	Lt.	Light	M.L.F.	Thousand Linear Feet
kHz	Kilohertz	Lt. Ga.	Light Gauge	Mo.	Month
Kip	1000 pounds	LTL	Less than Truckload	Mobil.	Mobilization
kJ	Kilojoule		Lot	Mog.	Mogul Base
K.L.	Effective Length Factor	Lt. Wt.	Lightweight	MPH	Miles per Hour
KLF	Kips per Linear Foot	LV	Low Voltage	MPT	Male Pipe Thread
km	Kilometer	m	Meter	MRT	Mile Round Trip
KO	Knockout	M	Thousand; Material;	ms	Millisecond
KSF	Kips per Square Foot		Male; Medium Wall	M.S.F.	Thousand Square Feet
KSI	Kips per Square Inch		Copper	Mstz.	Mosaic and Terrazzo
kV	Kilovolt	mA	Milliampere		Worker

M.S.Y.	Thousand Square Yards	O & P	Overhead and Profit	P&T	Pressure and
Mtd.	Mounted	Oper.	Operator		Temperature
Mthe.	Mosaic and Terrazzo	Opng.	Opening	Ptd.	Painted
	Helper	Orna.	Ornamental	Ptns.	Partitions
Mtng.	Mounting	OS&Y	Outside Screw and	Pu	Ultimate Load
Mult.	Multiple; Multiply		Yoke	PVC	Polyvinyl Chloride
MV	Megavolt; Mercury	Ovhd.	Overhead	Pvmt.	Pavement
	Vapor	Oz.	Ounce	Pwr.	Power
MVA	Million Volt Amperes	P	Pole; Applied Load;	Q	Quantity Heat Flow
MVAR	Million Volt Amperes		Projection	Quan.; Qty.	Quantity
	Reactance	p.	Page	Q.C.	Quick Coupling
MW	Megawatt	Pape.	Paperhanger	r	Radius of Gyration
MXM	Male by Male	PAR	Weatherproof Reflector	R	Resistance
MYD	Thousand Yards	Pc.	Piece	R.C.P.	Reinforced Concrete
N	Natural; North	P.C.	Portland Cement;		Pipe
nA	Nanoampere		Power Connector	Rect.	Rectangle
NA	Not Available; Not	P.C.F.	Pounds per Cubic Foot	Reg.	Regular
	Applicable	P.E.	Professional Engineer;	Reinf.	Reinforced
NBC	National Building Code		Porcelain Enamel;	Req'd.	Required
N.C.	Normally Closed		Polyethylene; Plain End	Resi	Residential
N.E.C.	National Electrical	Perf.	Perforate; Perforated	Rgh.	Rough
	Code	P.F.	Power Factor	R.H.W.	Rubber, Heat, & Water
NEMA	National Electrical	Ph.	Phase		Resistant; Residential
	Manufacturers	P.I.	Pressure Injected		Hot Water
	Association	Pile.	Pile Driver	rms	Root Mean Square
NEHB	Bolted Circuit Breaker	Pkg.	Package	Rnd.	Round
	to 240V	Pl.	Plate	Rodm.	Rodman (reinforcing)
N.L.B.	Non-Load-Bearing	Plah.	Plasterer Helper	Rofc.	Roofer, Composition
nm	Nanometer	Plas.	Plasterer	Rofp.	Roofer, Precast
NM	Nonmetallic Cable	Pluh.	Plumber's Helper	Rohe.	Roofer Helpers
NMC	Nonmetallic Cable with	Plum.	Plumber		(Composition)
	Corrosion-	Ply.	Plywood	Rots.	Roofer, Tile & Slate
	Resistant Sheath	p.m.	Post Meridiem	R.O.W.	Right of Way
No.	Number	Pord.	Painter, Ordinary	RPM	Revolutions per Minute
N.O.	Normally Open	pp.	Pages	R.R.	Direct Burial Feeder
N.O.C.	Not Otherwise	PP; PPL	Polypropylene		Conduit
	Classified	PPM	Parts per Million	R.S.	Rapid Start
Nose.	Nosing	Pr.	Pair	RT	Round Trip
N.P.T.	National Pipe Thread	Prefab.	Prefabricated	S	Suction; Single
NQOB	Bolted Circuit Breaker	Prefin.	Prefinished		Entrance; South
	to 240V	Prop.	Propelled	Scaf.	Scaffold
NRC	Noise Reduction	PSF; psf	Pounds per Square	Sch.; Sched.	Schedule
	Coefficient		Foot	S.C.R.	Modular Brick
N.R.S.	Non Rising Stem	PSI; psi	Pounds per Square	S.D.R.	Standard Dimension
ns	Nanosecond		Inch		Ratio
NTS	Not to Scale	PSIG; psig	Pounds per Square	sdwk.	Sidewalk
nW	Nanowatt		Inch Gauge	S.E.	Surfaced Edge
OB	Opposing Blade	PSP	Plastic Sewer Pipe	SE; S.E.R.;	Service Entrance Cable
O.C.	On Center	Pspr.	Painter, Spray	S.E.U.	
OD	Outside Diameter	Psst.	Painter, Structural	S.F.	Square Foot
O.D.	Outside Dimension		Steel	S.F.C.A.	Square Foot Contact
ODS	Overhead Distribution	PT	Potential Transformer		Area
	System	PTZ	Pan, Tilt, and Zoom	S.F.G.	Square Foot of Ground

S.F. Hor.	Square Foot Horizontal	T.C.	Terra Cotta	W	Wire; Watt; Wide; West
S.F.R.	Square Feet of Radiation	T.D.	Temperature Difference	w/	With
S.F. Shlf.	Square Foot of Shelf	TFE	Tetrafluorethylene	W.C.	Water Column; Water Closet
S4S	Surface 4 Sides		(Teflon)	W.F.	Wide Flange
Shee.	Sheet Metal Worker	T. & G.	Tongue & Groove; Tar	W.G.	Water Gauge
Sin	Sine		& Gravel	Wldg.	Welding
Skwk.	Skilled Worker	Th.; Thk.	Thick	Wrck.	Wrecker; Wrecking
SL	Saran Lined	Thn.	Thin	W.S.P.	Water, Steam,
S.L.	Slimline	Thrded.	Threaded		Petroleum
Sldr.	Solder	Tilf.	Tile Layer, Floor	WT, Wt.	Weight
S.N.	Solid Neutral	Tilh.	Tile Layer Helper	WWF	Welded Wire Fabric
SNM	Shielded Type NM Cable	THW	Insulated Strand Wire	XFMR	Transformer
		THWN;	Nylon Jacketed Wire	XHD	Extra Heavy Duty
S.P.	Static Pressure; Single Pole; Self-Propelled	THHN		XHHW	Cross-linked Polyethylene Wire
		T.L.	Truckload		Insulation
Spri.	Sprinkler Installer	Tot.	Total		
Sq.	Square; 100 square feet	T.S.	Trigger Start	Y	Wye
S.P.D.T.	Single Pole, Double Throw	Tr.	Trade	yd.	Yard
		Transf.	Transformer	yr.	Year
S.P.S.T.	Single Pole, Single Throw	Trhv.	Truck Driver, Heavy	Δ	Delta
		Trlr.	Trailer	%	Percent
SPT	Standard Pipe Thread	Trlt.	Truck Driver, Light	~	Approximately
Sq. Hd.	Square Head	T.V.	Television	ø	Phase
SS	Single Strength; Stainless Steel	T.W.	Thermoplastic Water Resistant Wire	@	At
				#	Pound; Number
SSB	Single Strength B Grade	UCI	Uniform Construction	<	Less than
Sswk.	Structural Steel Worker		Index	>	Greater Than
Sswl.	Structural Steel Welder	UF	Underground Feeder		
St.; Stl.	Steel	U.H.F.	Ultra High Frequency		
STC	Sound Transmission Coefficient	U.L.	Underwriters Laboratory		
Std.	Standard	Unfin.	Unfinished		
Ston.	Stone Mason	UPS	Uninterruptible Power Supply		
STP	Standard Temperature and Pressure	URD	Underground Residential Distribution		
Stpi.	Steamfitter; Pipefitter	USE	Underground Service Entrance Cable		
Str.	Strength; Starter; Straight				
Strd.	Stranded	UTP	Unshielded Twisted Pair		
Struct.	Structural	V	Volt		
Sty.	Story	VA	Volt/amp		
Sub.	Subcontractor	V.A.T.	Vinyl Asbestos Tile		
Subj.	Subject	VAV	Variable Air Volume		
Surf.	Surface	Vent.	Ventilating		
Sw.	Switch	Vert.	Vertical		
Swbd.	Switchboard	V.G.	Vertical Grain		
S.Y.	Square Yard	V.H.F.	Very High Frequency		
Syn.	Synthetic	VHO	Very High Output		
Sys.	System	Vib.	Vibrating		
t.	Thickness	V.L.F.	Vertical Linear Foot		
T	Temperature; Ton	Vol.	Volume		
Tan	Tangent				

Maximum Circuit Length in Feet for Various Power Requirements

| Amperes | Wire Size | Maximum Circuit Length in Feet | | | | |
| | | 2 Wire, 1 Phase | | 3 Wire, 3 Phase | | |
		120V	240V	240V	480V	600V
15	14*	50	105	120	240	300
	14	50	100	120	235	295
20	12*	60	125	145	290	360
	12	60	120	140	280	350
30	10*	65	130	155	305	380
	10	65	130	150	300	375
50	8	60	125	145	285	355
65	6	75	150	175	345	435
85	4	90	185	210	425	530
115	2	110	215	250	500	620
130	1	120	240	275	555	690
150	1/0	130	260	305	605	760
175	2/0	140	285	330	655	820
200	3/0	155	315	360	725	904
230	4/0	170	345	395	795	990
255	250	185	365	420	845	1055
285	300	195	395	455	910	1140
310	350	210	420	485	975	1220
380	500	245	490	565	1130	1415

*Solid Conductor
Note: The circuit length is the one-way distance between the origin and the load.

Minimum Copper and Aluminum Wire Size Allowed for Various Types of Insulation

Minimum Wire Sizes

Amperes	Copper THW THWN or XHHW	Copper THHN XHHW *	Aluminum THW XHHW	Aluminum THHN XHHW *	Amperes	Copper THW THWN or XHHW	Copper THHN XHHW *	Aluminum THW XHHW	Aluminum THHN XHHW *
15 A	#14	#14	#12	#12	195		2/0		
20	#12	#12			200	3/0			
25			#10	#10	205			250MCM	4/0
30	#10	#10			225		3/0		
40			#8		230	4/0		300MCM	250MCM
45				#8	250			350MCM	
50	#8		#6		255	250MCM			300MCM
55		#8			260		4/0		
60				#6	270			400MCM	
65	#6		#4		280				350MCM
75		#6	#3	#4	285	300MCM			
85	#4			#3	290		250MCM		
90			#2		305				400MCM
95		#4			310	350MCM		500MCM	
100	#3		#1	#2	320		300MCM		
110		#3			335	400MCM			
115	#2			#1	340			600MCM	
120			1/0		350		350MCM		500MCM
130	#1	#2			375			700MCM	
135			2/0	1/0	380	500MCM	400MCM		
150	1/0	#1		2/0	385			750MCM	600MCM
155			3/0		420	600MCM			700MCM
170		1/0			430		500MCM		
175	2/0			3/0	435				750MCM
180			4/0		475		600MCM		

*Dry Locations Only

Notes:
1. Size #14 to 4/0 is in AWG units (American Wire Gauge).
2. Size 250 to 750 is in MCM units (Thousand Circular Mils).
3. Use next higher ampere value if exact value is not listed in table.
4. For loads that operate continuously, increase ampere value by 25% to obtain proper wire size.
5. Refer to previous table for the maximum circuit length for the various size wires.
6. This table has been written for estimating purposes only, based on ambient temperature of 30°C (86°F); for ambient temperature other than 30°C (86°F), ampacity correction factors will be applied.

Maximum Number of Wires (Insulations Noted) for Various Conduit Sizes

Copper Wire Size	½" TW	½" THW	½" THWN	¾" TW	¾" THW	¾" THWN	1" TW	1" THW	1" THWN	1-¼" TW	1-¼" THW	1-¼" THWN	1-½" TW	1-½" THW	1-½" THWN	2" TW	2" THW	2" THWN	2-½" TW	2-½" THW	2-½" THWN	3" THW	3" THWN	3-½" THW	3-½" THWN	4" THW	4" THWN
#14	9	6	13	15	10	24	25	16	39	44	29	69	60	40	94	99	65	154	142	93		143		192			
#12	7	4	10	12	8	18	19	13	29	35	24	51	47	32	70	78	53	114	111	76	164	117		157			
#10	5	4	6	9	6	11	15	11	18	26	19	32	36	26	44	60	43	73	85	61	104	95	160	127		163	
#8	2	1	3	4	3	5	7	5	9	12	10	16	17	13	22	28	22	36	40	32	51	49	79	66	106	85	136
#6		1	1		2	4		4	6		7	11		10	15		16	26		23	37	36	57	48	76	62	98
#4		1	1		1	2		3	4		5	7		7	9		12	16		17	22	27	35	36	47	47	60
#3		1	1		1	1		2	3		4	6		6	8		10	13		15	19	23	29	31	39	40	51
#2		1	1		1	1		2	3		4	5		5	7		9	11		13	16	20	25	27	33	34	43
#1					1	1		1	1		3	3		4	5		6	8		9	12	14	18	19	25	25	32
1/0					1	1		1	1		2	3		3	4		5	7		8	10	12	15	16	21	21	27
2/0					1	1		1	1		1	2		3	3		5	6		7	8	10	13	14	17	18	22
3/0					1	1		1	1		1	1		2	3		4	5		6	7	9	11	12	14	15	18
4/0						1		1	1		1	1		1	2		3	4		5	6	7	9	10	12	13	15
250MCM								1	1		1	1		1	1		2	3		4	4	6	7	8	10	10	12
300								1	1		1	1		1	1		2	3		3	4	5	6	7	8	9	11
350									1		1	1		1	1		1	2		3	3	4	5	6	7	8	9
400											1	1		1	1		1	1		2	3	4	5	5	6	7	8
500											1	1		1	1		1	1		1	2	3	4	4	5	6	7
600												1		1	1		1	1		1	1	3	3	4	4	5	5
700														1	1		1	1		1	1	2	3	3	4	4	5
750 ↓														1	1		1	1		1	1	2	2	3	3	4	4

Metric Equivalent, Conduit and Wire (THW)

Conduit Size		Wire Amp.	Wire Size		
Inches	Millimeters		AWG		mm^2
1/2	15	20	# 12		2.5
3/4	20	25	10		4
1	25	30	8		6
1-1/4	32	45	6		10
1-1/2	40	60	4		16
2	50	80	3		25
2-1/2	65	100	1		35
3	80	130	1/0		50
3-1/2	90	165	3/0		70
4	100	200	4/0		95
5	125	235	250	MCM (kcmil)	120
6	150	280	300		150
		325	400		185
		360	500	↓	240
		415	600		300

Concrete for Conduit Encasement

Table below lists C.Y. of concrete for 100 L.F. of trench. Conduits' separation center to center should meet 7.5″ (N.E.C.).

Number of Conduits	1	2	3	4	6	8	9	Number of Conduits
Trench Dimension	11.5″ x 11.5″	11.5″ x 19″	11.5″ x 27″	19″ x 19″	19″ x 27″	19″ x 38″	27″ x 27″	Trench Dimension
Conduit Diameter 2.0″	3.29	5.39	7.64	8.83	12.51	17.66	17.72	Conduit Diameter 2.0″
2.5″	3.23	5.29	7.49	8.62	12.19	17.23	17.25	2.5″
3.0″	3.15	5.13	7.24	8.29	11.71	16.59	16.52	3.0″
3.5″	3.08	4.97	7.02	7.99	11.26	15.98	15.84	3.5″
4.0″	2.99	4.80	6.76	7.65	10.74	15.30	15.07	4.0″
5.0″	2.78	4.37	6.11	6.78	9.44	13.57	13.12	5.0″
6.0″	2.52	3.84	5.33	5.74	7.87	11.48	10.77	6.0″
Trench Layout								

Weight (Lbs./L.F.) of 4 Pole Aluminum and Copper Bus Duct by Ampere Load

Amperes	Aluminum Feeder	Copper Feeder	Aluminum Plug-In	Copper Plug-In
225			7	7
400			8	13
600	10	10	11	14
800	10	19	13	18
1000	11	19	16	22
1350	14	24	20	30
1600	17	26	25	39
2000	19	30	29	46
2500	27	43	36	56
3000	30	48	42	73
4000	39	67		
5000		78		

Size Required and Weight (Lbs./1000 L.F.) of Aluminum and Copper THW Wire by Ampere Load

Amperes	Copper Size	Aluminum Size	Copper Weight	Aluminum Weight
15	14	12	24	11
20	12	10	33	17
30	10	8	48	39
45	8	6	77	52
65	6	4	112	72
85	4	2	167	101
100	3	1	205	136
115	2	1/0	252	162
130	1	2/0	324	194
150	1/0	3/0	397	233
175	2/0	4/0	491	282
200	3/0	250	608	347
230	4/0	300	753	403
255	250	400	899	512
285	300	500	1068	620
310	350	500	1233	620
335	400	600	1396	772
380	500	750	1732	951

Conduit Weight Comparisons (Lbs. per 100 ft.) Empty

Type	1/2"	3/4"	1"	1-1/4"	1-1/2"	2"	2-1/2"	3"	3-1/2"	4"	5"	6"
Rigid Aluminum	28	37	55	72	89	119	188	246	296	350	479	630
Rigid Steel	79	105	153	201	249	332	527	683	831	972	1314	1745
Intermediate Steel (IMC)	60	82	116	150	182	242	401	493	573	638		
Electrical Metallic Tubing (EMT)	29	45	65	96	111	141	215	260	365	390		
Polyvinyl Chloride, Schedule 40	16	22	32	43	52	69	109	142	170	202	271	350
Polyvinyl Chloride Encased Burial						38		67	88	105	149	202
Fibre Duct Encased Burial						127		164	180	206	400	511
Fibre Duct Direct Burial						150		251	300	354		
Transite Encased Burial						160		240	290	330	450	550
Transite Direct Burial						220		310		400	540	640

Ampere Values Determined by Horsepower, Voltage and Phase Values

H.P.	Amperes					
	Single Phase		Three Phase			
	115V	230V	200V	230V	460V	575V
1/6	4.4 A	2.2 A				
1/4	5.8	2.9				
1/3	7.2	3.6				
1/2	9.8	4.9	2.3 A	2.0 A	1.0 A	0.8 A
3/4	13.8	6.9	3.2	2.8	1.4	1.1
1	16	8	4.1	3.6	1.8	1.4
1-1/2	20	10	6.0	5.2	2.6	2.1
2	24	12	7.8	6.8	3.4	2.7
3	34	17	11.0	9.6	4.8	3.9
5			17.5	15.2	7.6	6.1
7-1/2			25.3	22	11	9
10			32.2	28	14	11
15			48.3	42	21	17
20			62.1	54	27	22
25			78.2	68	34	27
30			92.0	80	40	32
40			119.6	104	52	41
50			149.5	130	65	52
60			177	154	77	62
75			221	192	96	77
100			285	248	124	99
125			359	312	156	125
150			414	360	180	144
200			552	480	240	192

NEMA Enclosures

Electrical enclosures serve two basic purposes: they protect people from accidental contact with enclosed electrical devices and connections, and they protect the enclosed devices and connections from specified external conditions. The National Electrical Manufacturers Association (NEMA) has established the following standards. Because these descriptions are not intended to be complete representations of NEMA listings, consultation of NEMA literature is advised for detailed information.

The following definitions and descriptions pertain to NONHAZARDOUS locations:

NEMA Type 1: General purpose enclosures intended for use indoors, primarily to prevent accidental contact of personnel with the enclosed equipment in areas that do not involve unusual conditions.

NEMA Type 2: Dripproof indoor enclosures intended to protect the enclosed equipment against dripping noncorrosive liquids and falling dirt.

NEMA Type 3: Dustproof, rain-tight and sleet-resistant (ice-resistant) enclosures intended for use outdoors to protect the enclosed equipment against wind-blown dust, rain, sleet, and external ice formation.

NEMA Type 3R: Rainproof and sleet-resistant (ice-resistant) enclosures that are intended for use outdoors to protect the enclosed equipment against rain. These enclosures are constructed so that the accumulation and melting of sleet (ice) will not damage the enclosure and its internal mechanisms.

NEMA Type 3S: Enclosures intended for outdoor use to provide limited protection against wind-blown dust, rain, and sleet (ice) and to allow operation of external mechanisms when ice-laden.

NEMA Type 4: Watertight and dust-tight enclosures intended for use indoors and out—to protect the enclosed equipment against splashing water, seepage of water, falling or hose-directed water, and severe external condensation.

NEMA Type 4X: Watertight, dust-tight, and corrosion-resistant indoor and outdoor enclosures featuring the same provisions as Type 4 enclosures, plus corrosion resistance.

NEMA Type 5: Indoor enclosures intended primarily to provide limited protection against dust and falling dirt.

NEMA Type 6: Enclosures intended for indoor and outdoor use—primarily to provide limited protection against the entry of water during occasional temporary submersion at a limited depth.

NEMA Type 6R: Enclosures intended for indoor and outdoor use—primarily to provide limited protection against the entry of water during prolonged submersion at a limited depth.

NEMA Type 11: Enclosures intended for indoor use—primarily to provide, by means of oil immersion, limited protection to enclosed equipment against the corrosive effects of liquids and gases.

NEMA Type 12: Dust-tight and driptight indoor enclosures intended for use indoors in industrial locations to protect the enclosed equipment against fibers, flyings, lint, dust, and dirt, as well as light splashing, seepage, dripping, and external condensation of noncorrosive liquids.

NEMA Type 13: Oiltight and dust-tight indoor enclosures intended primarily to house pilot devices, such as limit switches, foot switches, push buttons, selector switches, and pilot lights, and to protect these devices against lint and dust, seepage, external condensation, and sprayed water, oil, and noncorrosive coolant.

The following definitions and descriptions pertain to HAZARDOUS, or CLASSIFIED, locations:

NEMA Type 7: Enclosures intended for use in indoor locations classified as Class 1, Groups A, B, C, or D, as defined in the National Electrical Code.

NEMA Type 9: Enclosures intended for use in indoor locations classified as Class 2, Groups E, F, or G, as defined in the National Electrical Code.

Labor-Hours

Description	L.H.	Unit
NEMA 1	1.330	Ea.
12"L x 12"W x 4"D		
NEMA 3R	1.600	Ea.
12"L x 12"W x 6"D		
NEMA 4	4.000	Ea.
12"L x 12"W x 6"D		
NEMA 7	8.000	Ea.
12"L x 12"W x 6"D		
NEMA 9	5.000	Ea.
12"L x 12"W x 6"D		
NEMA 12	1.510	Ea.
12"L x 14"W x 6"D		

Screw Cover - NEMA 1　　　*Hinged Cover - NEMA 1*

Rainproof and Weatherproof, Screw cover - NEMA 3R

Sheet Metal Pull Boxes

⏶ Means Forms
SPEC-AID

DATE _____

DIVISION 16: ELECTRICAL

PROJECT _____ LOCATION _____

Incoming Service: ☐ Overhead   ☐ Underground

	Primary	Secondary
Voltage		
Unit Sub-station & Size		
Number of Manholes		
Feeder Size		
Length		
Conduit		
Duct		
Concrete: ☐ No ☐ Yes		
Other		

Building Service: Size _____ Amps   Switchboard _____

Panels: ☐ Distribution _____ Lighting _____ Power _____

Describe _____

Motor Control Center: Furnished by _____

Describe _____

Bus Duct: ☐ No   ☐ Yes   Size _____ Amps   Application _____

Describe _____

Cable Tray: ☐ No   ☐ Yes   Describe _____

Emergency System: ☐ No   ☐ Yes   Allowance _____ ☐ Separate Contract

Generator: ☐ No   ☐ Diesel   ☐ Gas   ☐ Gasoline _____ Size _____ KW

Transfer Switch: ☐ No   ☐ Yes   Number _____ Size _____ Amps

Area Protection Relay Panels: ☐ No   ☐ Yes _____

Other _____

Conduit: ☐ No   ☐ Yes   ☐ Aluminum _____

☐ Electric Metallic Tubing _____

☐ Galvanized Steel _____

☐ Plastic _____

Wire: ☐ No   ☐ Yes   ☐ Type Installation _____

☐ Armored Cable _____

☐ Building Wire _____

☐ Metallic Sheath Cable _____

☐ _____

Underfloor Duct: ☐ No   ☐ Yes   Describe _____

Header Duct: ☐ No   ☐ Yes   Describe _____

Trench Duct: ☐ No   ☐ Yes   Describe _____

Underground Duct: ☐ No   ☐ Yes   Describe _____

Explosion Proof Areas: ☐ No   ☐ Yes   Describe _____

Motors: ☐ No   ☐ Yes   Total H.P. _____ No. of Fractional H.P. _____ Voltage _____

☐ 1/2 to 5 H.P. _____ ☐ 7-1/2 to 25 H.P. _____ ☐ Over 25 H.P. _____

Describe _____

Starters: Type _____

Supplied by: _____

Page 29 of 30

307

⚓ Means Forms
SPEC-AID

DIVISION 16: ELECTRICAL

Telephone System: □ No □ Yes   Service Size _____   Length _____
  Manhole: □ No   □ Yes   Number _____   Termination _____
  Concrete Encased: □ No   □ Yes   □ Rigid Galv.   □ Duct   □ _____

Fire Alarm System: □ No   □ Yes   Service Size _____   Length _____ Wire Type _____
  Concrete Encased: □ No   □ Yes   □ Rigid Galv.   □ Duct   □ _____
  □ Stations _____   □ Horns _____   □ Lights _____   □ Combination _____
  Detectors: □ Rate of Rise _____   □ Fixed _____   □ Smoke _____
  Describe _____   Insulation _____   Wire Size _____
  □ Zones _____   □ Conduit _____   □ E.M.T. _____   □ Empty _____
  Describe _____

Watchmans Tour: □ No   □ Yes   □ Stations _____   □ Door Switches _____
  □ Alarm Bells _____   □ Key Re-sets _____   □ _____
  □ Conduit _____   □ E.M.T. _____   □ Wire _____   □ Empty _____
  Describe _____

Clock System: □ No   □ Yes   □ Electronic   □ Wired   □ _____
  □ Single Dial _____   □ Double Dial _____   □ Program Bell _____
  □ Conduit _____   □ E.M.T. _____   □ Empty _____
  Describe _____

Sound System: □ No   □ Yes   Type _____   Speakers _____
  □ Conduit _____   □ Cable _____   □ E.M.T. _____   □ Empty _____
  Describe _____

Television System: □ No   □ Yes   Describe _____
  □ Antenna _____   □ Closed Circuit _____   □ Teaching _____   □ Security _____
  □ Learning Laboratory _____   □ _____
  □ Conduit _____   □ E.M.T. _____   □ Wire _____   □ Empty _____

Lightning Protection: □ No   □ Yes   Describe _____
Low Voltage Switching: □ No   □ Yes   Describe _____
Scoreboards: □ No   □ Yes   Describe _____   Number _____
Comfort Systems: □ No   □ Electric Heat   □ Snow Melting   □ _____
  Describe _____
Other Systems: _____

Lighting Fixtures: □ No   □ Yes   □ Allowance _____   □ Separate Contract
  □ Economy   □ Commercial   □ Deluxe   □ Explosion Proof   □ _____
  □ Incandescent _____
  _____ Foot Candles _____
  □ Fluorescent _____
  _____ Foot Candles _____
  □ Mercury Vapor _____
  _____ Foot Candles _____
  □ _____   Foot Candles _____
  □ Step Lighting _____   □ Planter Lighting _____   □ Fountain Lighting _____
  □ Site Lighting _____   □ Poles _____   □ Area Lighting _____   □ Flood Lighting _____
  Dimming System: □ No   □ Yes   □ Incandescent   □ Fluorescent _____
  Ceilings: □ T Bar   □ Concealed Spline   □ _____
  Emergency Battery Units: □ No   □ Lead Acid   □ Nickel Cadmium   □ 6 Volt _____   12 Volt _____
  Describe _____
Special Considerations: _____

Page 30 of 30

Index

Index

Index

Index

Notes

Notes

Notes

Notes